C000194902

*From behind the walls of the death row
blocks of the USA's tough
come the voices c*

ROBERT FIELDMORE LEWIS - I candidly of his freewheeling criminal career, and his time on the row with savage sex killer Ted Bundy...

WAYNE HENDERSON - a free spirit trapped within the California Corrections system, writing of his own dubious murder conviction, and the nightmare of prison life...

MARK DEFRIEST - the only man on Florida's Death Row without a death sentence, his will to escape earning him several life sentences in "the cell from Hell"...

CARL PANZRAM - the noble psychopath, and original "killer author", writing here of his incredible worldwide murder spree, soon to form part of a major motion picture...

GERARD JOHN SCHAEFER - the infamous multiple murderer, who has become the most disturbing crime writer of our time. Reliving the grim details of crime and punishment from his own life, he reports from Hell with an unblinking eye worthy of De Sade...

OTTIS TOOLE - twisted killer... genial man-monster... deranged sidekick to Henry Lee Lucas... "devil's child"...

DANNY ROLLING - tormented drifter... armed robber... mass murderer? Rolling now faces a total of five life sentences and five death sentences - read of the past that haunts him, and of his love for editor Sondra London...

JOSEPH O'DELL - as he continues to endure years of torment on Virginia's Death Row, science seems to bear out his claims of innocence. In his *Prison Letters & Diaries*, he reveals how a man holds on to his sanity in a world of ugliness, violence and pain...

There has never been a crime book like **KNOCKIN' ON JOE** - by turns funny and intense, poignant and sickeningly harrowing. Readers may pray that they never come closer to the world of violent offenders and incarcerated criminals. Told in their own distinct voices, the stories of the men themselves ring loud and, sometimes appallingly, clear. **KNOCKIN' ON JOE** is also the story of a woman's obsession - the extraordinary, fearless Ms. London tells how her abiding fascination for the men of violence has pulled her close to the abyss...

KNOCKIN' ON JOE
(Voices from Death Row)
This first edition published July 1993
by
Nemesis Books
Unit 4
Millmead Business Centre
Millmead Road
London N17 9QU.

Printed and bound in the UK
by
Woolnough Bookbinding Ltd.

British Library Cataloguing-in-Publication Data.
A catalogue record for this book is
available from the British Library.

All material in this book Copyright (c) Sondra London /
Nemesis Books 1993, except for the following:
"Hotel Kalifornia" by Wayne Henderson,
and "On a Highway to Hell" by Mark DeFriest,
copyright held by the authors;
Nemesis are particularly grateful for the kind permission
of Amereon Ltd. to include "Excerpt from the Memoirs of Carl
Panzram", taken from the book *Killer - A Journal of Murder*
by Thomas Gaddis and James O. Long (Amereon House);
for the kind permission of Mutesong / Dying Art to include the
lyric "Knockin' On Joe" by Nick Cave;
for the kind permission of A. M. Heath Ltd. to include the short
extract from *In the Belly of the Beast* by Jack Henry Abbott;
and for the kind permission of Little, Brown (USA) for enabling us
to quote from *False Starts* by Malcolm Braly.
All material by Robert Fieldmore Lewis; "You Might As Well
Assume I'm Lying" by Wayne Henderson; all material by G. J.
Schaefer; "I couldn't stop... so I just kept going..." by Ottis Toole,
all originally Copyright (c) 1989 - 1992 Media Queen.
Copyright now held by Sondra London / Nemesis Books.
All rights fully reserved in every case.

KNOCKIN' ON JOE

(Voices from Death Row)

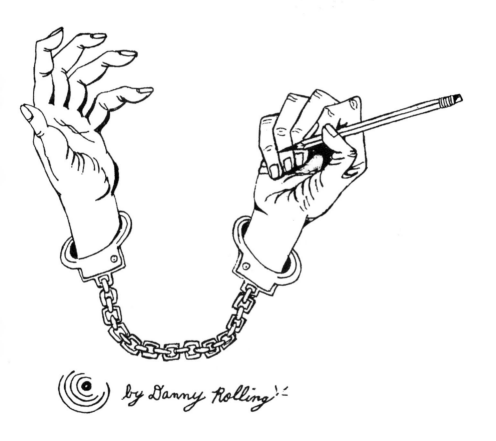

by Danny Rolling

These chains of sorrow, they are heavy, it is true.
And these locks cannot be broken, no, not with one thousand keys.
O jailer, you wear a ball 'n' chain you cannot see.
You can lay your burden on me -
You can lay your burden down on me -
You can lay your burden down upon me.
But you cannot lay down those memories.
Woe-ooo woe-oo woe-oo - woe-ooo woe-oo woe-woo - Here I go!
Knockin' on Joe!
This square foot of sky will be mine till I die. Knockin' on Joe.
Woe-ooo woe-oo woe-oo - All down the row. Knockin' on Joe.

O Warden, I surrender to you. Your fists cain't hurt me anymore.
You know these hands will never wash your dirty Death Row floors.
O Preacher, come closer, you don't scare me anymore.
Just tell Nancy not to come here -
Just tell Nancy not to come here anymore -
Tell Nancy not to come.
And let me die in the memory of her arms.
O Woe-oo woe-oo woe-oo - Woe- oo woe-oo wo-ooo - All down the Row.
Knockin' on Joe.
You kings of halls and ends of halls.
You will die within these walls.
And I'll go, all down the row, Knockin' on Joe.

O Nancy's body is a coffin,
she wears my tombstone at her head. (X2)
She wears her body like a coffin.
She wears a dress of gold & red (X2)
She wears a dress of red & gold.
Graverobbers at my coffin before my body's even cold.
It's a door for when I go, Knockin' on Joe.
These hands will never mop your dirty Death Row floors.
No! You can hide! You can run! O but your trial is yet to come.
O you can run! You can hide! But you have yet to be tried.
You can lay your burden down upon me...
You cain't hurt me anymore.
Knockin' on Joe.

NICK CAVE

Note: "Knockin' on Joe" was an early twentieth century term used by prisoners in the southern USA, as a euphemism for injuring or mutilating themselves to avoid demeaning or degrading labor. The best known case is probably Clyde Barrow, who cut off two toes to escape his work detail.

CONTENTS

INTRODUCTION
MURDER ROAD by Sondra London   1

Part One - "Regular Joes"   11

1.   ROBERT FIELDMORE LEWIS
     by Sondra London   12
     DON'T CALL THIS PRISON MY HOME
     by Robert Fieldmore Lewis   17
     LIFE & CRIMES OF BEAUTIFUL BOBBY
     by Robert Fieldmore Lewis   32
     ALONE ON DEATH ROW WITH TED BUNDY
     by Robert Fieldmore Lewis   50
2.   WAYNE HENDERSON by Sondra London   68
     YOU MIGHT AS WELL ASSUME I'M LYING
     by Wayne Henderson   70
     HOTEL KALIFORNIA by Wayne Henderson   88
3.   MARK DEFRIEST by Sondra London   102
     ON A HIGHWAY TO HELL by Mark DeFriest   110

Part Two - Charismatic Psychos   125

1.   THE STORY OF CARL PANZRAM   126
     EXCERPT FROM THE MEMOIRS OF
     CARL PANZRAM   131
2.   GERARD JOHN SCHAEFER by Sondra London   139
     STARKE STORIES by G. J. Schaefer - including:
     NEWCOCK   161
     DEATH HOUSE SCREAMS   164
     JESSE IN FLAMES   167
     EARLY RELEASE   172
     NIGGER JACK   196
3.   OTTIS TOOLE by Sondra London   217
     "I couldn't stop... so I just kept going..." by Ottis Toole   228
4.   THE ROLLING PAPERS by Sondra London   230
     "Judge, there's just a whole lot of suffering and sorrow to go
     around in this world..." by Danny Rolling   245
     NO PLACE TO BE by Danny Rolling   247
     THE DEATH PENALTY by Danny Rolling   254

Part Three - KNOCKIN' ON JOE

     JOE O'DELL by Sondra London   260
     THE PRISON LETTERS & DIARY OF JOE O'DELL   266

The Editor

INTRODUCTION

MURDER ROAD
by Sondra London

Murder as a Dramatic Device

Murder is America's number one growth industry. Because of its epidemic proportions, understanding why the killing goes on has become more crucial than ever. Not only are actual murders touching more and more of our lives, but anyone who owns a TV set knows how fictional murder dominates our imagination.

Have you ever noticed how often a story uses the primal conflict between life and death to heighten interest? The characters in the story might merely contemplate death, but more often than not, somebody winds up on the killing floor. And the audience loves it.

Because of its timeless power as a dramatic device, murder occurs far more frequently in art than in real life. It is a facile device providing red-hot copy , stunning visuals, and a quick climax to a tense situation. It has become the ultimate snappy comeback, glossed with the superficial allure of the quick, energetic gesture. Thus we have trendy dinner parties enacting the murder of one of the guests, and the underground magazine that urges *Murder Can Be Fun.*

Our ideas about murder come less from personal experience than from stories we have seen and heard. Since a combination of taboo and economics defines what is seen in the mass media, the tastes of buyers are reduced to the lowest common denominator by the sheer weight of numbers. While the fantasy of murder may be the favorite focus of our entertainment industry, still, the largest number of paying customers prefer to be shielded from too much ugly realism. For most of us, our own vulnerability is so great we can't stand to look at murder close-up, because the illusion of security is so much more comfortable.

The murder dramas offered up by the mass media present a sequence of events reassuring us, once again, that all's right with the world: the sprightly old lady quizzically contemplates the shapely corpse sprawled on the Persian rug, while the jaunty music rises and the scene fades to a heart-warming message from the sponsor. Or the nasty killer knocks off a charming victim or two, then the handsome cop in the trendy suit flattens the villain and kisses the mandatory pretty girl as they speed off into the sunset in the Testarossa.

Of course, the popularity of *Miami Vice* or *Murder She Wrote* is nothing new; Will Shakespeare routinely littered his stage with corpses, and a Greek tragedy was not a success unless violence claimed half of the case.

The Old Testament provides a marvelously bloody panorama. But the killers of old were honored, not reviled. We read of mass slayers racking up higher and higher scores, while the ancient people glorified them, chanting, "Saul has slain his thousands, and David his ten thousands."

Today, such overt encouragement is frowned upon, but within their own minds, mass and serial killers may well be fulfilling their image of an ancient and honorable tradition. Danny Rolling, now facing the death penalty for the stabbing deaths of five college students, tells me he feels like he comes from another time. In stories and songs romanticizing his criminal career, he often refers to himself as Jesse James. Recently he boasted that for me, he would fight a sabre-toothed tiger, not to mention his closest neighbors - real-life killers and thugs getting in his face about our relationship. When I begged him to forego fighting over me, he wrote wistfully of "legends of lion-like men and beautiful lasses who stole their hearts away ...a magical, simpler time when one won the favor of his Lady Fair by how well he could wield a two-edged sword and stand his ground against his enemies. I realize you said that such things do not impress you. I understand this .. still, it must have been a glorious era for man".

Today's killers all share one fate: some are regular Joes, some are charismatic psychos, but having crossed that line they become one of "them", and are shunned by "us". Their physical presence is no longer tolerated, and their ideas, feelings and works are dismissed as well. Yet, isn't there a vital significance to their stories? After all, even on Death Row there is life.

Most killers can describe their crimes, but in-depth insight into the roots of their violent behavior is rare. Most of then cannot verbalize their homicidal impulses. Most will tell you that they just killed someone, and that's it. The short version of your average killer's tale is a complaint that he is a victim too, or that he was framed. Even those who have thought seriously about these matters are rarely in a position to frankly disclose their observations, since they inevitably have an appeal pending, and don't want to ruin their chances of release or a reduced sentence.

On the road of life, there's a crossroads at a place called Murder Road.

That's where two lives meet; one comes to an end, and the other takes a permanent detour. What's life like out there on that road where murderers and victims make that fatal connection?

I wanted to find out, so I set out on Murder Road myself, and started asking questions. The victims' voices have been stilled - only the killers can speak. The answers are still coming back from accused, convicted and confessed killers all over America, in the form of stories, poems, artwork and songs, as well as telephone calls, prison visits... and real-time involvement in ongoing cases.

This, then, is "the rest of the story" that comes out only after the giddy Murder for Fun crowd has left the theater and the cameras have been turned off. This book takes you into the prisons on the other side of that fatal crossroads, to meet the killers who live there. As D.H. Lawrence once said, "It is lurid and melodramatic, but it is true." While some may be the charismatic psycho-killers beloved by the media, others are more or less regular Joes who carelessly wandered onto Murder Road and now find themselves out past the crossroads. By definition, anyone who kills becomes a killer, but in most cases, the event that forever after defines their status has happened only once, and because the circumstances are so various, generalizations about killers are meaningless.

And then you have Genus Serial Killer - those with a compulsion to kill and kill again. It is in them that homicidal pathology takes its most virulent form. For the serial killer, the murderous encounter doesn't "just happen". It stems from a powerful drive, not merely the occasional angry impulse, like "I could just kill my boss." Nor is it merely an unfortunate by-product of business, drugs, greed or passion. For these persons, murder becomes an obsession that colors every aspect of their existence. Killing for its own sake is a way of life, encompassing the preparation, execution and aftermath, along with the maintenance of a passable semblance of normality. The motivations are rarely personal: on the contrary, the victims of these crimes are most often hapless strangers, taken out just because they are there. "Sometimes I felt like a vampire," said Ted Bundy, and Henry Lee Lucas summed it up, "I just hated."

The lack of personal relationship places this type of crime into a dimension more social than individual. We like to feel we can avoid a fata encounter by taking precautions, following safety tips, and not talking to strangers. Once we realize that this is not enough to stop a killer, that nothing is enough, it is profoundly disturbing. P Lundsgaarde observes in

Murder in Space City, "The killer who chooses a stranger as his victim overtly threatens the preservation of the social order." And Ralph Stone, an FBI-trained profiler and investigator of thousands of murders once advised me, "Bottom line is, if one of these guys decides he wants you, there's nothing that we or you or anyone else can do to stop him. You're his."

Into the Abyss

These days it seems it's only prisoners and their friends that actively pursue the ancient art of personal correspondence. When a person is forced to give up the pastimes that comprise our lives, in order to reach out and touch someone, he can always fall back on the old tried-and-true way to escape: pen and paper, stamp and envelope, and someone on the other end.

Prisoners lead lives of consummate boredom. Once a prisoner gets into any of the arts, it's like having a magic key, and he can pass through the walls of time and space, and live - even if it's just for a few fleeting moments - in another world. And having a friendly, inquiring mind meet you there makes it all come alive in a most gratifying way.

At times it seems that an unusual percentage of the prison population write or draw. But today we, as free people, take immediacy of communication for granted. When we want to contact a friend, we just ring them up. Or we drive or fly to them. The mail is used for very little besides bills and ads.

In the United States, access to violent offenders is extremely limited. There is a strong resistance to allowing convicted felons to be studied. Perhaps it is because those of the "burn 'em" persuasion are afraid that research will reveal some kind of medically-grounded disorder, which will then justify that tiresome "bleeding heart" argument that these people need *HELP*, not execution. It strikes at the very foundation of the mandate envisioned by the Corrections Mentality. Since it is too much to expect for this situation to change any time soon, many types of psychological and medical information will remain unavailable.

But stories, drawings and correspondence are still tolerated in most prisons, and these are the tools I have used to pursue my independent studies aimed at shedding light on the inner worlds of these men who have been ejected from society for offending to the maximum extent.

While I usually keep the personal distance prescribed by convention and good form, my most valuable materials comes from those cases where I have become personally involved. Perhaps that's why I get the stories I do,

4

because so few are willing to actually go down into the abyss to see how the "monsters" are doing. But how ironic when you find the shadowy monsters turn out to be little boys in men's bodies, hungering like all of us for that human touch. And what strangely beautiful gifts they present to their curious lady visitor.

Because these individuals have traversed such extremes, their souls have become like locked rooms hiding mysterious secrets. They seldom see their experiences and observations as valuable, having been programmed for years to believe that they are utterly beneath contempt. It takes a certain sensibility to draw them out, and that is what I bring to the table: an appreciation or the strange fruit of their enigmatic dreams, and their sincere attempts to confront the truth they have found.

For each case, I take an in-depth approach, spending an enormous amount of time getting to know the unique qualities of each individual, rather than depersonalizing them with generalities based on their crimes. While I develop an empathy for my subject, I always take care not to actually sympathize to the extent that his dramas start paying in the theatre of my own mind. It's a constant balancing act between identification and analysis.

To learn from a person, you must put yourself in his place, follow his train of thought, and feel his emotions. While you follow the thinking of your subject to some extent, you never become like him. You remain yourself...but it's not easy. You draw close for a while, close enough to get a sense of these often-foreign ideas and emotions...but you must always pull back to restore the integrity of your own boundaries.

I have often had cause to contemplate the words of Friedrich Nietzsche: "Whoever fights monsters should see to it that in the process he does not become a monster. And when you look into an abyss, the abyss also looks into you."

But while one must maintain a certain professional distance, on the other hand, in order to capture a mystical treasure, you must confront a fire-breathing dragon - not to slay him, but to charm him with your gentle touch so he will reveal his treasures just to have the pleasure of your company. Cesare Pavese put it another way: "The only way to escape the abyss is to look at it, measure it, sound its depths, and go down into it."

Getting involved with a criminal is a dangerous matter, because when you concentrate deeply on any personality for an extended time, you find yourself drawn into their world. It's not just an abstract subject you are focusing on, it's a man - and in these cases, your subject might be as unpredictable as a wild tiger. And even though your dangerous pussycat might cuddle up to you while you scratch behind his ears, still you must always be aware that he might just as easily rake your flesh to the bone with his razor-sharp claws, just to break the boredom of living in a cage.

And while you're in his cage studying him, remember he's also studying you. There comes a moment when you find yourself standing stock-still, rapt and mutually fascinated, your heart beating as one with his. And suddenly, everything begins to matter, really matter.

Springfield Gothic

Four years ago I set out to learn about crime, murder and killers - having no idea where this peculiar pursuit would take me. Until a year ago I lived the life of a self-professed media queen, as I cultivated my killer correspondence from a cute color-coordinated condo I couldn't afford. But as I became more and more engrossed in my subject, I began to neglect those pesky little things called bills. The facts of life strongly suggested that I put the requisite hours into my computer consulting business. But I still haven't grown up, I guess: I never learned to care more about money than my real love: researching, learning, producing intriguing material. Obviously, this couldn't last. I lost the condo to foreclosure, sold the furniture for gas money, packed the Macintosh in the bank's Honda, and went underground, barely a step ahead of the repo man. I counted on the fact that my bill collectors couldn't find me. But I always made sure that my favorite felons could. I need them just as they need me, and we both had work to do.

For a while I made out all right, polishing off a movie screenplay from a million-dollar waterfront mansion with private security, a heated pool, and daily gourmet food. But Hurricane Andrew blew all that away, and I barely escaped with one carload of my most precious possessions: my original manuscripts, tapes, and diskettes - and of course, my Baby Mac. I was flying on the wings of all of my angels as I nipped along, at the leading edge of the wrath of God.

For a passing moment, I accepted the hospitality of a 6'9" 300 pound Hell's Angel, with a KKK tattoo on his massive biceps: a Big Bad Biker Behind Bars. I moved my files and my Baby Mac into a flea-bitten apartment with his biker babe, on the premise that I would write a book about how his father killed his mother. But it was not to be.

I was already involved with Danny Rolling, the mysterious singing drifter who has staked out more and more of my heart with his angels and his demons, and I had no appetite for anything less exotic than the world he has shared with me. So when the BBBBB hit me with written threats couched in offensive language, that was it: I booked out. Honey, I might fraternize with killers, but don't get me wrong. I don't *DO* abuse.

Once again, because I was still pursuing my non-paying writing projects with a single-mindedness that was more and more often being referred to as obsession, I found myself living like a character out of my own screenplay, in a ramshackle trailer with a hillbilly mechanic playing Lynryd Skynyrd at a brutal volume as he slid into his nightly alcoholic stupor. Huddling close to my Baby Mac in a tiny closet, I pressed on: bringing forth the first volume of *The Rolling Papers* and *Knockin' on Joe* at the same time.

But my hillbilly host was only waiting for me to respond to that certain little gleam in his eye, and once he realized that was never to be, I had to leave there too. Such is the life of a woman flying blind into the darkest night: fleeing a well-lit and deadly-predictable rut to pursue an outrageous dream with no backers, no assets and no guarantees. Because of my obsessive involvement in my work, *which does not pay*, the past year has been a death-defying high-wire dance, performed with no net.

After I fled the lurid glow of the trailer's neon beer signs, I sought refuge in a nesting ground for every kind of violence, an ugly place with a pretty name: Springfield.

The Springfield district of Jacksonville, Florida, is more than your typical burnt-out inner-city high-crime area. It's beyond surreal: it's absolutely *TILTED*. It's a combustible mixture of violence, insanity and despair... the noxious fumes from the paper mills and the sulphurous water...the musty odor of unwashed human flesh and bodily secretions...the flashing weapons and open wounds...the scarred faces and burnt-out eyes of the dispossessed...the sounds of broken glass, gunfire and sirens providing the percussion over the undercurrent of muttered threats, hysterical laughter and screams in the night...the men boasting they'd just as soon kill you as thump the ashes off their cigarette...the women seeking shelter in Almighty God...cracked-out, dropped-out, illiterate kids...this is the backdrop for the broken lives of its children.

The mean streets of Springfield produced two of the killers whose works are included in this book: Ottis Toole and Bobby Lewis. And Joe O'Dell grew up right across the river. As Bobby recently wrote while he was involved in Danny Rolling's hair-raising multiple murder confessions: "This is easy compared to Springfield."

I write these words from the top floor of a crumbling old haunted house ruled by a holy-ghost spirit-filled, pistol-packing grandma who not only has had two serial killers shaking in their boots, but has known more than that in the Biblical sense. "Bullshit walks," she likes to say, "but my .38 Special walks and talks." And seeing her steely eye and her regal bearing, you believe.

The extent to which I have taken my research gives a whole new meaning to the term "participatory journalism". The rebel yells and gunfire in the night begin to sound almost normal. And the baby munches on the rat poison while his teenage mom zonks out on MTV: vacant. And on the front porch, a derelict howls at the moon, clapping his hands and chanting "I'm gonna *KICK* your ass, gonna *KICK* your ass..." as he slowly slithers down into an oblivious heap.

When I first visited this human swamp last year, I asked one of its denizens how those two scroungy murder machines Henry Lee Lucas and Ottis Toole could pursue their violent crimes for so long without anyone noticing them. In reply, he whipped out a big ugly butcher knife and rubbed his thumb along its edge as he leered, "Hell, you're talking to a serial killer right now!" I don't doubt it. *Eau de Springfield.*

The general situation is pretty grim, but I'm learning how the other half lives in a way that reading or hearing about it just cannot convey. Last week, my research into the social circumstances that breed uncontrollable violence got even more serious: I was arrested and put in jail. I had committed the heinous offence of driving my trusty Honda with an expired tag and a suspended licence, while failing to appear for a court date on a similar offence at my last domicile. Because I still hadn't given up my monomaniacal pursuit of the work I love in order to become a financially responsible member of society, I was handcuffed behind my back and transported to the County Jail, where I spent a very convincing 18 hours developing empathy for my fellas. I sat in the cramped holding cells and stood in the crowded halls, writing a 25-page letter to my prison pals as a member of the Prison Brother-and-Sisterhood: just call me Inmate London, a/a/a 93-325947, yes *SIR*. You might be pleased to know I acted up - not much, mind you, but a little bit.

This "*MO MACHO*" lady cop was strutting around the hail looking for any opportunity to vent a heavy charge of built-up sadistic hostility. I caught her eye and tapped my stripped wrist, mouthing the question, "*TIME?*" She tossed her smart-ass reply over her shoulder: "Time? You got a *LOTTA*

time!" And my cellmates gasped as I spat back *"FUCK YOU, BITCH!"*
I might still be in there right now if she'd caught that foolish remark. The
male prisoners, dogs that they are, bark every kind of obscenity with
impunity, but apparently more decorous twittering was expected of us lady
jailbirds.

Oh, there's no doubt this work has changed my life. Like the old song
says, in every crime you take something away and you leave something
behind. And so it is with life. Just as I have an impact on the lives of
prisoners I work with, I can't get involved with them to the extent that I have
without their touching, and to some extent, changing, my own life. Since my
style is to go all the way with the things I do, the impact of this season in hell
has been quite extreme. It has alienated family, friends, and would-be
employers. I've seen people actually shrink from me in fear and distaste,
blaming me for the crimes my subjects have committed as if I were a criminal
myself, instead of a writer. I've been dismissed as everything from an
airhead prison groupie to a calculating con artist, exploiting the emotions of
the poor defenseless convicts I work with to rip them off for their stories.
They say I'm just in it for the money. If only they knew - they wouldn't
believe it anyway.

Just this week, the local newspaper described how I have been ripping
off my most recent killer "victim". As a jealous inmate described my latest
scam to reporters, "Danny Rolling spends most of his time talking about
London, and shows off sketches before he mails them to her. He said he
believes Danny is naive to London's intentions to profit from her relationship
with him." Then he goes on to complain that Bobby Lewis has threatened
to kill him if he tried to convince Rolling that I do not love him. "He asked
me if I liked living. That's a pretty good threat there." Claiming that I have
led Danny Rolling on with my intimately worded letters, he says, "The
woman has got him convinced they're in love. What we're dealing with is
fraud." Then his girlfriend chimes in, "She told me she was going to get
that story, and the only way she could was to earn his trust. I'm afraid that
he's going to go off the deep end when he finds out he was scammed." Oh
PLEASE....

Robert Fieldmore Lewis

Part One

"Regular Joes"

"Caryl Chessman ... acted out the drama of the individual vs. the state, played his role without compromise, and died bravely. I saw his last night on television ... he was at ease. I could sense how he liked the attention ... They asked if he expected to die on the morning, and he smiled and said, 'Yes, they have me now. I think it's over.' He taught them the power of the written word when he came to prominence with his first book. He had shouted from his cell and the world was listening ... They forbade him to write and confiscated his second book because he had written about Death Row. What else was he to write about? They were asking the court to act as if they believed the state had assigned Chessman something to do while waiting to die, to write this book, and to turn over to them any money it might earn. A federal judge dismissed this contemptuously. And it seems to me this miserable attempt to silence a condemned man and hustle him to his death is the sorriest abuse of free speech since the notorious Sedition Act."

*- Malcolm Braly, **False Starts***

1

ROBERT FIELDMORE LEWIS
by Sondra London

Not that Bad

In June of 1989, a lifer at Florida State Prison saw a tabloid story about *Killer Fiction* [*See section on Gerard John Schaefer in Part Two*], and shot a kite over to fellow-inmate Schaefer, asking how he could obtain a copy of his book. Schaefer obligingly gave him the Media Queen address, and he wrote to me, introducing himself as Robert Fieldmore Lewis, otherwise known as Beautiful Bobby by the string of girls he had walking the streets of Jacksonville. He informed me that if it was crime stories I was after, I should forget Schaefer's bullshit, and listen to *his* stories, which were better, because they were *true*. Mentioning that he had spent a year alone with Ted Bundy and had escaped from Death Row, he enclosed a copy of his post-sentence investigation as a sort of macabre resume.

I learned that Bobby Lewis was thirty years old in 1977, when he was sentenced to Death Row. One evening in January of 1976, Joe Richards, a 46-year-old small-time Jacksonville crook, was at his comfortable river-front ranch home, reclining in bed in an intimate conversation with two close friends of the female persuasion, when his brains were blown all over the walls, the ceiling, the floor, and the horrified ladies.

There had been a tense situation brewing in the Jacksonville underworld for about a month. Bobby Lewis had robbed a dope dealer, and the dealer hired Joe Richards to get his money back. In pursuit of the bounty, Richards had been harassing not only Lewis but several of his associates, causing them to become increasingly irritated. The post-sentence investigation explained exactly how the tension was resolved:

"The entire top right portion of the head was disintegrated, multiple wounds were evident in the right upper arm and lower forearm, and the upper right torso. The right thigh exhibited an apparent entry wound, as did the lower right calf area. What appeared to be blood, brains and skull matter was evidenced throughout the bedroom, adjoining bathroom and hall area, on the walls, ceiling and floor. A large mass, which appeared to be the principal portion of the brain, was located on the floor approximately three feet west of the bed."

There were other people and other issues involved in the case, but although Bobby Lewis hated Joe Richards and was glad he was dead, he stated that he was not present at the house on Trout River that night and he was not guilty of murder.

Nevertheless, he was sentenced to die. Recommending execution, the state's attorneys stated that in their opinion, Bobby would kill again regardless of whether or not he was inside or outside of prison; that his record showed he was totally unable to remain at large without breaking the law; that he was incorrigible and could not be rehabilitated; and that he had forfeited his right to live.

Next to this grim prognosis, Bobby had pencilled in a goofy goggle-eyed smiley-face and scrawled, "I'm not all that bad!"

A Regular Joe

At this point, I was extensively involved in my work with Schaefer and had no intention of ever working with another convict. Schaefer was the only one I had ever known, and I knew him long before he was locked up. I was still under the standard impression that convicts were all alike: dangerous, nasty, undesirable creatures who were not fit to live, much less communicate on a level with refined, law-abiding ladies like myself. I still thought I was just going to publish *Killer Fiction*, maybe *Killer Serial*, and that would be the end of that, and I could go back to some semblance of my previous life.

I tried to blow Bobby off, informing him coolly that I was a bitch, I was busy, I wasn't interested, I wasn't paying anything...but I *would* like to hear about Ted Bundy. With that, my singular new career moved into the next phase, and from this point on, there would be no turning back.

Schaefer never liked Bobby, and Bobby quite naturally returned the favor. While my relationship with Schaefer was not a romantic liaison, still he had come to consider me "his". He strenuously denied being jealous, but freely admitted he believed that he deserved my full attention and resented any intrusions. For his part, Bobby disapproved of Schaefer, as much for his choice of literary material as for his crimes, and resented being mentioned in the same article (as happens from time to time). I constantly received letters from each one, imploring me not to have anything further to do with the other. I found it laughably childish, but now I realize it was serious. As time went by I noticed that other convict writers would often show the same tendency, and I began to look at such behavior as a primitive territorial dispute, both instinctive and inevitable.

While my prior experience with budding creative writers included tutoring at a college level, I really had no idea how to help men in cages become literary lions. When Bobby Lewis entered my life, there was no book to go by, no role model to consult. I had no plan and no format. I had been playing a fairly dominant, autocratic role with Schaefer, forever giving him assignments, and he responded eagerly. Regardless of other problems I might have had with Schaefer, when I critiqued his writing he took it like a real pro, and applied my suggestions to his next effort.

Now here we had Bobby, a high-school drop-out with an inferiority complex about his dismal spelling and grammar. What worked with Schaefer wasn't going to work with Bobby. What would work? I was going to have to find that out the old-fashioned way, by *doing* it - mistakes and all.

His original intention was for me to come in and interview him, and then write up his stories myself. But since prison regulations forbid visiting more than one inmate at the same institution, this was not possible. When he realized he was going to have to push the pen himself, he was almost too embarrassed about his grammar to even try. He had never thought of his own writing as any good. But I assured him I don't judge people by their grammar. I just want to find out what they have to say. I did edit his writing, but I didn't just correct the spelling and put the punctuation in the right place. I encouraged him, coached and trained him, and gave him new ideas. Once he gained confidence, he began to get a kick out of this writing thing.

And out from under the initial roughness, emerged a charming, natural-born storyteller with fascinating tales that distinctively portray his sunny personality and underworld elan. A Bobby Lewis story moves forward with the inevitability of a living thing, without artifice or pretension, with a heartbeat. And therein lies it's power. When he writes a story, it stays the way he wrote it, giving it the gritty, in-your-face realism of a home video.

It was working with Bobby that first taught me the revolutionary concept that killers are just people. Sure, Bobby's been to Death Row for killing a man, but the appeals court gave him life, and he'll finish up his mandatory 25 years pretty soon. He'll be in his mid-fifties when he gets back on the street, and when he does, he won't be incorrigible or psychopathic. He'll just be a regular Joe - a sports fan who likes to laugh, eat, get high, have sex, listen to music, gamble, and goof off. I wonder if he'll still be a writer. I sure hope so.

The Creative Convict

Even though my collaboration with Bobby Lewis has produced some good stories, their creation has been neither uneventful nor untroubled.

Bobby had some important lessons to teach me about working with these bad boys. They are not professional artists or writers. The give-and-take of a healthy writer-editor relationship is rarely present. The tough macho shell they project turns out to not so tough after all, but rather brittle, without the resiliency of your everyday hero, the humble writer who comes up with ideas, has them rejected, and goes right back and comes up with more. Prisoners can't tolerate criticism, and they don't take to being told what to do by anyone, much less a woman. It was touch and go with Bobby. Several times I came close to losing him, and more than once I told him to get lost.

Anyone who attempts to write the truth about their life goes through an intoxicating transformation process that is both exhilarating and disturbing - even more so for a man like Bobby, because the events that lead up to imprisonment are always painful. As he struggled with confronting the truth about himself, powerful emotions he had been running from for years come to the surface. He had no idea how to handle them.

"I am emotional, I am sensitive. I'm sure prison has sort of warped me. And I got all types of defence systems at work to survive this everyday bullshit! And I began to feel I was just in more bullshit - I got to admit I don't understand you. I got so hot the other day I went off and tore half my cell up. I have not threw a fit like that since I was a kid! I was hot for a couple of days. Then I got your card and I laughed for a half hour. I started to wonder am I going nuts or are you! That night I went to bed and spilt a lot of tears! That also made me mad, as it don't do much for the tough guy image!"

Christmas of 1989 marked the end of the most active phase of our collaboration to date. That was when hell froze over. Everyone knows it never snows in Florida, but that winter at Florida State Prison (aka *HELL*) the snow blew in directly onto some of the prisoners through windows that had been broken out by a rampaging goon squad, and even in that sub-freezing weather, there was no heat whatsoever. Though Bobby tried to maintain his buoyant demeanor, he wrote, "Have you ever just got in a mood where you did not want to do nothing? Or you just keep putting things off?"

But it turned out not to be just an attitude problem. Bobby was sick. He caught the flu like everyone else on his wing, but by the time he was taken to the emergency room, he was in critical condition with pneumonia, and was confined to a hospital with tubes in his chest throughout most of 1990, only returning to life and to FSP in September.

During his long convalescence, I missed my buddy, and sent him get-well cards and letters of encouragement. I also called the prison hospital regularly to enquire about him, for two reasons. Of course, I found out about his condition, but more importantly, I put the prison system on notice that somebody cares about this inmate, somebody knows where he is and who is responsible for his care. Many inmates swear that prison hospitals are killing grounds for troublemakers, that they are tortured and beaten to death and their remains buried in the unmarked graves nearby. It's never been proven, but the stories have been circulating for years. The way the system works, they say, is that only the prisoners with no outside contacts are killed. This is one of the most powerful motivations for an inmate to write stories, give interviews, and gain recognition by the media: to gain a small measure of immunity from the ultimate in prison abuse. I didn't want to lose Bobby to benign neglect or worse, so I made sure the prison knew somebody was watching.

Art as Life

Just as our life becomes our art, so we see that art can return the favor by becoming life. This intertwined quality of life and art was soon to take yet another twist, and this time, it would make all the rest just look like practice.

In May of 1992, Bobby met a guy who reminded him of his old pal and everyone's favorite serial killer, the darkly charismatic Ted Bundy. The state of Florida had been in a traumatic state of deja vu since the 1990 slayings of five college students over a three-day period just as fall classes began. Five million dollars were spent investigating before charges were finally brought against Danny Harold Rolling in November of 1991. In May of 1992, he was sent to FSP and placed on the wing where Bobby Lewis worked. Everyone may be calling him the new Ted Bundy, but I was soon to find out that Danny Rolling is *different.*

Danny told Bobby he had a lot of offers from writers to work with him on his exclusive story, but he had turned them all down. Bobby showed Danny a movie script I had written about his love affair with a mixed-race girl down in South Carolina, during his time on the lam from Death Row. After reading it, Danny decided that I was the writer he wanted to work with. But that, as they say, is yet another story...

DON'T CALL THIS PRISON MY HOME
by Robert Fieldmore Lewis

If I Am An Animal

As I try to portray the events of life in this prison, and to convey the tension and emotion in these events, I find it hard to put into words. I dropped out of school in the ninth grade, and English was always my worst subject. But bear with me, because the stories I tell are true.

If any prison official, judge, lawyer or policeman claims that I am lying, I'll be glad to stand any lie detector tests, voice stress tests, or other examinations by an impartial party, and I will challenge my accusers to take the same tests. That should determine who is telling the truth.

I know many people will say this is just another convict trying to make a buck off the suffering he caused to other people. Sorry, folks, but I do not make one cent from this. Part goes to the lady who was kind enough and had the courage enough to help me do this book, and part goes to charity. The only thing I stand to gain is a hard time, harassment by guards and prisoners, and perhaps the loss of the transfer I've been waiting fourteen years to get. Then why, you ask, do I do it?

Overcrowding and lack of funds make prisons dangerous to everyone. If someone will just take the trouble to tell the truth about how it is, then maybe someone can do something about how it will be in the future. The public wants to keep us in prison for a long time, but they won't pay the price. Politicians don't push the issue because they don't want to seem soft on crime.

Every taxpayer and every politician has reason to be alarmed, since what they go on ignoring every day will only cost them more in the long run. The American prison system is a national disgrace, and Florida is one of the worst. Walls are coming down all over the world, and before Americans scream for human rights in the prisons and mental institutions of Russia and other countries, we'd better take a look in our own back yard.

Millions of Americans live behind walls that are not coming down, but instead are getting bigger and stronger every day. There are already millions of us. We are a minority, but each day we are growing - getting bigger, smarter, more dangerous, and a lot less human. And unless you pass a law to just kill us all, remember that sooner or later we are coming back to see you.

The moral fiber of life on the streets has changed with the influence of drugs like heroin, crack, and ice, and the prisons have changed too. Now we have the worst of every group under one roof to become more like animals, more cunning and well-versed in ways to beat the law. This place strips away all hope and self-respect, until life reaches a level of existence that has all the hallmarks of a blockbuster horror flick - but this is no movie, this is real.

I had to smile the other day when I saw on TV an animal shelter surrounded by people protesting the treatment of animals - their inadequate space, their food, their solitary confinement. And these good people were mad. They demanded changes. They screamed about their tax dollars and cruelty and said to do it right or shut it down.

But as I sat in my cell in 32 degrees weather, huddled under a thick blanket because I had no jacket and there was no heat, I realized those animals had heat in the winter and air conditioning in the summer. They had more room than I do. Their diet was better, and their housing was healthier.

I realized that the vast majority of people consider us less than human. We have been convicted of crimes, and the animals have done nothing. If that be the case, then all I am asking is to treat us at least as well as the other animals you keep in cages.

I am 5'8" and 180 pounds, and I live in a 6 x 10 outhouse with a bunk in it. What I am fed keeps me guessing - is it animal, vegetable or mineral? I may be bad, but I'm not bad enough to eat something when I can't even tell what it is.

I exercise four hours a week in a 20 x 20 steel cage with 15 other men.Name one animal anywhere of a similar size that does not have many times the space I do. Add smoke and noise 24 hours a day and welcome home!

You call me an animal, you say I am inhuman. You built this prison you call my home. You buy my food, you pay my keepers, you keep me penned up here for life. If I am an animal, then what does that make you?

Don't Call This Prison My Home

Each person handles time in prison differently, and builds his own defense system to survive in this surreal madhouse.

It's like a Noah's Ark for all the sick and the bad, the rejects of life - at least two of every kind of asshole that walks this earth. They come every size, shape and color and a lot of foreign languages. And some of the very worst are here at the East Unit of Florida State Prison at Starke, where I have lived for the past 14 years.

There are approximately 40,000 people in the Florida prison system. This building holds 1,200 and over 300 of them are on Death Row. Over a hundred are in a mental ward, and 500 are on lock-up. They have been sent here from every other prison as the trouble-makers, the fuck-ups. About 300 are in population on a trial basis to see if they can stay out of trouble so they can transfer. The idea is to be any place but here. This is the hellhole of the system. The men here are the baddest, the sickest, the craziest in the state, and they have little respect for themselves or anyone else. This is where they bring people to kill them.

As long as I have been locked up, it still takes a few minutes to get adjusted when I wake up each morning. After a couple of cups of coffee and a joint, and a little meditation, I can block it all out.

The man who survives prison is the one who creates the most protective devices to deal with the first signs of trouble. When I go anywhere, even to the shower every other night, I am handcuffed behind my back to go there and come back. While I enjoy my five minutes of cold water in the winter and hot water in the summer, naked men are standing around hollering and whistling at other men, looking for just one sign of fear that will let them bust some asshole wide open so they can own another man.

When a new man comes in here, the first thing he is tested for is if he will fuck. Next test is if he will snitch. So it's, "Hey how about a shot of that ass?"

Or they rob your cell, take your family photos, your radio, your watch. And you and everyone else knows exactly who did it. So then you have to fight and maybe kill or be killed, or else you go snitch. If the guy tries to take the easy way out and snitches, the rest of his time in prison there may as well be a large sign on him saying *OPEN SEASON - DO WHAT YOU WANT TO ME.*

On our wing there are a hundred men, so we have the combined smell of unwashed bodies and clothes and a hundred shit-jackets. A cloud of tobacco smoke and funk hangs in the air. The noise level most of the time is at the level of a jet engine. I often wonder what the combined effects of noise pollution and smoke pollution have on a prisoner's nervous system. It keeps everyone on edge, along with all the petty bullshit that we get from guards and give to each other, especially over long periods of time.

On the wing next to me are a hundred men who didn't make it - the bug wing, where every day they throw shit and piss at each other and scream, cry, beat the walls, and cut and burn themselves. You'd be amazed at how many men hurt themselves to get attention of any type - to go to the clinic and see a nurse, to hear just one or two words of comfort and sympathy.

Most prisoners have nobody outside. They get no mail, they can't even buy a Coke, because somebody has to send you money so you can be issued a book like food stamps to buy what you want. This is probably true of 80% of the prisoners in the Florida prison system. Fifteen percent get money from family or friends, letters, packages, and visits, and they do OK. The other five percent are the ones that run drugs, gambling and other vices inside, and these are the ones that rule supreme.

Grass is the major product of the prison, and there is a lot of money in it. I did it for years here and made and wasted a lot of money. I used to buy so many Cokes for the people that worked for me that my Coca-Cola bill ran over $100 a week. I got out of it a few years ago, but people still give me a lot of gifts of smoke. It eases the tension and makes my day.

This type of living changes people and forces them to be other than they want to be. There are a lot of things prison takes from a man, but there are other things that you don't have to give up. And if people understand that bringing trouble to you is like asking for death, then you don't have these problems. There is no place that is even 50% safe. Prisoners have 24 hours every day to think up things to do. Guards only have 8 hours a day to figure out how to stop them.

Prison guards have tried to break me. There is very little they have not done or tried to do to me. A lot of sick puppies work here. One guard on Death Row used to bring in grass and then back up to the bars to give the men a shot of ass. They just fired the psychiatrist for trading head jobs with his patients. Must be a new form of treatment for the mentally ill.

The price of a man's life is as cheap as his asshole. My day is full of watching men dehumanize other men. I see men turn queer for tobacco, or from fear, or just for the touch of another human being. They used to distribute a form of state tobacco free to the prisoners that had nothing, and when it stopped a few years ago, I was amazed at the people who became punks and sold their assholes to be able to smoke. What that must do to a man's soul, I can't imagine. I'd rather be dead myself.

About 80% of all men in prison are involved in homosexuality. Whether they pitch or catch it's all the same. I never have, and I've been locked up a good portion of my life. I'm sure a shot of ass or a head job from a man may feel good physically, but I just don't have any part of me that is turned on by a man. I just plain like women too much. I miss sex a lot because I was sexually active outside. When I see a big old muscle-bound ugly motherfucker with his towel pulled up to his chest - legs shaved and eyebrows plucked - swishing his way to the shower, I say to myself, anyone that would want *that* has got to be one sick puppy. My mind and my hand have got me through all these years.

But they have crazy rules. If a man is married, his wife can't send him a picture of herself in a bra and panties. But he can have a cell full of *Hustler* and *Penthouse*, bare tits and pussy everywhere. So he can't look at his wife, but he gets all he wants of strangers!

Prison is big business - one of the top ten industries in Florida. Inside graft and corruption reigns. This prison has been run for over one hundred years like an old slave plantation. There is a huge clique that runs these places to the second, third and fourth generations. As they intermarried and grew, they got ever more powerful positions in the system. Members of these families or their friends get the contracts for the prisons. What a position of power for a company to be in! For example, the people that make the canteen sandwiches know its product automatically goes to 40,000 people with no competition. You eat their food or you don't eat at all. I've handled paperwork for years in this place, and we are talking major kickbacks at all levels!

Blacks for the most part run the inmate society today. They're in the majority, and I give them credit because they stick together against the other races. The Spanish groups do the same. The whites as a group are the biggest pussies. It's interesting to consider how whites as a group react when they don't control the power. There are exceptions to every rule, and at the top of the social structure are the killers - the ones that people just don't fuck with because they are pure trouble. Like all animals, prisoners prey on the weak. They go to the easy shots. Babykillers and ladykillers are the most hated, along with former cops and guards.

Prison talk is full of hate and resentment. It goes *Nigger Cracker Spic Fuck-boy Dick-sucker Snitch* on and on and on like that day and night like a record stuck in one lifelong groove. As I'm writing this, a couple of black punks have been arguing over which one is the best dick-sucker, and one told the other that he could suck a basketball through a garden hose! That shut the other one up, so he must have won.

So this is for all my hardass outlaw counterparts on the street that will someday wind up here with us. Boys, get you an asshole-enlarger and start practising. Or come prepared to kill or be killed - 24 hours a day, seven days a week, 365 days a year, year in and year out, for the rest of your life.

The White House

I had just turned 13 a month earlier when I was sent to reform school on Halloween day, with some candy and a few dollars. My mother worked as a maid and my father as a laborer, and with no brothers or sisters, I had more or less raised myself.

What got me sent away was stealing a car. Everybody else had one, and I was at the age where I wanted one too. My first day there I was beat up twice and had all my stuff stolen. I went to bed that night scared and crying. I was small for my age - about 5'4" and 110 lbs. I was puny, but I swore that night I would get tough. By the next four months I had put on 30 pounds, kicked the shit out of the two that got me the first day, and won the Golden Gloves trophy for my weight. We fought against all the other reform schools in the South.

The reform school at Mariana, Florida looks like a big southern college campus with little cottages, beautifully kept up, with about 1,000 boys aged 8 to 16. In fact it is the cruellest, most sadistic place I have ever been, and to read my life is to know I have been in some bad places.

In back of the kitchen was a small white brick house about 10 x 20 that used to be for cold storage, but was used to torture and beat kids. The instrument was a razor strop - the kind that goes on an old-fashioned barber chair to sharpen a razor. It was about 3 feet long, 3 inches wide, and half-inch thick. If you were just beat black and blue that was called a pinky, and you got off easy. A bad beating was determined by how many places you got busted open and how bad you were bleeding when it was over.

I had fought my way up amongst the boys until I was one of the physically baddest ones there. But I was afraid of the white house, as I had seen those people break the spirit of so many other tough boys.

Inside was an old army cot with a mattress and a pillow covered with teeth marks and blood stains. When they started to beat you, they would tell you how many lashes you'd get. If you cried out or moaned in pain, they would start over. For four months I had been wondering how I would handle that, and later that night I was to find out.

When I had first come in, I was tested to see if I would fight, and I did. It was also a test to see if I would snitch, which I did not. If I had not fought that first day, the first night I would have been fucked, and turned into a punk.

Now as an old-timer, I knew it was my turn to test the new cocks as they came in. I remembered how the two boys beat me the first day, and I tried to test the new ones in other ways. The cottages each held about 80 boys, with 40 at each end dormitory style, and a cottage father than lived upstairs in the middle. Each cottage had a clay basketball court with two baskets nailed up on boards about 10 feet high. Each kid has a job or area to clean up, and it was my job to assign the new kid a job.

Earlier that day one of our baskets had fallen off the pole, and when it was nailed up, it was two feet shorter than the other one, since we had to do it by standing on each other's shoulders. It was a freezing winter day, about 15 degrees with a strong wind. About 3.00 p.m. I took the new kid outside and told him his job was to water the basketball pole each hour on the hour, since we had a big game that week against another cottage, and the short basket was theirs. I told him if it didn't grow as tall as the other one by game time, I was going to kick his ass. It was easy to see he thought I was crazy, but too scared to do anything but say OK. For hour after hour we watched him water the pole and laughed at him.

That night everyone had gone to sleep and forgot about the new kid. The night watchman found him outside at 2.00 a.m., crying and half frozen in his thin PJs watering the pole. When he asked the kid who told him to do that, he told him.

I was in bed dreaming of some fat young pussy, when I was snatched out of bed by my hair and held off the floor. Then I was spun around and kicked in the ass all the way to a car outside. I was cold and scared, as I knew my time to go to the white house had come. I don't think to this day anything has ever scared me so bad - not even the electric chair. I had to tell myself I would not scream. Each time I heard the belt drag the floor and then tap the wall, that meant I was about to get hit. I would loosen up the muscles in my ass, because when you tighten up, that's when it splits you open. They usually just hit you across the ass, but this night because they had to get up and come out in the cold, they beat me across my back and legs too.

Each time I was hit, I bit into the pillow and screamed inside my mind. I was too scared to scream aloud, too scared they would start all over again. I got 20 lashes. By the time it was over I was almost naked, as my PJs were nearly torn off me. I was bleeding in a couple of places, but not too bad. I had managed not to tighten up my muscles, and not to cry out. I was proud that I took their worst and was not broken.

When I got back from the cottage, I went and got in bed just like I was. All the lights were out, but I knew all the boys were up. They asked me what happened. I told them the new kid snitched on me, I'd been to the white house, and I'd get his ass tomorrow. I went to sleep beat but proud.

I didn't know it but about ten of my friends on my end of the building got up and got a blanket and eased to the other end to give the kid a blanket party. That's when four boys each take a corner of a blanket and pull it down over a bed so they can let the rest beat the kid under the blanket, and he could not see to tell who had done it. Blanket parties were fairly common, but these boys went all out. They knocked out a lot of the kid's teeth and busted him up good.

I was asleep and did not know a thing until again I was snatched out of bed by the same men. They kicked and beat me out to the car. The real scary thing this time was that I did not know why. One the way there, one told me, "So you think you're tough! We'll see who's tough!"

I was hollering, "But I ain't done nothing!"

"You lying little bastard! Shut up!" he yelled and punched me in the head.

As soon as we got inside I was thrown on the bed and they went crazy. I had blisters from my head to my feet. The next day, all I could remember was thinking that they were killing me, that I was dying. But I would not scream or beg, as I knew that was what they wanted. I passed out.

I woke up screaming in the hospital as a nurse was putting salt and vinegar solution over my wounds to kill the infection and close the cuts. I spent a week in there, and in that time my hatred for all forms of authority grew until all I could think was, "Wait till I grow up!"

Well, I am grown up now, and you see how my life turned out. The men who beat me that night continued to beat many other kids like me for years, until they beat two so bad they almost killed them. There was finally a big investigation, and most of them were fired. But one went on to become the head of the Parole and Probation Commission for the State of Florida. These men will be remembered, as there are reform schools with plaques all over the state that carry the names of the most sadistic group of men I ever met. They are used as examples to kids in reform schools of what they should strive to become.

But I would rather be a crook, and to have done all the crimes I have done, than to have treated one kid the way they treated me. You may think things have changed. But with overcrowding and shortages of every kind, the system can't control the rape, robbery, slavery, drugs, gambling, killing and every kind of cruelty and inhumanity that dominates our prisons today.

You say you pay your taxes, it's not your problem? I hope you sleep well tonight, but one last thought: one out of every ten Americans has been to prison or is currently in prison, and the number is growing each year. And nine out of ten prisoners will one day be free.

Freedom Isn't Everything

I was in the Jacksonville jail, convicted of murder and waiting to go to Death Row, when my father died.

The judge said I could go to his funeral but I would have to find two policemen to escort me and pay for their day's work. My lawyer, my family and I tried, but everywhere we got the same answer: *No way.* They said my friends would just try to break me away and somebody was bound to get killed.

At last I came out of my cell to call my mother and let her know I couldn't come. She was crying and I was crying too. The two guards put me back in my cell. I had known them for about six months and they had always been decent and polite to me, and I to them. About fifteen minutes later these two men called me back out. They had called the judge to find out if they had the authority to take me to my father's funeral. The judge had said yes, but advised them against it. All the other guards at the jail had told them not to do it.

One of them said, "Bobby, I am a Christian, and I lost my father not too long ago. I know what you're going through right now, and I take it as my Christian duty to take you to your daddy's funeral."

He pointed to the other guard and went on, "Now this is my friend, Bobby. And he's going along with us because he won't let me go without him. Everyone is saying you're going to run and you'll probably have both of us shot. Now, I know you can do that. But I'm gonna ask you as a man - not for me, but for my friend here, who is going along with this because of me. I want you to look in the eye and tell me that you won't try to escape and you won't let my friend get hurt."

I said, "Mister, if you'll take me to my daddy's funeral, not only will I not escape, I will stand with you against anyone who tries to free me. You could take the cuffs off me and I would not run."

"I believe you, Bobby," he said, and he handcuffed me and took me out of the jail. When we got in the police car, there was no cage between us. The same man turned around and took the cuffs off me, saying, "I'm not going to cuff you, since it won't make any difference if you are lying to me. When we get to the funeral, we won't act like police, so as not to embarrass you."

They had changed their uniforms to suits, and when we got to the funeral home, they sat in the back. I went to my mother, and was surrounded by my friends. Probably half of them were armed in case Joe's friends tried to get me.

We left the funeral home and went to the grave site. The guards stayed in the car. At times 50 to 75 yards away, and I could have walked away or unarmed them any time I wanted to. I knew it and they knew it! I walked around for over an hour with my people until it was time to go. I hugged my mother and told her how much I loved her. I hugged and kissed my friends, and then I walked back to the police car and opened the door and got in.

If you don't think my every instinct was burning to run, knowing I was headed for Death Row and that I would never have another chance like that... I never wanted anything so much in my life as to run.

The only thing that kept me there was to show my ultimate respect for these two men, the only two men in the county that trusted me, took my word, and risked their lives for me. They even stopped and bought me a good meal on the way back to the jail. To this day, there is nothing I would not do for either of them.

When we got back to the jail, I got out of the car without cuffs and walked in by myself. There were maybe ten off-duty guards that had stayed over, since they were worried for these two men and would not go home until there were back safe.

As I walked toward the jail, I heard one of the guards tell another, "I don't believe it!" These men had shown me the ultimate respect and consideration when I needed it, and I would have gladly died before I'd have done any less.

Getting Away with Murder

After five years on Death Row and many more in the rest of prison, I began to understand the road that takes some murderers to the electric chair while others are sentenced to life or less.

Should you find yourself on trial for your life, the best you can hope for is a very complicated case that lasts a long time. Mass murder, kidnapping victims across state line, robbery & sexual assault - the worse the better. Because compared to someone who just got into an argument and killed another person, your trial will be much longer and more expensive.

If the things you do are bad enough to get national attention, then you can look forward to good lawyers in private practice wanting your case for the free publicity and advertising their firm will get by handling you. The better the lawyer, the better your chance. And then there's always books and magazine stories you can sell to make more money to be able to afford a long appeal and the over-priced necessities that must be bought in prison.

But best of all, the more complicated your trial, the better your chances of getting off Death Row, because once you have been found guilty the only thing that matters are the technical mistakes in your trial. If any of your constitutional rights have been violated, then you get to start all over again with a new trial.

So take a few tips from a man who beat Death Row: if you want to get away with murder, follow the Robert Lewis Code.

1. *DON'T* commit the crime. While this is always your best insurance against execution, it is far from foolproof. It is not true that lawyers, judges and witnesses are more careful with death penalty cases. By my estimation, about one out of a dozen Death Row inmates is actually innocent. Don't be deceived; innocent people *are* executed.

2. *DO* accept a plea bargain, even if you are innocent. There are men who have been executed after refusing a deal with the state to plead guilty to manslaughter and serve ten years. The state felt its case was weak enough

to offer the deal, but the defendants felt they actually weren't guilty. Do you want to end up on the hot seat when you might get out in ten years?

3. *DO* commit murder in the North. Just like on racism, there is a Mason Dixon line on the death penalty. Most northern states just don't have it, and those that do seldom use it. Over 90% of all executions are in the South.

4. *DO* have friends in high places. A good example is a friend of the governor who killed some of his own family and ran into the street trying to kill more. He was able to plead guilty to 15-20 with no mandatory sentence. He didn't even have to go to the regular reception area, but was sent to an honor work release camp to teach other prisoners how to act on the outside.

5. *DON'T* be poor. Few of those accused of murder can afford private lawyers and investigators. A Texas millionaire was recently acquitted after spending several million dollars, even though there were eye witnesses and a lot of evidence against him.

6. *DON'T* kill anyone important. The best way to escape Death Row is to kill a black or another racial minority. National statistics show it's open season on minorities. Any police investigation will be perfunctory at best. Chances are you won't even be arrested, but in the off chance you are tried and convicted, you won't get the death penalty.

7. *DO* be a woman. Women have committed many murders since the death penalty came back in, but few have received the death sentence and only one has been executed. Why? It's just not good public relations for a governor to kill a woman or even ask that one be killed, especially when there are so many men you can kill for the same crime and have public support for it. The death penalty is a politician's dream come true. What other issue can get his name and picture in the paper without political opposition or debate? A smart politician knows when he's got a good thing.

Zipgun

Back in '76 when I first went to Death Row it was one wildass place - lots of drugs and weapons.

Everyone had a homemade knife or a zipgun. This was usually made out of a short piece of pipe with a hole in the top for a fuse, packed with match heads and anything at all for shot, from ball bearings to glass to small pieces of metal out of a can.

That night I had just got two pounds of good Mexican dirt weed in the mail. I got all my grass in free, sent in large brown legal envelopes with a lawyer's name on the outside. Back then they did not open the legal mail, they just gave it to you. So I'd have a couple of pounds sent every two weeks to someone different on the floor under a different lawyer's name. Because it didn't cost me to get it in, that left a lot to party with, and I had 17 eager killers to help me. This lasted two years until one of the men had his wife send him some of her used panties in the mail. They had to be well-used because they smelled so bad it made the guards curious. They called for a lieutenant and he opened the package. That gave them the bright idea to open the rest of the packages that had come in that day. Yep, you got it. Two pounds down the fucking drain, and the end of a two-year party.

But back to the story. Now, at Florida State Prison there are three floors to a wing, with 17 cells on each side of each floor, and that night we had one empty cell out of our 17. Right after supper they brought this black man in, fighting and raising hell. They threw him and all his property in the cell. Said he'd come from Q-Wing, where he had ripped his shitjacket and sink off the wall. He didn't have a death sentence, but that was the only open cell in the prison at the time.

I was fixing up 15 packages of about five joints each for that night of TV. I thought what the hell, be neighborly and send the new man one! I should have known we had a real asshole when he didn't even bother to say thanks.

Well, everyone lit up and got a good buzz, getting ready for TV and showers. At shower time they pop one cell door at a time and you walk to the shower. After about ten minutes they come back to lock you up. You cold shower and go visiting, get a shot of ass, settle your problems or whatever.

Everyone had headphones for their TV or radio and used them to be considerate of everyone else. The new man had no TV, but he had a radio and he turned it wide open. I was in Cell 13 and he was in Cell 7, and I couldn't even hear my TV with headphones on. So I hollered down, "Hey! Cell Seven! How about turning your radio down?" and what do I get back but, "Fuck You, Cracker, this is my radio!" So I hollered back at him, "Play it, Nigger! Enjoy it while you can!"

In Cell 16 was one crazy little dude that made some of the prison's best zipguns. He would shoot anyone I told him to, as I used to give him all the stems and seeds out of my smoke. That's what he liked to smoke - like I said, crazy. So I shot him a kite - that's a prison term for a small note - saying when you come out for showers how about scaring that nigger. Just shoot in his cell, you don't have to hurt him. And I sent him some stems and seeds.

He wrote me back that he would, as he had just finished making a new zipgun out of a Coke can and wanted to try it out anyhow.

So Stoney hollered down, "Nigger, you got five minutes to get quiet or you gonna be quiet for life!" The black dude hollered back, "Suck my dick, Cracker! Suck my dick!"

Well, that's all Stoney needed. When he came out, he stopped at my cell to show me his zipgun and to tell me he was going to shoot that nigger for real. I said, "Stoney, just scare him, that's OK."

"No" he said, "he told me to suck his dick and I'm gonna kill his black ass." Then he hollered out, "Here I come, Nigger!"

Well, the man must have been on the lookout because when Stoney got there, he had his mattress off his bed and was holding it in front of him.

I watched in my mirror as Stoney got in front of Cell 7 and squared off in a pistol stance - one arm extended, a Bic lighter in the other to light the fuse - and it went off with one big *BANG!* Smoke was everywhere. The nigger screamed once and then all got graveyard quiet as Stoney staggered over to my cell.

Blood was pumping out a small hole in his neck. He had powder burns on him and piece of blown apart zipgun in his hand.

I handed him a wet washrag and told him to wipe his face and hands off and throw the rest of the zipgun out the window. I was drinking coffee and smoking a joint. Stoney said, "Give me some of that."

There was a steady squirt of blood shooting out of the little hole in his neck each time his heart beat, and Stoney held one finger over the hole while he took a swig of coffee and then a toke.

All this happened before the guard got from upstairs down to our tier. As a general rule back then when a zipgun went off they were slow getting there.

I heard the guard holler, "Get the medic and the goon squad! There's one shot and blood everywhere!"

Smoke still covered the hall.

The guard unlocked the gate at one end and came down to help Stoney. As he approached, Stoney passed me the joint and I flipped it in the shitjacket. The guard got Stoney by one arm and told him, "Come on, we got help on the way." He walked him toward the black dude's cell. All this time not a sound had come from him, and I wondered what shape he was in.

As Stoney and the guard passed the black man, he had a bar of soap in his hand and he threw it at Stoney. It hit the floor with a sharp *BANG* and then bounced up and hit the guard. The guard yelled, "It's the nigger in Cell 7! He shot me in the foot!"

A goon squad of about ten guards had just got to the grill gate, so they rushed Cell 7 and you could hear one badass beating going on. After about ten minutes they dragged him out, and an hour later a guard came down to tell us that Stoney was OK and would be back tomorrow. And the black dude was fucked up, so we wouldn't have to worry about him any more.

Meanwhile I had been missing a good TV program, so I put up another joint and put my headphones on. What the fuck, one more day on Death Row.

Football

My second year on Death Row, we got to go to the yard twice a week for four hours - a small fenced-in area about 20 x 40 feet. One bright fall day during football season, we picked sides, six men to a team. There were nine whites and three blacks.

The first play we ran, all three blacks got hurt. The one that hiked the ball hit the one in front of him in the mouth with the top of his head. They both fell over and landed on the third black, who hurt his leg.

When the guards turned around they saw nine whites standing over three blacks with blood on them. They went crazy and swore it was a race riot. We all told them it was nothing of the kind, but the superintendent came over to tell us no more football. He took the football away from us and was bouncing it up and down in one hand. I told him that if he didn't give us back the football, I was going to run away from home. I was smiling, and he laughed, "Go ahead, Bobby, but I'm keeping this football!"

Well, the very next weekend I made that escape I had been planning for so long. And just for the record, I had permission straight from the top. I wonder, did he ever wish he had given me back that football?

LIFE & CRIMES OF BEAUTIFUL BOBBY
by Robert Fieldmore Lewis

I've been in every kind of crime all my life. There is no crime I can think of that I have not done at least once - and I was damn good at what I did! I've always lived by my own rules. I never wanted to be a doctor or a lawyer or a preacher. I wanted to be an outlaw from the start and I worked hard at it. One thing that's just not in me is *GIVE UP*.

When I was six, I left home in Jacksonville, Florida on my bike. I stopped for a rest in Georgia (fifty miles away) and the police took me home. I've always been adventurous, to say the least.

When I was ten I stole a boat. I took a friend and my dog, and we headed out across the Atlantic Ocean for China - yeah, *CHINA!* This time they had to send the fireboats out into the ocean north of Jacksonville to rescue us.

I've traveled all over the United States. I used to go to New Orleans and hang out in the blues and jazz bars. That was some great music and some great times! I did my first armed robbery in New Orleans. It was like a Richard Pryor movie - the whole scene was ridiculous. I got my first two whores at the same time! The things they taught me... I was sixteen then and I loved every minute of it. I had my one and only deal with a fag there too - one of those S & M deals.

When I was 17, I was caught with some 16-year-old pussy and the judge told me I had a choice, prison or the armed forces. It was amazing how patriotic I got all of a sudden. I was in the Army Airborne for about a year, but I hurt my foot and got a medical discharge. It was honorable.

I was sure glad when they let me go. I was 18 and it was 1964. I headed straight to Hollywood, California to be a hippie and do drugs. Made a few trips to Mexico to smuggle. I've been involved in drugs one way or another since then. I was at Woodstock doing LSD. All I do now is kick back and smoke a joint from time to time.

A lot of the things I've done have been so silly. Like the time I read the book *Iceberg Slim* and was inspired to go to New York to be a big-time pimp. You'll love the way that one comes out! I have been in prostitution on and off for years from coast to coast and have lived a very wild sex life. When the news people asked some of my girls on the street if I had a nickname they said they called me "Beautiful Bobby", because I was always so sweet to them.

The police didn't like me in Jacksonville because I made fools of them time and time again. Like the time I got pulled over for a traffic violation when I had 100 pounds of grass in the car and no licence. I convinced the cop that I was his superior and I was on my way to a big drug bust. I told him he was in the middle of an undercover operation, and to get right on back into his bubblegum machine and hide behind the 7-11 if he wanted to keep his job - and he *did*! It was all over the papers. I was charged for impersonating an officer!

But I have done a lot of serious crimes when I was told they couldn't be done. Like the time I robbed the mob of drugs - but even that was funny. Most of these people I am free to talk about, since they are either in prison or dead. The statutes of limitations are up on 95% of everything I tell, and the rest I will tell in a way that I can't be prosecuted for, but can be proved to be true.

Like the time several of us on Death Row were investigated for over $100,000 worth of income tax returns filed from this place. We got the money, all right! It went for drugs and escapes. Several prison guards got fired, and I was accused of being one of the brains involved.

But I'm very much a different person now than then. Against all odds I am not the animal they portray me to be. I have not let all this fill me with hatred or rob me of my sense of humor. I'm very easy going and I see humor in almost everything. If I couldn't laugh at myself I would have hung myself years ago. I'm not ashamed of my life or anything I have done. I am a survivor. I should be dead a hundred times over in a million different ways.

As to any and all crimes and my part in them, I will admit them and tell them in an honest way, whether they make me look good or bad. As to being a cold-blooded killer, I would kill, with no problem, any person who was trying to kill me or one of my family and friends. And that's a fact.

The murder I was convicted of, I did not do, and I have proof that I was physically unable to pull that trigger. But I have done a lot of crimes that would require killing, and I was willing to take that chance to get what I wanted. I have robbed mostly big dope dealers and other criminals. I have never bothered or hurt an average person, or a business. Hey, outlaws have principles too!

Move Over, Iceberg Slim

In 1963, I was sixteen. I only had one girl on the street, but she loved to fuck day in and day out. I got my hands on the book *Iceberg Slim.* After studying the book, I figured I was as smart as Slim, and if he could conquer

New York so could a guy from Jacksonville the girls were calling Beautiful Bobby.

So I took my one whore and my two suitcases and caught a Greyhound for the Big Apple. The ride was uneventful, except for a head job in the back of the bus to break up the monotony. We got to the bus station in downtown New York - a huge building about three stories high that covers an entire city block. It was about 2.00 a.m. and we were tired and dirty.

As we headed through the door, a huge black punk dressed as a woman called out, "Hey Baby, want to party?" I told her, "No thank you," and thought, what a town!

We went inside and sat on a bench. I bought a newspaper and told her to look for a place to stay. I had about $2,000 in one suitcase and about $500 in my Levis. I told her to stay with the suitcases while I went to wash up, because I had to piss bad. I told her when I came back she could go wash up and then we'd find us a place.

Well ten minutes later when I came back, my suitcases were gone and so was my whore. I couldn't believe she would run off on her own, but she could easily be led or tricked. I mean we are talking one beautiful girl here, but she was as dumb as she was pretty.

I started to check the bars that are all around the station. I went through about ten of these without finding her before I stopped in one that didn't have too many people to have a beer. There was a young man not much older than me shooting pool. He said, "Hey, you want to shoot for a beer?" I had to give it a try, and as we played I told him my story. He told me that he knew everyone and if the whore could be found he would find her. I won three games and three beers. He told me I could crash at his place, but first he had some business to take care of, and when he go through he'd come back and get me. Unless I wanted to go.

Back then I was not much smarter than the girl I was looking for, so I asked him , "What's up?"

He said, "See that guy at the end of the bar? He just got off a ship and he has about three or four thousand on him. I'm waiting for him to get drunk and leave the bar. Then I'm gonna roll him. If you want in you can have half." That sounded pretty good to me. The plan was to make friends with him and tell him we had wild women that loved to fuck. Then he'd want to come with us to party. So we sat with the guy and bought him beer, and he bought us a lot more beer. I was starting to get pretty drunk when he said, "Let's go party!" So we walked out the bar and down the street about a block, and cut through an alley - my partner in front, me in the middle, and the sucker behind me.

About half way down the alley, the sucker punched me in the back of the head. As I spun around to get him - yep, you got it! - my new partner punched me in the back of the head. Well, they kicked my ass and took all my money, including my spare change. My shirt was ripped, my nose was bloody, and both of my eyes were black.

Since I had nowhere else to go, I walked back toward the bus station. I needed to wash up and I was broke. Looking back on my first hour in New York, I was feeling really dumb - I'd lost my whore, my suitcases, my clothes, and every cent I had, and had gotten the shit kicked out of me. As luck would have it, the same black punk I saw when I got off the bus to conquer New York was leaning against the same wall. She said, "Uh-uh, Honey! What happened to *you*?!"

"Shut up, dammit, I need a dime." The punk giggled and opened her purse and fished out a dime. So I went and did what any red-blooded American boy would do - I called my mother. I said I was in New York and the damn Yankees were killing me. I told her how I'd had my ass kicked and robbed, and asked her to please wire me the money to catch the next bus South!

You say, what about the girl? Well, I still don't know what happened to her, but I hope she made out better than I did. Years later I was to go back to New York many times, and that city paid plenty of interest on my loan. But I was in another business then, and that's another story!

Instant Marriage

I was living with a topless dancer, and all we had in common was sex.

We argued every time we were not in bed, so I seldom stayed at home. I had been gone two days with a friend and two other topless dancers. We had been partying all over most of North Florida and South Georgia, and everyone was wasted on good smoke when we passed a sign that said INSTANT MARRIAGE. One of the girls decided she wanted to get married. We got into a long discussion over who was going to marry who, because we had been swapping for the last two days. As we got the blood tests, and all the way to the chapel, we still had not figured it out. When the preacher and his wife came out, he asked who was going to marry who. I said, "We don't know!"

He said, "Well, if you don't know I sure can't tell you. Y'all let me know when you get it figured out."

So I got a coin out. It was heads I would marry one, tails I'd marry the other. After the flip, someone said two out of three. So we flipped some more. You should have seen the preacher and his wife! Well, I married the one named Louise. When we woke up the next afternoon in a motel in Jacksonville, I didn't even remember it because we had got drunk to celebrate the marriage. I told Louise I was sorry but I had to go home. I gave her $1,000 and she gave me her address on Jacksonville Beach, and said if I changed my mind I'd always be welcome.

When I got home the dancer I lived with was pissed. She kept bitching, wanting to know where the hell I had been for the past two days. The woman was totally unreasonable! So finally I just told her, "Nowhere, I just went up to Georgia for a couple of days to get married." Let me tell you, that woman was as mad as any woman I ever saw! After two days of non-stop verbal abuse I told her she had to shut up and give me a break.

"Break!" she screamed, "If you want a break, why don't you go live with your damn *wife*!" You see what I mean about being unreasonable? So I said, "That sounds like a good idea!"

I packed up. I stuck my gun in the front of my Levis and was off to the beach and my wife. It was a two storey duplex, and when I got there it was about 7.30 a.m. It was a hot summer morning and I could see the door to the upstairs apartment was open. I got my two suitcases and up the stairs I went. I opened the screen door with my foot without knocking since both hands were full. I stepped into the living room and put the suitcases down. I heard people talking in the kitchen, so I headed that way. When I walked into the kitchen, I was not even thinking of the pistol in the front of my Levis. Louise had her back to me at the stove cooking in a short nightie.

Two sailors in their underwear were sitting at the table talking to Louise while she cooked breakfast for them. As I appeared in the doorway they got real quiet. I saw them look at the gun and look at me. As Louise turned around, one of them asked her, "Who he?"

Good old Louise could see they were worried and wanted to put them at ease. So she said, "Don't worry. It's just my husband."

Well, folks, it's a good thing the kitchen had a door that led to a fire escape that led to the beach, because if it hadn't I would have had to pay for one! I just don't think the Navy teaches good manners, because before I could say a word, they were gone in a puff of dust.

When Louise and I stopped laughing, I went out on the fire escape and hollered at these two fools on the beach in their underwear to come back, it was OK. I even left my gun inside. They hollered back, "No way! Just throw our clothes out the back door and go inside, then we'll get them!" That made me mad because I can't stand unsociable people. But I threw their clothes out there, and Louise and I hid behind the kitchen curtains for the next ten minutes, smoking a joint and watching them sneak up on their clothes. We laughed so much I thought I was about to fall in love with this woman I married a few days ago. But it was not to be. Turned out we liked each other just fine, but she liked pussy even more than I do, and that's saying a lot! So after a couple of months we drifted apart and I was off to my next adventure.

Texas

B.Lewis 89

In the late sixties I had long hair, a beard, and a pretty healthy grass business in Jacksonville, Florida. When I couldn't score in Miami or Atlanta it was off to the wild west.

It was a long trip, but I could always find some good Mexican weed dirt cheap. I was driving across Texas in a car I had registered in a false name with five thousand dollars hidden in the spare tyre and one thousand dollars in my Levis. I thought I would try Laredo first and if I couldn't score there, I was sure I could in San Diego.

I was sleeping in the day and driving at night, because there was less chance to be noticed or have police problems. A lot of the South still did not go for long haired men. It was about 1.00 a.m. and just me and the radio, when red flashing lights came on in back of me. Fuck, I thought, and wondered what I had done. I looked at the speedometer and saw I was ten miles an hour over the speed limit. I thought, what the hell, I'm clean, I'll get my ticket and go on.

So I pulled over and the Texas Highway Patrolman pulled over in back of me, got out and walked up to my car.

"You was ten miles over the limit, Boy. Let me see your licence."

So I got it out and handed it over, and he walked back to his car and got in. I could see him talking over his microphone to the station. We were like this for about five minutes, me just sitting in my car and him in his. I felt OK because I knew I didn't have anything to worry about. About that time another Texas Highway Patrolman pulled up in front of me and got out. The one in back got out of his car and they met at the back of my car. I was trying to hear them but I couldn't. When they walked up to the door and asked me to get out, I did. One said, "Boy, you got drugs in that car. We know your type."

I said, "I ain't got shit in this car. Why don't you just go on and give me a ticket or whatever you're gonna do? I got a long trip ahead of me."

"Oh yeah? Where you going, Boy?"

"Any place but Texas."

Well he didn't like that remark one bit, so it was the old turn around and spread them. They searched me pretty good but didn't find anything on me but the money.

"Boy, what you doing with all this money?"

"Shit, where I come from that's not much, but maybe it is in Texas." As you see, we were getting to know each other pretty well by this time, but I guess they wanted to know me a little better, because they locked me in the back seat of their squad car while they searched my car. After about a half hour of this, they came and let me out. The one in front got in his car and drove off. The one in back said, "I want you to follow me. We're going to see the judge."

"What judge?"

"Oh, just down the road. You just follow me, and no funny stuff, hear? Or else I'll drive you and have your car pulled in and you'll have to pay to get it back!"

"Lead on, let's go see your judge."

So he walked back and got in his car, and pulled in front of me. I pulled out to follow him, thinking, fuck, what bad luck! I wasn't ever sure what town I was near, but I figured it was just your typical speed trap. They'd hit me for my money and I'd be on my way.

We pulled off the interstate and drove about three or four miles to town. The whole town was about two blocks long, and we pulled up in front of a little square wood building not much bigger than an outhouse. The cop got out and motioned for me to follow him, so I got up. He put a key in the door and opened it up and turned on the light. It looked like a miniature courtroom. He told me to sit down and I'd better not try to run off. He opened a back door and said he'd be right back and closed the door behind him.

I am thinking, what a fucking idiot! Why would I run off? I got up and went to the back to look out the window. I saw the cop go to an old wooden house maybe fifteen feet out back. The lights went on and the door opened and he cop went in. The whole thing was starting to get amusing to me. This was like no court I had ever seen, and even the way they acted was funny. I just wished they would hurry up so I could get back on the road.

Well, about five minutes later I got my wish. Mr. Texas Cop and some old man came in. The old man looked at me and looked at the cop, and said, "This the one that was speeding?", like there was someone else in the room.

"That's right," the cop said, "Ten over."

The old man looked at me and said, "Thirty days on the P-farm."

"Wait a minute," I said.

The old man said, "I did not tell you to speak."

I said, "I did not ask. This ain't no fucking court!"

"Sixty days!"

"Why don't you cut the crap? Just give me my fine and I'll be on my way."

"I said sixty days."

I was hot. I said, "Look, this ain't no trial, this is bullshit. And I am not going to do no fucking sixty days!"

The old man said, "That's right, you're not going to do sixty days, you're going to do a hunnerd and twenty! Keep talking and we'll get to a year!" By now we were both shouting. The old man glared at me and turned and walked out the back door.

I looked at the cop and said, "Is that old fucker serious?"

The cop laughed and said, "Yep! He does get a mean side when I wake him up in the middle of the night." Then he said, "Give me your car keys. And take all your stuff out of your pockets and put it on the desk." So I gave him the keys and watched him go out front and lock up my car. I was taking my stuff out of my pockets when he walked back in and said, "Keep ten dollars," and walked back out the door.

He was gone about five minutes and came back in with a pair of coveralls with a big P painted on them and an old pair of brogans. He said, "Put these on." So it was out of the clothes and into my new outfit. I'm thinking, no way in hell am I gonna stay here no 120 days. I got smoke to buy! Shit! They've got my car, my money, my ID...

The cop put all my stuff in a large brown bag and got out his keys, opened one of the desk drawers and put it inside and locked it up. Then he told me, "If you want to eat, tell me. I'll take you over to the gas station across the street and you can buy something."

I said, "I belong to you now. Aren't you supposed to feed me."

"You get dinner and supper out on the road camp if you work. You want breakfast you can buy it, I don't care one way or another."

So I told him to lead off. Here it was 3.00 a.m. and we're going across the street. I was feeling like a damn fool - the brogans were too big, the overalls were too big, and I had no shirt. We went in the gas station. Some old fucker behind the counter giggled and said, "What you got there? That one of them there hippies?"

The cop smiled and said, "That's our new help for the next 120 days." The old man laughed at that. I was starting not to like the old men of this town. I got me a Coke, a couple of sandwiches, and a bag of cookies, and back across the street we went. He told me to sit, and handcuffed one arm to the chair. He went behind the other desk and put his feet up and started to eat.

"OK," I said, "Where am I going?"

"About an hour or so, a truck'll be by here to get you on the way out to work. Tonight they'll take you to a road camp outside of town. You be good and you may get out early."

I thought, a lot earlier than you think, asshole! So we sat like that for a little over an hour - the cop nodding out, and me trying to figure out this shit. A horn blew and woke the cop up. He smiled and said, "Your ride's here." He uncuffed me and outside we went. There was a ruck with sideboards like you tote cattle in. I got my bag of cookies. There were two prison guards. The Mexican one had a pistol and the white one had a shotgun. The one with the shotgun hollered, "Look what we got!"

All the men in the back of the truck laughed. I looked at them. There was about 15 Mexicans, three blacks and one old white man - the one with the shotgun. He said, "Don't just stand there, we got work to do!"

So I climbed up the side where the tyre was and got in the back. He said, "You try to run, I'll shoot."

"Yeah," I said. So he got in the front and started to pull off. I felt someone pulling at my bag. He said, "I want," and gave me his mean look. I said "OK," and turned loose the bag,. He smiled and got a handful of cookies. He put one in his mouth and went to pass some out to another man. That's when I kicked him in the nuts as hard as I could. He screamed and dropped to the floor. I kicked him in the mouth and knocked out a couple of teeth. Two of his friends made a move for me. I hit one and the other jumped on my back.

The truck slammed on the brakes. The two guards jumped out and pointed their guns, yelling, "Break it up!" As soon as everyone stopped, the white guard said, "OK, everyone out!"

So two men lifted the tailgate. We all got out, except for the one I kicked in the nuts. He was all balled up on the floor moaning and spitting blood. He looked at me and said, "I gone fucking kill you, I gone kill you."

"Yeah," I said, "I can see that."

Shotgun walked over to me and said, "You do that?"

I didn't say nothing. He hit me in the pit of the stomach with the barrels of the shotgun, and then upside the head with the stock. It knocked me down and knocked the breath out of me, and tore the top of my ear and scalp. In a couple of minutes I got back up and just looked at him. He said, "I do all the fighting here."

I said, "Yeah, you're real tough." He went to hit me again, but the other one stopped him. He said, "Hey, we got to get to work."

So everyone got back in the truck. The Mexican I fucked up was now holding on to the side of the truck. When everyone was back in the truck, he started again. He kept muttering out of his broken mouth, "I gone kill you." I just looked at him.

We drove out of town and hit a dirt road. It was not even daylight yet, but by the time we drove down this road maybe a half hour, it was starting to get light. It looked like an ocean of cotton as far as you could see in any direction, grown up five feet off the ground. I thought, oh shit. Cotton.

There was already a couple of other trucks out there. One had a lot of large bags. The guard said, "Everybody get a bag and a row." This bag has a strap that goes over your shoulder and must be six or seven feet long. I was getting mine when the shotgun guard came over to me and said, "You work to eat. You don't work you don't eat. And any more trouble - " and he just smiled at me.

I looked at him, thinking just give me one chance, asshole, and I will fuck you up and that's a promise!

Everyone else was already working when I walked over to a row and started. I was between an old white man and a young black. They were picking this shit from top to bottom. I picked a few off the top until I caught up with them. Soon as I did the old man said, "Yeah, you better watch that Mex. He will try to kill you." The black guy said, "That's right, man. He done cut up a couple people."

"I said, "Well I'm not doing too bad so far."

The black guy said, "Yeah, but when we get back, there are maybe 1500 Mexicans - ten blacks and five whites."

"Yeah?" I said, "Well, I guess I'll just have to leave. Why don't you run?"

"Can't you see there's no place to run? Since I been here one man did run and he was waiting on the road that afternoon to get picked up. Said he didn't want to die of thirst."

"Hey, how do we get water?"

"Just call 'Waterboy.' A trustee totes a water bucket."

So I hollered, "Waterboy!" and sure enough up popped a Mex with a bucket of water. As I was getting my drink, he said, "You gone get it tonight."

"Yeah, so I understand," I said. I drank all I could. The black saw what I was doing and said, "Don't drink so much - you'll get sick when the sun gets on up!"

I just kept drinking. After the Mex left I told the black guy, "If I get enough of a lead, I'll take you with me. You want to go?"

"Naw, man, I only got two weeks left."

So I said, "OK," and started walking forward. After I went about fifty yards, I was a good twenty yards in front of everyone else. The two guards were inside the truck in the shade and didn't seem to be paying attention. I thought, just a little further.

I went maybe twenty more yards and then bent down and ran low for maybe fifty yards and looked back. I could see one guard standing on the side of the truck, but he wasn't shooting. So I took off again. I ran till when I looked back the truck was just a dot. It had not moved. I didn't know where I was or how to get to town except on the road we came down. I eased over to about twenty yards off the road and started to walk. I was going to stop anything that come down that road.

By about 2.00 p.m. my mouth was cracking and I was real thirsty. I still could see nothing but that fucking cotton. I wondered if I was going to have to give up that afternoon on the road too, just to survive. I picked up a small rock and sucked on it. That helped a little bit and I looked back. I could see a cloud of dust on the road, so I headed for the road. Whatever it was, I was going to stop it. And if it was the guards, well we would just have to deal with that. So I got in the middle of the road, figuring whatever it was could not go around me.

A car, or sort of a car, slowly came to a stop. Most of the body had been cut off so it was open like a truck in back, and full of kids. An old man and woman sat in the front. I walked up to the car and said, "I'll give you five dollars to take me to town." I had about seven on me. The old man pointed to the back. I got in and off we went. One of the kids had a jug of water. I pointed to it and the kid gave it to me. It was hot, but it was the best water I ever tasted.

Soon as we got to where I could see the town ahead I pounded on the roof and the old man came to a stop. I gave him five dollars and got out. I circled around back of town and found an old garage. I went in and stayed there until about 2.00 a.m. By then I was real thirsty and hungry again, so I headed for the filling station I was in the night before, since that was the only place with lights on.

I found an iron rod about 2 feet long and picked it up. I eased up on the side of the station and looked in the window. The old man was in back of the station. My car was still in front of the little courthouse, so I thought what the fuck, I'm mad. I just walked right across the street, busted the courthouse door open, and pried open the drawer on the desk. There was my bag. I grabbed it and looked outside. The old man was back in the station. I walked out, got in my car and took off. I hit the interstate at over a hundred miles an hour and just kept it to the floor. I expected to see red lights any time, but after about thirty minutes I eased off. There was an expressway overpass going north and south, so I hit that and headed south all the rest of the night.

Before it got light, I stopped and changed back into my own clothes, and the next day I was in Laredo. There are two Laredos, one in Texas and one just across the bridge in Mexico. I had a Mexican friend who had done time with me in Florida, so I drove over to his house. Ruiz lived on the American side. He wasn't home, but his sister Consuelo was. She was thirteen and she was crying. I asked her where Ruiz was.

"Gone to kill some boys."

"What for?"

"They messed with me."

"What you mean mess?"

"You know."

"You mean they raped you?"

"They had sex with me but I wanted them."

"How many?"

"Eight."

"Do you know where your brother is right now?"

"Looking for them."

"He got the same car?"

"Yes."

So I started driving around and before too long I found him on Main Street. He was glad to see me but he was hot. He told me a bunch of assholes had raped his sister.

I said, "I just talked to her and she said she wanted them."

"Don't matter. She's too young. I gone kill them."

"Well, look. I need to cop a hundred pounds." It was going for about fifty a pound and he knew he could get a cut.

He said, "Yeah, OK. But it'll take me a couple of days."

So we went back to his house and while we were smoking and eating and drinking, he said, "I gone go looking again."

"You got a gun?"

"Yes."

"I mean one I can use while I'm here."

So he went and got me an old .38 and came back and gave it to me. I said, "Why don't you just leave it alone, man?"

"She fucks everybody. But it's got to stop." He insisted on going to look for them.

I said, "If you want to wait till tomorrow, I'll help. But I got to get some sleep."

So he showed me a room and left. I took a shower, smoked a joint, got in bed and went right to sleep. When I woke up Consuelo was in bed with me naked, saying "You want to fuck me?"

"No!" I told her, "Get your ass out of the bed!"

"You do too, look how hard you are."

"I'm gonna tell you one more time. Get out of the bed."

She tried to get next to me again, and I threw the covers back and got up and grabbed her by the arm and pulled her to the door.

"I gone tell Ruiz you fucked me!"

I was mad and sleepy so I said, "Yeah, well you tell him this," and I dragged her over to the couch and put her over my knee and blistered her ass. And I do mean blistered. She screamed and cried. I let her fall to the floor and crawled back to bed.

It seemed I had just got to sleep when Ruiz was shaking me awake. He had ahold of Consuelo and he said, "Bobby, she said you raped her, man. Is she lying?"

"Hell, yeah, Ruiz. She came and got in bed with me naked and I beat her ass. Get her to show it to you."

He looked at her and said, "Let's see your ass."

She took off running with Ruiz right behind her. I heard *WHOP! WHOP!* as she got that ass beat again.

I went back to sleep and didn't wake up until noon the next day. I walked in the kitchen and Ruiz was there.

"Did you find them?"

"No. She ran away again," he said. "But I got a buy set up for you."

"OK, how we gonna do it?"

"I got to do it by myself. They don't trust no gringos. But I want you to go so you can watch."

"OK, when?"

"Tonight. First we gone go look for my sister and then we go by there."

So we went riding and smoking and looking. He showed me a house and where I could watch from about a block away. As we headed back for his house, he said "There they are!"

We went chasing a car full of Mexicans. I could see Consuelo in the back seat. The chase lasted about ten blocks and they got away.

So we went on back to the house to wait for dark. About an hour later Consuelo came home. Big argument. She finally went in the bathroom to shower, and Ruiz said, "Man, why don't you take her back to Florida. I'd rather she be with you."

I said, "No thanks. Don't you have some place to send her?"

He told me their mother and father had burned to death the year before and he had the job of raising her.

Later that night we went to score. He went to the house and I watched. It all went real smooth. We got back home and took the grass in the bedroom. His house sat way out by itself, so I felt safe as we were checking it out.

But I heard something out back. I put out the light and said, "What's that?"

A low voice said through the bedroom door, "We know you're in there. We want the dope. We got Consuelo, Ruiz."

I said, "Who's that?"

Ruiz said, "The ones she's been with."

I said, "Oh, shit."

Ruiz called out, "You got her, you keep her. But get out."

A couple of pistols and a shotgun went off several times through the door at us. I shot back four times, and kept two.

I heard a lot of noise and running and I started to get up. That's when I realized I'd been hit in the knee. I had blood all down my pants leg.

Ruiz said, "Man, you been hit in the head."

"No, it's my knee."

"Your head too."

I put my hand to my face and sure enough I got blood all over it. We eased out to the living room and there was a good puddle of blood there too. So I was not the only one hit.

I went to the bathroom and turned the light on. I'd been hit in the cheek with a splinter of wood. I thought, no problem, but when I pulled the wood out it hurt like hell. I took my pants off as my leg was really starting to hurt and I was still bleeding. There was a patch of meat missing where I believe the shotgun hit me. It bounced off the bone and took a piece of meat with it. So I got a towel and sheet, washed my knee off, and poured a bottle of beer over it. We're talking big time pain now! Ruiz got a pressure bandage on it and helped me out to the couch so I could put my leg up. Then he patched up my face the best he could.

I smoked a couple of joints and had a beer, which wasn't easy since the wood punched a hole right through my cheek and it burned with each swallow.

"Ruiz," I said, "you think they hurt your sister?"

"No man, I think she set us up. I gone kill that little whore."

"Man, it can't be easy for her after losing your mom and dad. We ain't lost nothing."

"You're shot."

"I'll be OK. If she comes home what you need to do is take her and go somewhere else."

"Man, my car ain't going too far."

"You can have mine. I got to catch a bus back anyway, as I'm not gonna drive through Texas again."

I told him the whole story and we both laughed. About an hour later Consuelo came home. She was scared and told us one of the boys was hit real bad and was at the hospital.

I told Ruiz we'd best get packed and leave. So he went out and got a lot of boxes, packed up my grass, and took it to the Greyhound station to ship to me in Jacksonville. Then he came back to tell me the bus was leaving in two hours. He got me a pint of whisky, a bag of joints and some bandages, and we fixed the leg up. He gave me an old cane he had, and in two hours they had me on the bus home.

That was one miserable trip. I did not get up for anything but the bathroom, and that liked to killed me. When I got to Jacksonville I hurt so bad I could just barely get out of the bus. I called the house and a woman I was living with from Texas, of all places, came and got me and the smoke. When we got in the car, she stared at me and said, "What happened to you?"

"Just visiting your old home state, girl, and don't ask me to take you there!"

Gangster Poodle

The man that went to Death Row with me for killing Joe Richards looked and played the role of the gangster to the hilt: alligator shoes, dress slacks, silk shirts - Eddie wouldn't be caught dead in Levis.

He is a big guy - about 6'4" and about 200 pounds. Joe Richards was even bigger - 6'5" and 230 pounds, and he was super bad. Mob connections. When he'd been in the Atlanta Federal Pen he ran the place. Both Eddie and Joe took the badass role very seriously. There I was at 5'8", about 180 - hair halfway down my back, well-worn jeans with Walt Disney patches all over them, a T-shirt and sandals. I had my left arm in a sling from a knife wound, but that's another story.

The whole town knew we were at war over a big coke house we had robbed from some other bad guys. Joe had been promised half to get it back.

So for a couple of weeks he had been threatening us, telling us he wanted the stuff back or he would kill us, our kids, our dogs and everything. Typical gangster shakedown.

Eddie wasn't in on the drug robbery. Joe said Eddie owed him because he got a fix in at the courthouse for him. All the bad boys in town had asked us to talk it over and see if we couldn't make a deal. If we couldn't there would have to be a killing and that would put the heat on everyone. As Eddie and I rode over there I figured someone was going to die. I knew there would be about ten men with Joe and that everyone would be armed. I had my .45 pistol. It was a summer morning as we pulled up in Eddie's Cadillac. Everyone was in the yard hanging out and drinking beer.

Joe was washing his car and the star of this story, the poodle, was jumping around dodging the water bouncing off the car. As we pulled up, Joe knew who it was, but didn't turn around, as he had his role to play. Joe was not married and had no family - nothing but this poodle. Pound for pound, Joe was probably the most dangerous man I had ever met, but he loved that poodle. He would get it groomed and trimmed, its nails painted, its coat dyed different colors, and he'd put all kinds of crazy outfits on it. He spent big money on all this and would brag that the dog would listen to nobody but him.

As we stepped out of the car you could feel the tension in the air. About this time, the poodle ran across the yard and jumped up on Eddie. He wrapped his front paws around Eddie's legs and started to hump him. I guess he was just feeling horny and Eddie must have looked like a big, fancy well-dressed poodle. Or maybe they used the same cologne. The whole yard got real quiet. I braced myself to see Eddie set a new world record for how far a poodle could be drop-kicked. It got so quiet Joe finally had to turn around.

Well, folks, I've already told you how Eddie carried himself, and especially with a dozen of the most dangerous men in town looking on, I was ready for some deadly action. I didn't move. Out of the corner of my eye, I saw Eddie reach down and pull the little dog off his leg. He stood back up and turned the poodle on it's back and cradled him in one arm like a baby. The poodle had a hard-on. I had no idea what Eddie was going to do. The feeling in the air had gone from tension to electricity. Everyone knew that when Eddie hurt that dog somebody was going to die. I had one eye on Joe, who had the look of a crazy man in his eye, and the other on Eddie as he reached over with his other hand and with two fingers, started to jack off the poodle real fast. Folks, I saw true love in that poodle's eyes. He had all four legs spread wide open, and his head turned in my direction with his tongue hanging out.

I was trying to keep my eye on Joe, because I was sure he was about to go for his piece. I never tried so hard in my life to hold my composure, and it has been said I'm a little on the tough side myself. I wanted to be ready to shoot back, but as hard as I tried I must have lasted at the most a second and a half. I screamed. I laughed so hard I was laying down in the yard kicking my feet in the air. So hard I hurt and tears were running down my face. I was 99.9% sure Joe was about to kill us, if not for what Eddie was doing, then for me laughing. I lay there laughing hysterically, waiting for the bullets to hit me. When I could stop enough to see through the tears, I saw Joe was gone. I figured he had gone inside to get something to kill us with. After a few minutes of everyone trying to make small talk about everything but Eddie and his new friend, we got in the car and left. We never did get to have that talk. Two weeks later Joe was dead. Amazing how that poodle changed all our lives that day!

ALONE ON DEATH ROW WITH TED BUNDY
by Robert Fieldmore Lewis

Bundy's First Night On Death Row

At the time I met Ted Bundy, I was the only death row prisoner on the bottom floor of Q-Wing, with the electric chair only 30 feet from my bed. I was kept there as a form of mental punishment because of my recent death row escape.

I was doing quite well for myself as the major grass supplier for the prison. I'd pay up to $250 a pound plus $300 to the guards to bring it in. I'd sell it mostly as nickel bags, or $20 for a matchbox. That pound would get me $3,500 to $4,000. Then I'd have to pay the people who sold for me and take all my expenses out of that. So I would clear about $2,000 each. Business was good. After my escape from Death Row, I was well respected by the other prisoners, since I had done what they'd only dreamed of. The head dope man of any prison in many ways runs that prison, and I had a lot of people working for me. I could get anything into the prison, up to and including real guns.

That morning started out the same as usual. I got up, lit a joint, drank my coffee, and turned on the radio for the early morning news. The big news of the day was that Ted Bundy was to be sentenced. I was expecting him to be sent to Death Row. I'd heard and read a lot of stories about him, and had formed my opinion that if he was guilty, he was one sick puppy. I was soon to learn that my first opinion was more than right, and that he may have set new standards for being a sick puppy. But I was to learn that and much more about him and his character over the next few years.

The news went off and I switched to a good hard rock station to start one more boring day. Other than the guards and the prisoners who would make an excuse to come by to cop, I had nobody to talk to for 23 out of 24 hours, and had been this way for about a month. There was no worse place for the State to put me except the chair.

About 2.30 that afternoon I heard a lot of guards coming down the stairs. Oh shit, I thought, probably a shakedown. There hadn't been one for a while and I had about a half to three-quarters of a pound of pot under my bed.

Besides that, I had just got two gallons of some ass-kicking prison wine made of orange juice and sugar, and that was under the bed too.

But I was surprised to see a very large sergeant who was known as an ass-stomper shoving a prisoner very hard towards the cell next to me. The man was whining and complaining at the way he was being handled. The other guards were laughing as the sergeant pushed him in the cell. The sergeant said, "Well, Bobby, I got you a real asshole to talk to now." Then he looked at me and said, "If anything happens to him, I'll make sure nobody sees anything." He laughed but I knew he was only half kidding.

Then he looked at Bundy and said, "I know Kimberly Ann Leach's family. A lot of us here do. And we just want you to know we're real happy to have you here." The guards laughed and turned to go, but they promised to come back and see him.

As they went upstairs, Bundy said who was that big bastard and was he serious? And that he was Ted Bundy. He was shaking. It was obvious he was really scared. I told him that the guard was Sergeant Spraggins and that there was no worse guard here to have for an enemy. And that I was Bobby Lewis.

"Hey man, ain't you the one that escaped?"

"Yeah."

"I've been reading about you and seeing you on TV."

"Yeah, I've been in the news almost as much as you!"

It was true at that time, at least in Florida. My escape from Death Row and the plot to hijack a helicopter to bust out five other prisoners had received quite a lot of media attention.

"I've escaped a few times myself."

I could see he was trying to impress me as he kept talking, or trying to save face as I had seen how scared he was when the guards brought him in. Then he said, "When are they going to bring my bed linen and toilet paper?"

"They're supposed to give it to you when you come in. You'll have to ask the guard."

Then for the next ten minutes no one said anything much, and I laid down. I was surprised they put him next to me. I found out it was for security. He had gotten the death penalty for the Chi Omega murders, but he still had to go to the Kimberly Ann Leach murder trial. Over the next couple of months, they would take him down to the court and bring him back every day. We'd go over his case and his defence. They were afraid that if they put him on the regular Death Row he would get hurt. Babykillers and womankillers are the lowest of the lowlifes in this place, and it was quite common on Death Row to have a stabbing or a shootout with zipguns. Bundy was getting too much media attention for them to take a chance that he'd get hurt, because they'd catch the heat for it.

I don't like people who do what he did any more than anyone else. As a matter of fact, a couple of months later I was next door to Arthur Goode, a child torturer who liked to brag about it all day long.

I tried to blow him up and shoot him. He wrote the FBI that I was trying to kill him, and that the same Sergeant Spraggins was letting me, and the guards wouldn't do anything about it. So the FBI came here to investigate. That's all in the records.

I was thinking about how I was going to handle Ted. I admit to being curious about him, as I'm sure everyone was at that time. Even back in jail before I went to Death Row, I'd always thought I'd like to write a book some day about my life in crime and in prison, and if I lived, I knew it would make a good book. So I set out on purpose to learn as much as I could about Ted.

About this time the guard came by for a cell check. Ted asked him for bed linens and toilet paper, a blanket, toothbrush and toothpaste, shower shoes - all the things he was supposed to get when he came in. The guard just looked at Ted and said, "Sergeant Spraggins says if you want anything you got to ask him."

As he left, Ted asked me what that meant. I told him it meant he was not going to get anything but trouble if he bothered the Sergeant.

"But what am I going to *do*?" Ted whined.

I told him I'd give him some stuff, and I gave him some of all the things he needed, plus a lot more. A coffee cup, spoon, fork, paper, pen, stamps, and a lot of other small stuff. He kept saying, "I've got money, I'll pay you." It was obvious he was grateful to me that I would help him, and not fuck him up as the sergeant had suggested.

I wanted to put him at ease with me, so I asked him if he smoked grass. "Hell, yeah!" was his answer, so I lit up a couple of joints and we got off. About 30 minutes later we had supper, which was no good. So I ordered some steak and fries to be brought down to us, which impressed Ted to no end. Then they brought the mail down. I had about 40 letters.

Ted said, "Shit, you know all these people?"

I told him, "No, but I've been getting mail from all over the world for weeks. It's mostly people who've read about me - book and movie offers, requests for magazine interviews, fags, Christians, women in love, hate mail. Just the usual mix of shit."

I told him he'd probably get it too, and by the next week he was getting 50 to 100 letters a night, just like me. All kinds of shit. But he got a lot more hate mail and weird letters.

We had our showers, and by then it was about 7.00 p.m. No guards would be by until 11.00 p.m. So I reached under the bed and pulled the wine out. I asked him, "Do you drink?" and he said, "Yeah!" He was real surprised that I had something to drink and had a lot of questions about how it was made and so on. It takes about a half gallon to get really drunk and it doesn't taste bad at all if it's done right. This was done to perfection, and we got down to some serious wine drinking and reefer smoking.

Ted had a million and one questions about the prison, the guards, other prisoners, and me - how I had all the things I did and could get things like the steak and fries. It was all new and amazing to him. He had been under a lot of emotional strain in the last several months, and said he had not had a joint or a drink since he was arrested.

We talked a lot, just as a way to feel each other out. Over the next year Ted was to become totally dependent on me for just about everything that affected his daily life. And that night I was to get a glimpse of what made Ted Bundy into a slobbering-at-the-mouth maniac.

By about 11.00 p.m. we were each well fucked up between the wine and the smoke, and Ted said, "I got to lie down before I fall down." I told him to go ahead, and I laid down to think about Ted. So far he seemed to be a real nice, polite guy. It was obvious he had a lot of intelligence, and he showed a good personality and sense of humor as we were getting wasted. It was kind of hard to put the Ted I partied with together with the Ted I'd been reading and hearing so much about.

It was real quiet down there, with nothing but my radio turned down low. I was just about to go to seep after 15 or 20 minutes, when I heard noises - the kind of noises a man makes when he's getting to the height of passion fucking a woman and talking to her. Except in this case it was Ted talking to Ted in his drunken sleep. This is what I heard :

"Oh God, YEAH! I've got blood all over me! Ah! Ah! Guts everywhere! Ohhh...I've got her heart in my hand! It's beating! AH! AH!"

By this time I was wide awake and out of bed. He was carrying on really loud. I got my mirror and put it outside, so I could see into his cell. It was dark but there was enough light from the guard tower right in front of us for me to see. And it looked like he was in bed asleep - but talking. Then he screamed out, *"I'm coming! She's dead!"* He screamed *"AHHH!"* and then he went on mumbling.

I beat on his wall until he got up. I told him, "You crazy bastard! You were talking in your sleep about a girl you killed and split open and how you were holding her heart in your hand while you raped her!" Well, he freaked out big time. I told him that if one of the guards came by at count and heard him doing that, they would be at his next murder trial testifying against him. He was so excited and crazy acting. He said, "Please, Bobby, please don't tell nobody." I said I would not, and did he want to smoke one to calm down? He said he did so we smoked several.

Ted said he was afraid to go back to sleep because he might start again. I told him to go ahead, I would listen and wake him up if he did. I laid back down and thought to myself, "*WOW*, what a crazy bastard!" And as I lay there, I started to revise my opinion of earlier that day. I guess twenty minutes went by like that. I was just starting to nod off again when out of the blue I heard a shriek like a woman in a monster movie when the monster grabs her.

It scared the shit out of me. I jumped straight out of my bed, my sheets and blanket flying. I got my mirror and looked again. Ted was asleep.

He was absolutely still and quiet. He made no more noise that night, but it was quite a while before I was able to go back to sleep.

Ted's Lesson

Bam Bam Bam! I beat on Ted's wall. I could hear the food upstairs and wanted Ted to be up so the guards wouldn't hang around. Today was to be his first whole day at the prison, as he had come in late the day before.

"Ted! Hey, Bundy!"

"Yeah, yeah, what?"

"Get up - breakfast!"

"Damn, what time is it?"

"About 4.30 or 5.00."

"God damn! They bring it this early every day?"

"Yeah."

"Hey, Bobby - listen man...about last night-"

"Later, Ted. Here they come."

In time it gets easy to tell by the sounds who the guards are. I could tell most of them just by the sound of their feet. But all of the guards wore a different amount of keys in different places, and they made different noises. It used to amaze Ted that I could tell him who was coming before he could tell anyone was even headed our way.

"All right! Up and get it!" said the guard.

"What you got?" I asked.

"S.O.S."

I said, "Shit, I pass," and Ted, "No, I'm not hungry."

"Coffee?"

"No."

"Me neither."

"What, you two too good to eat this? I eat it!"

"Yeah, it's probably better than what you get at home."

"You better watch your mouth, Lewis!"

"You asshole, what are you gonna do? Put me in prison? Kill me? What, asshole, what!" I was yelling after him as he left.

Ted said, "Hey, man, they don't do nothing to you when you talk like that?"

"Yeah, sometimes they kick ass, Ted. But me and that asshole been through it enough by now that he knows it's a waste of time!"

"Damn, that shit looked bad!"

"Yeah, I'm gonna have some coffee and donuts. You want some?"

"Where you gonna get the coffee?"

"We get instant at the canteen. They have a little hot water bug you have to buy to heat your water. I'll get you one today."

"How much is it?"

"Couple of dollars."

"OK." He was quiet for a couple of minutes, and then he said, "Hey, man."

"Yeah, Ted."

"I appreciate all you're doing, and about last night. I can't believe I was talking about that."

"Well - you were. How else would I know?"

"Yeah. But Bobby -"

"Ted, I told you don't worry. I'm not gonna say anything, but you got to watch it. Do you always get like that when you get high?"

"No, I get pretty wild when I drink sometimes. But not on grass."

"OK, I got two more gallons coming down today. I'm gonna sell one and drink one. You want any?"

"Yeah!"

"OK."

"Hey, Bobby, that big sergeant gonna work today?"

"Yeah, and I'll tell you this. You'd best not run off at the mouth at him or he will kick your ass. He's gonna ride you for a while, and if you show it bothers you, it will get worse. It's best to act like it's no big deal. Then he'll get tired of you, and leave you alone when you don't amuse him anymore."

"OK, man. What time does he work?"

"The seven to three shift. Here's a joint."

"Shit."

"Well, light it up! And look, here's the coffee and donuts."

"OK."

After a little buzz and the snack we began to rap.

"Man, that escape was pretty neat."

"It wasn't too neat - here I am."

"I escaped a couple of times myself."

"Yeah."

" And I don't plan to stay here."

"Ha! Ha! That's funny. Believe me, Ted, it's not that easy."

"You did it!"

"Yeah, but it was as much dumb luck as it was me being any good. And believe me, they're gonna tighten this mother down now."

"Well, I'm still gonna do it."

"I hope you do."

"How about you? You gonna try again?"

"Ted, you don't just drive up your first day and say, 'Hey man, I'm gonna escape, how about you?' "

"But you're OK, Bobby."

"Yeah, right. How do you know, Ted? You've known me less than 24 hours. I may be a guard planted here. You just got my word. Who am I?"

"Those other guards said you were Lewis."

"Yeah, Ted. Don't you think they would lie if I was not? Ted, listen. If you're gonna have any sense - if you're gonna do anything here - you got to play it close to your chest. Every person here can get a transfer if they just give up an escape. Especially a Death Row escape - and especially you! You got a hard way to go, Ted. You got a lot to learn."

"I got to go to Lake City for the Kimberly Ann Leach thing. I may get a shot there."

"Ted, you know they're gonna have a ton of security and news around you."

"Yeah, but it's a little town - no bigger than the one I get out of in Colorado. I went through the ceiling and out the guard's living quarters next to the cell."

"Well I doubt they keep you there, Ted. They'll probably just take you back and forth every day."

"No man, I got my lawyer to make them keep me there."

"I doubt it, but you can try."

"Hey man, why you got to be so negative about everything I say?"

"Ha ha! Ted, I'm not negative. I'm trying to answer your questions the best I can. I'm no yes-man. If you ask, you get my opinion. I may be wrong, but it's what I think. Let me put the music on."

"Yeah! You like hard rock?"

"Uh-huh. Here, roll a couple more while I shave and wash up."

"OK."

After a few minutes I heard, "Hey, Bobby."

"Yeah Ted."

"I'm gonna pay you back for all this."

"Ted, look. There's just you and me and Old Sparky down here. No telling how long we'll be here, man. There's nobody else to talk to. You don't have to thank me every time I do something. You don't have to pay me back. It's easier on each of us if we get along. If you did all the things they say you did, I don't care too much for that - nobody here does. And you're bound to have problems sooner or later. I got my own problems and my own life to worry about, so let's just try to get along, OK?"

"Yeah, man. But I'm not guilty."

"That's not how it sounded last night, Ted. You were scared to death when I woke you up and told you what you were saying."

"Yeah, man, but that was just a nightmare or something."

"Yeah, I'll go for the *or something.*"

"Are you saying I'm lying?"

"Look, Ted. I'm sure you are guilty as hell. So save all the bullshit! I don't need it and I don't want to hear it! I don't care how many women and kids you killed - that don't mean shit in this place. We got men in here. And me and you can either get along or not. So it's up to you."

"Yeah, man, you're right, I'm just nervous. Shit, I've got to get out of here!"

"Ha! Yeah man, don't we all. You got that shit rolled yet?"

"Yeah."

"Well light up, light up!"

"Yeah, Bobby. Hey, where do you get all this shit from anyway?"

"Mostly from guards. I got a couple on the pay roll. So when you see one came down and hang around my door, go to the back of your cell, because they won't do business with you watching."

"OK, sure, no problem."

I laid back and put on my headphones to think. I thought, shit. I'm probably stuck with Ted. This fucker attracts people like flies on shit. There were already tour groups to see me - *The Man Who Escaped From Death Row* - like I was their prize trophy. Now with this fucker down here it's gonna look like a goddamn zoo. At least until the newness wears off.

I had been running the grass business for the institution right off death watch. Since these group tours had been coming down to look at me, it had been fucking with business. So what to do. Drink what wine I got and stop making any more of that. Send most of the smoke to one of my homeboys in population to sell. I can just keep me a fat stash to stay right. At least until they move Ted or me, or these people stop coming through to stare at us. I can see I got to school Ted fast or he's going to get me busted through sheer stupidity. There's just no other way to do it, I got to get started right now.

"Hey, Ted! Let me talk to you!" So we each walked up to the bars by the 8" wall that separated us. You couldn't look directly at the other person, but it was easy to reach around and pass something.

"Ted, there's a lot you need to learn to keep the guards and prisoners off your ass. For a while you don't have to worry about prisoners. But the guards are gonna ride you if you go off. It just amuses them."

"I'll tell my lawyer!"

"No, Ted. Most of what they do is petty. And the lawyer won't care."

"Mine will."

"OK, let's say yours does, then. Let's say he tells the news people the mean old guards are picking on you. First the prison people are gonna say it's not true and smile. The news is gonna run it as a public interest story, and the public is gonna be happy as hell!"

"Happy?"

"Ted, as you may have noticed, womenkillers are not the most popular acts in town! You got to grow up. You're smart, Ted. I can see that. So use it!"

"OK man, I'm gonna try."

"Hey, that's the new shift coming on. They'll be down in a minute."

"Is Spraggins gonna be down?"

"Yeah. Just take it easy. Here they come!"

Sergeant Spraggins stepped up to Ted's cell and said to another, "Well! Let's check on our new asshole!"

He called over to Ted, "Good morning, asshole. Sleep good?"

No answer. "Hey asshole, I'm talking to you! I said did you fucking sleep good?"

"I'm no asshole."

"You'll be anything I want you to be. And when you talk to me you say OFFICER or SERGEANT SPRAGGINS. Or I'll write you up. Hey asshole, where'd you get that stuff in your cell?" Not a word from Ted.

Sergeant Spraggins turned to the other guard, and said, "Give me the keys. " He popped Ted's door and went in. "What's this shit ? Asshole, this in contraband! I didn't give this shit to you!" He was talking about all the small stuff I gave Ted the day before. "Anything you want, you ask me for it, you hear?"

"But you can't-"

"*Asshole!*" Spraggins shouted as he walked right up to Ted's face. "I told you once and I'm not gonna tell you again! You call me OFFICER or SERGEANT SPRAGGINS! You got that, asshole?"

"Yes sir. I mean Sergeant Spraggins, yes sir!"

"That's better, asshole." Sergeant Spraggins walked back and locked Ted's door then walked over in front of my cell.

"Lewis, did you give this stuff to Ted?"

I smiled and shrugged.

"Well, you're just throwing your shit away. I'm gonna take anything I don't give him myself!"

I just shrugged my shoulders again.

The guards walked off, and as they went upstairs, Ted said, "That crazy bastard. I'm gonna tell my lawyer. He'll be here today, and I'm gonna get that bastard fired. I'm gonna - "

"Ted, you're not gonna do shit but get into more trouble!"

"I don't care! I'm gonna tell my lawyer!"

"OK, Ted. You tell your lawyer. Do it your way, and when you get ready to learn, you give me a holler. I don't have time to waste on you. I'm reading a good book. Later!"

So I kicked back to read. About an hour later they came and got Ted to go see several lawyers that had come to see him. While he was gone, I moved all my smoke except for my stash out to population, and started to clean up, thinking about what a headache Ted was going to be until he learned. He ate dinner out there and came back about 4.00 p.m. looking happy.

"Bobby, I told those lawyers I wanted to be kept at the Lake City Jail. And about Spraggins, I'm gonna show that big fucker he can't fuck with me!"

"Yeah, right, Ted."

"Well I am!"

"I said right."

So we didn't talk much until after supper.

"Ted, I'm gonna knock off the rest of this wine. You want some?"

"Yeah, sure."

"Here, roll the smoke while I get the wine out."

And we sat down at the bars and got a good buzz going until about 5.30 when the mail came. At that time the next shift came down complaining about all the mail Ted and I were getting from all over. Among all the other usual stuff, he got a large poster from Carole, and a letter from a woman from Jacksonville who promised to do anything for him.

"Look at this picture, Bobby. This crazy bitch wears black to all my hearings. She loves me. I'm thinking of putting her or this other one, Carole, on my visitor's list."

"It's not that easy."

"My lawyer can handle it."

"Right."

As I glanced through my mail, Ted asked, "You got any tape or glue?"

"Yeah, what's up?"

"I'm gonna put this poster on the wall."

"If you do, Spraggins is gonna tear it down."

"No he's not. I told you the lawyers said they were gonna take care of Spraggins!"

"Right. Here's some tape."

"What's wrong? Every time I tell you my lawyer's gonna do something, you just say *RIGHT*."

"Well Ted, I do try to tell you, but you don't want to listen! So we'll just wait and see. Believe me, you'll know tomorrow."

"What's that mean?"

"Just what it sounds like. You'll find out what pull your lawyers got in here. But fuck that shit, Ted. Let's get high!"

"OK." Then he asked me for more of the things Spraggins had taken from him that morning, and I gave them to him again.

We had finished about half the gallon each when I heard Ted giggling. So I got my mirror to see what was so funny. He was sitting in a lotus position, and he had a wash cloth, twisting and twirling it in his hands. Then he would throw it up and try to catch it. When he missed, he giggled and grabbed it up and choked it, and then giggled some more.

I called him. I even beat on the wall but he did not answer, he just kept at it. Then about sixty seconds later he sort of snapped, and said, "What are you hollering about?"

I said, "What the fuck are you doing, Ted?"

He said, "Watch! Watch!" and went right back into his act. I thought *OH SHIT*. So I just poured the rest of the wine down the toilet, washed the bag out and stashed it. It looked like Ted was going to get us shook down for sure. But by the time I had done all that, he crawled in bed and went to sleep. I laid over there with a good buzz and my music and thought to myself, "Check this crazy bastard out!"

I knew one thing for sure, Ted just got his last wine from me, as it was clear he goes to another place. On this thought, I drifted off to sleep myself.

The next day after breakfast, here come Spraggins and about five guards. He opened the door to Ted's cell and shouted, "Shakedown, asshole! Strip!"

Ted said, "What!?"

I hollered over, "Do what he says, Ted!"

"Move! Strip butt-ass naked!" he yelled.

Ted stripped. I heard Spraggins tell him to run his hands through his hair, stick out his tongue, lift his feet, lift his balls, and turn around and spread his cheeks.

Ted said, "What?" again and Sergeant Spraggins went off. He rushed at Ted and pressed him against the wall with his chest.

"Asshole!" he shouted in his face, "I told you to call me SERGEANT SPRAGGINS or OFFICER when you talk to me! And I told you to bend over and spread the cheeks of your ass! You don't want to do what I tell you? So let's say I want an excuse - any excuse - to kick your fucking ass! Every minute of every day I'm gonna look for you to fuck up! Now, asshole, you bend over and spread your cheeks or I'm gonna spread them for you!"

As Ted bent over the other guards started laughing, and I heard Ted crying.

"Check this asshole out! It looks used. I'm an expert on assholes, and that asshole is used!"

I heard Ted crying as they tore the poster off the wall and took all his stuff. Ted must have moved, because next I heard, "I did not tell you to move. Spread those cheeks. I'm telling you that is one used asshole! Is your asshole used, asshole?"

"No Sergeant Spraggins."

"Well, I think you're lying, asshole. But if it ain't used now, it will be soon! Your lawyers are gonna be here at 9.30 to see you, asshole. So get ready, I'll be back to get you. Then you can tell them about this, asshole! I'll be back tomorrow to see you again." The guards all laughed.

"Stand up, asshole!" Ted stood up. "Asshole, why are you crying?" Ted didn't speak. "You reckon all the families of the women and kids you killed are crying? Huh, asshole?" He put his face up close to Ted's. "Well, I *love* to see you cry. I'm gonna *love* having you here, because you belong to *me*. And I'm gonna see how much I can make you cry. You understand that, asshole?"

"Yes, Sergeant Spraggins." And when they left Ted was still crying.

After the guards were gone, I said, "Ted, wash your face and smoke this joint."

After about ten minutes, Ted said, "That bastard's really crazy. I thought he was gonna fuck me up!"

"Yeah Ted I thought he might fuck you up myself."

"Man, he's gone too far. I got his ass this time. I'm gonna get him fired."

"Ted, you don't learn easy, do you?"

"You'll see, I'm gonna get him, and I mean today!"

About 9.30 they came to get Ted, and he didn't get back until about 2.30 p.m. He was quiet.

"Well Ted, what happened?"

"Man I got a bunch of pussies for lawyers! They let those people scare them. They told them I was causing problems and all kinds of shit and for them to talk to me. I told them about Spraggins and about my poster. They told me to try to be good. I think I'm gonna fire their asses."

"What? Ted, look - you come from one world, and now you are in another. All the rules are changed, you dig? Either you learn or they teach you. You gonna be real lucky if Spraggins don't kick your ass."

"Shit, I don't understand this place. These rednecks are crazy."

"Yeah Ted, that's about right. They're crazy like a fox, but don't underestimate them. They're smart in their own ways and this place is theirs! You'd better tighten up your game. And here's some more stuff... I know Spraggins got all your stuff."

"I'm gonna keep it, but I'll give it back at breakfast before Spraggins comes around."

"That's a good idea, Ted. You're starting to think. Here's a joint, but I poured out the rest of the wine. You sort of went crazy last night."

"Was I talking again?"

"No, you were sitting in the middle of the floor twirling your wash cloth and giggling."

"No I wasn't!"

"OK Ted, then what did we do last night?"

"Well - uh - I don't remember."

"Yeah, but I do! You can believe me or not, Ted, but that's what you were doing."

"Well, I must have been fucked up."

"Yeah, you must have been. Have you decided on your visitors yet?"

"I' m going to write that girl in Jacksonville. She sort of hinted that if I need money to let her know. If she comes through, I might keep her."

"How about the other one?"

"Shit, I already got her. Who comes to see you?"

"I got an old girlfriend out of Jacksonville. After I got busted, her brother married her for me with my ID so she could come visit me."

"No shit! Ha ha! Yeah!"

"She does me good. You may have to get married too."

"Yeah! I may if the rest of these people are like Spraggins. Boy I sure hate to see him in the morning."

"Yeah, I know what you mean."

So we smoked a little and wrote letters until lights out.

The next morning Ted passed me all his stuff before Spraggins came down. He just sort of growled at Ted a few times and went on. He did take all of Ted's stuff one more time, but after than he got tired of playing with Ted, and pretty much left him alone.

Death Row Shakedown

After Ted Bundy and I got off Q-Wing, by chance we were both moved to adjacent cells on S-Wing. This looks like a regular wing, except the 100 men on it are waiting to die. There are two sides with a pipe alley down the middle, seventeen cells to a floor, three tiers high.

Ted and I were sitting on the floor talking about the latest issue of the *East-West Journal*. We had each had a visit that day, and had scored some smoke and got some pussy in the bathroom from our old ladies. So all things considered, it was a good day. But there was a war brewing on the wing.

A black convict named Thomas Knight had seen his people arrive in their car and they were waiting to see him in the visitor's park. That day on the 7-to-4 shift, we had a reall asshole for a guard working the wing and he told Thomas that he was not going to get a visiting period. Thomas told him if he did not get to see his family, he would kill him or the first guard he could get his hands on. The guard laughed at him and walked away.

Thomas was a quiet guy who stayed to himself. But he was very serious. He had several black belts and he was in real good shape, at over 6' and 200 lbs. He could be bad when he was mad, and this time Thomas was mad. The guard on duty gave him hell until he got off at four. When the new shift came on, the two guards were OK. One, an older man, was as good as you could expect for a prison guard. We had supper and it was shower time. Everyone expected Thomas to do what he said, as that was the type of person he was. Now I don't know, but I've been told what happened that night. As the old guard came to get him for showers, they say Thomas stepped out with a homemade knife and stabbed the guard to death. The old man pleaded for his life, but Thomas had gone past the point of caring. On Death Row, a visit from family is the most valued thing a person has.

They came and took Thomas away. We heard they kicked his ass real bad, over on the famous Q-Wing. At that time, it was used quite a lot for that purpose. I'd had a couple of bad beatings over there myself.

Now there was even more tension than ever, as no matter if it's just one man who does something in prison, as a rule everyone is punished in some way.

A couple of days went by and nothing happened. Then early one morning we saw a lot of extra cars coming to the prison. We figured it was a tour group coming to look at the electric chair and the animals in their cages.

Shortly after breakfast we found out it was no tour group. It was a lot of guards brought in from other prisons so they would not be recognized. They had black tape over their name tags and the rank on their shirts was covered. There were fifty or more of them.

On my floor they started at my cell. "OK, asshole, strip!" I knew what was coming. Resistance is what they pray for so they can kick ass to get revenge.

I stripped naked, and had to lift my feet, lift my balls, run my hand through my hair, and then bend over and spread the cheeks of my ass so they could look for weapons and contraband. The entire time they were shouting abuse and threats. I heard them at other cells doing the same thing.

And then I heard Ted start to complain. The guard yelled, "Hey! I got Bundy here and he's *not happy!*"

I shouted, "Ted, shut up and do what they say!"

The one in front of me yelled, "*You* shut up, asshole!"

As I turned around the handcuffs were so tight they cut into my flesh. I was shoved naked into the shower and locked in. After a minute, here came Ted the same way. As they put others in showers on other floors, you could hear men struggling and the ones that resisted being beaten. One prisoner was thrown down a flight of stairs, and another had his arm broken.

I told Ted to be cool and not to complain, no matter what. He was real scared. Ted had a habit of whining and complaining about everything. I told him if he didn't keep his mouth shut this time he could get his ass killed.

Next I heard shouts of, "*Hey, stop! That's my stuff! You can't take that!*" Guards were walking by with big garbage cans. I had a lot of personal items in my cell like everyone else - letters and pictures from loved ones, my radio. Mostly a lot of junk, but there was the only picture I had of my father who had died not too long before, and there were my legal papers.

When Ted and I were shoved back in our cells, there was nothing - not even toilet paper. Noting but one sock under my bed. As I stood there thinking of what I had lost, I realized there was an important letter from a man who had testified against me and had written to say he was sorry he had lied. And I realized they had just thrown my life away.

Then I heard Ted starting to complain again. "Ted for chrissake!" I said, "Shut up, or they're going to fuck you up too!"

One of the guards said, "That's right! Both of you shut up!"

So it went, all day long. They went cell to cell, destroying property, beating prisoners. Later they took some to the hospital. Others they moved to Q-Wing until their bruises cleared up.

Now the prisoners pledged revenge. We flooded the wing, beat on the bars, and went on a hunger strike that was to last ten days. Finally we reached our people and our lawyers, and the news media found out what had happened. Lawsuits were filed, and a couple of years later, the State of

Florida paid off over 150 lawsuits. The payoffs were made quietly and they were kept out of the news.

Today Thomas Knight has changed his name to an African name and that is all he answers to. He has been on Q-Wing for over ten years with few privileges and much abuse. I expect him to be executed next year [1991]. He is the only man I am sure has been treated worse than me.

I don't agree with what he did. I liked that old man they say he killed - he'd always been decent to us. But I still have to respect Thomas Knight, because he has been through hell and he's still a man. He knows what it means not to be broken, not to beg or humble himself, and not to go crazy.

I had to laugh at all the bullshit about Ted Bundy and pornography. When he was about to be executed he made these statements blaming pornography for what he did. He had all the psychiatrists and anti-porn groups hollering, "I told you so!"

In prison, magazines with naked women are prized possessions. They're called fuck books, and are passed from hand to hand until they fall apart. I was around Ted Bundy on Death Row for ten years on an almost day-in-day-out basis, and I never once saw him with a fuck book. He did love true detective and crime magazines and TV shows with rape or torture as the main theme. Other than that, he did a lot of reading - mostly history, religion, education, yoga and health books. Ted was a health nut. He used to meditate and do yoga for hours and was 90% vegetarian. If he loved pornography so much, I don't know why I never saw him with any when it was all around.

Ted changed moods and beliefs faster than anyone I ever met. Any time he read something new, he would go off on it. Like if he read an article about sugar causing cancer, he would go on a big crusade against sugar. That would go on until a new article or TV fad came along and then he'd go back to using sugar and be off on the new deal. Anti-porn groups were in the news a lot about the time he was executed, so it seems like Ted was just trying to get in on the latest fad as usual.

For a person with Ted's education, he was the most immature or unworldly person on Death Row. His innocence at life made me wonder if it was an act at first, but as I saw other cons run games on him and trick him out of his money and drugs, I realized that it was not an act.

Ted reminded me of the woman in the movie with so many personalities.

I never could totally figure him out. That's important in prison, because one real mistake here means death.

The only time Ted got really crazy was when he was drinking. I'll bet there was not a crime Bundy ever did when he was not drunk. After his college girlfriend dumped him, I guess he went a little nuts and couldn't deal with it. She was the only person I am sure he loved. He just went for the bottle, and that was always the worst thing he could do.

With all I disliked about what Ted had done, I still was able to see good qualities in him, laugh with him, and look out for him. It seems for some reason life had given him the sickness inside him. I can't believe any baby is born to turn out like Bundy, and a lot must have happened inside to make him what he was.

2
WAYNE HENDERSON
by Sondra London

It all started because of the big titties. We're talking giganto mammalian appendages: "A pair of tits with a girl attached," as the lady has so poignantly expressed how she's known. Justice Howard was known only for unveiling her 44-FFFs on the silver screen until she decided to unveil a bit of her intellect as well, in her ragamuffin biker verse, a selection of which I added to the offerings of my Media Queen underground publishing empire in early 1990. An ad for her booklet, *A Taste of Justice,* netted a query from a writer known for his articles in various underground publications, who identified himself as Wayne Henderson, "an indigent prisoner - currently a guest of the Folsom branch of the Hotel Kalifornia." He requested a copy of the provocatively-illustrated poems, apologetically saying he was "unable to offer anything (like money) in exchange."

"Bah, humbug!" I replied, saying I would be glad to send him the Justice Zine and other amusing items as well, but that he need not feel he had nothing to offer. I invited him to send me the true story of how he got in trouble. Intrigued, he replied that his criminal record had been unimpressive - that is, until this time. "The present case is a doozy, I've got to admit: I was convicted of four counts of murder, two of armed robbery, and one of auto theft." At age 33, Wayne introduced himself to me as a first-termer, down since April of 1982, when his housemates wound up dead and he was caught on the other coast with van, jewelry and a few other items.

In the three years I have been corresponding with Wayne, I've found him to be a creative and highly intelligent individual, immensely talented in the visual arts, with eclectic literary tastes ranging from pictures of naked ladies to *The Meaning of the Qumran Scrolls* and *The Tao of Physics.* Wayne's most ambitious project is his unpublished book-length *Exegesis of the Gnosis,* an analysis of the correlations between the Hebrew Sephiroth and the chakras, demonstrating his thesis that the mystic/esoteric traditions of the oriental religions (Judeo/Christianity, Buddhism, Tao, etc.) can all be traced back to one original source. He is not only well-versed in arcana, but he manages to stay abreast of current trends in the international literary underground as well. He's published a number of articles about prison nutcases for *Kooks,* as well as theological stuff for *Dharma Combat* and *Reflections in a Golden Eye.* No Joke Publications has put out several collections of his short stories under the title *Return to Summer,* and

SteamshovelPress published an earlier version of his article *Hotel Kalifornia*, which appears in expanded form here. While Wayne has also published some erotic fiction, I can't vouch for how good it might be, as I discourage prisoners from sharing their erotic ruminations with me.

As a part of a scheme to shelter an inheritance, he offered me a thousand dollars, if I would drive to a bank in Florida and withdraw a pretty good chunk of money that was deposited under his name. He directed me to contact Kerry Thornley, the legendary Discordian philosopher, putative paranoid schizophrenic, and confessed conspirator in the JFK assassination. He felt that Kerry's presence was somehow necessary to this mysterious mission, and that my life was incomplete until Kerry became a part of it. It took more than a year to follow through on this bizarre pilgrimage, and we never did get that money, but I did manage to get myself embroiled in the "Kennedy curse" by putting Kerry on national TV and thus bringing down all sorts of hauntings and skulduggery upon myself forevermore.

I figure it's all Wayne Henderson's fault....

Wayne Henderson

YOU MIGHT AS WELL ASSUME I'M LYING
by Wayne Henderson

It's one of those basic assumptions - ask any guy in prison if he's innocent, and he'll swear up and down that he is. It's axiomatic: the sun rises in the east, birds fly south for the winter, pro wrestling is rigged, and convicts lie like rugs. So please, just assume that I am lying; no sense questioning our basic assumptions right at the beginning. No telling where that would end.

I won't bore you with a recounting of my childhood. Not that it was overwhelmingly bad, nor was it unbelievably good. My family always had enough money, and although I did find myself on the receiving end of a few sexual assaults when I was a child, and was badly traumatized by the death of my adoptive father, I'd have to say I came through it well enough. None of the really unpleasant things, such as my origins (my mother was a cheap prostitute, who sold me to the people I knew as "mom" and "dad") came to light until I was well past the age when it would matter, so all in all I'd have to say that the roots of my "life of crime" don't stretch back into my childhood.

I began my criminal endeavors back in my teens, mainly to support my growing love of electronic experimentation. I taught myself to repair old TVs and radios that I'd liberate from a nearby dump, and would recondition them for pocket money. Electronics parts were a snap to acquire. I made regular trips to a local science-goods firm and simply pocketed what I needed from the showroom. No "criminal intent" involved. It was just easier to pick up what I needed and split. I graduated, in time, to every teen's favorite - the fake ID - and have kept my talents honed over the years. I've enjoyed switching names and identities as often as I'd switch living quarters. Not because I was on the run, but rather for the sheer joy of accomplishment. Unless I miss my guess, I've still got a few identities on ice out there, and I might just resort to them, once the courts give me my retrial and torn me loose. By that time, I'll need them for my own protection. Once I've won my retrial, I intend to blow the lid off a few well-kept secrets that I'm sure a few of San Francisco's finest will find disquieting to say the least. Other criminal acts are, however, relatively unimportant. I could write about my check-cashing scheme, or the great connections I've made among border-runners over the years, but that would be wandering too far off course. Besides that, there are a few really good, stand-up people who've done me favors over the years whom I am loathe to implicate.

More than anything else, my present situation is the result of stupidity. Had I been more careful about my associations, I wouldn't be sitting here in Folsom Prison, typing this up on an outdated manual typewriter, while I wait for my appeal. I'm not claiming the blame for myself; I simply made the mistake of walking into a bad situation and letting myself get caught up in other people's concerns. No, the real blame has to fall squarely on the shoulders of others - people who should know better than to do the things they do under color of authority, and expect to get away with it. I believe in karma, and I'd hate to have the karma of those who are actually responsible for this mess.

I suppose it's only fair for me to lay out the facts and let you form your own opinion. It all started innocently enough in May of 1980. I was staying at a rooming-house in Tampa, Florida, resting up and setting some plans for my next tour, when I met Velma, an attractive older woman recently separated from her husband. I've always been an advocate of safe sex. I like to think that any man worth his gonads will protect his lover from unwanted pregnancy. So the choices being use of a condom or sex with a woman who can't get pregnant, I generally choose the latter - and Velma assured me she was beyond such concerns. We not only enjoyed a good sexual relationship, we also found we worked well together. Most of our jobs were side-by-side. Working at motels, hotels, and apartment buildings, we made a good team. After working in the Tampa area long enough to build some traveling funds and acquire a car we could live with (and if need be, in) we took off for a cross-country jaunt.

Velma had been raised in one of those staunchly conservative Baptist families in Missouri, had married her first suitor, and lived a relatively stable domestic life traveling the south with her husband, an alcoholic house painter who beat her regularly and treated her like a slave. When he abandoned her there in Tampa, her only thought was to get back to him - that is, until I seduced her one night, suddenly changing her perception of the way things ought to be. She never dreamed of getting involved with a younger man. She was, after all, a Baptist from Missouri, and the mere thought of anything beyond the missionary position with her lawfully wedded husband had never crossed her mind. It took me all of a month to introduce her to all of my favorite amusements; rock'n'roll and new wave music, marijuana, and a more expansive interpretation of sexuality. I was ecstatic. Not only did we work well together, but I'd finally found a playmate worth keeping.

We traveled through the south as far as Texas. I've never been overly fond of the south. I suppose it's the subtle snubs my Yankee accent draws, the sort of snubs I've never offered any southerners I've met up north. So we finally re-routed ourselves northward, stopping in Chicago for an extended stay. To me, Chicago was the turning point. I wanted to head east, back towards New Jersey, but Velma was hot to see California. I let her sway me, and that's a decision we'll both regret for a long time.

I'd been to California once before, back in '76, and I wasn't overly fond of what I'd seen. I'd been staying in Hermosa Beach at first, and later gravitated to LA. It just wasn't to my tastes. But since Velma wanted to see California, I thought that to make the best of a bad trip, we'd try northern California first rather than heading south. Though I normally have no trouble making money when I travel, the San Francisco Bay area proved to be a hard nut to crack. By this time, I had gotten my start in the tattooing profession, and turned a decent dollar at it, working out of hotel rooms along the way, staying only so long as business was brisk, and then moving on. The Bay area, though, was a rough road to go. We weren't able to find a place to stay in Berkeley, so we had to camp out in the car. And there was no way I could tattoo people in the car.

It took us a while to gather enough money just to move across the bay to Frisco. Actually, once we'd set up the tattooing equipment in a hotel room in Oakland, the money came in pretty easily. It was getting the initial money together, just to get that room in Oakland, that took the time. And I must say I think I did pretty well, considering that there's precious few while folk in Oakland; blacks just don't get tattoos.

Frisco was no picnic either. Though we were able to set up in a hotel room in the tenderloin district, I found it difficult to get customers in as often as I'd hoped. Let's face it, being set up on the third floor isn't as good as a relatively open motel. Nonetheless, we were able to get by and accumulate a small cache of emergency money. Even this would not have been possible, though, without the relief checks from the city to cover the rent.

At the time we had a '71 LTD from Texas that had served us as both transportation and sleeping accommodations. We had acquired it to replace our Nova, which was on its last legs and didn't provide enough room for my toolchest. I fill in the gaps in our finances by being able to fix just about anything - a talent I picked up in my earn years. Before meeting Velma, I'd not only supported myself, but had also advanced my education with the money my talents had provided. Our LTD was a great asset, one we'd be hard-pressed to do without. And we were careful to keep it moving, parking it in a different block every night, so as not to run afoul of the unusual parking situation and the towtrucks that we encountered in Frisco. All for nothing, for one night, while moving it to a new parking spot, she conked out on us - ran out of gas right in the middle of Market Street, between Fifth and Sixth. We pushed her over to the side of the street and left a sign in the window explaining that she was out of gas and we'd move her in the morning. But our car was towed nonetheless, leaving us stranded in San Francisco.

Without proper transportation out of the city, our plans had to be altered. We'd expected to move on within the month and now we had to acquire a vehicle. The LTD was a total loss to us; I wasn't about to pay more to get it out of the impound yard than I'd originally spent to buy it, and I wasn't sure I could get it back anyway. There was some question as to whether she was "street legal", and I was certain that the Texas plates were outdated.

We first met Ray and Angie at the Jack-in-the Box restaurant at Seventh and Market. At first, we simply knew Angie as a regular. We were welcomed at her booth and introduced to the Seventh Street people who congregated there. Though we still planned on leaving Frisco at our earliest convenience, the stay was becoming a bit more bearable. Not only due to the friendliness of the Seventh Street people, but also the extra money. It seems that those among them who had a little money wanted tattoos, and preferred to get from one of their own.

Angie introduced us to Ray, her live-in, and the four of us would party together regularly. Since Angie had been a hooker, she had a few good connections, and the weed came less expensive than before. After a week or so of regular partying, and only about a month after first meeting them, Ray and Angie asked us to move in with them and split the rent on their apartment. At first, we weren't overly enthused. I didn't know whether I could continue tattooing there, as it was in a black neighborhood, and I could just see our capital dwindling until we had nothing left to purchase the new vehicle we needed. Ultimately, however, it appeared that I couldn't do much worse. Business in the tenderloin was drying up, so we decided to go ahead and move in with them, at least for long enough to acquire transportation out of Frisco.

Before I moved in, I had no idea that Ray was involved with druggies - serious drug people, some bikers, a supplier, and the less-savory segments of the Frisco street crowd. Nor had I known that though Angie swore she'd left "the life", she was still turning a few tricks, and black tricks at that. Ray asked me to advance him a bit over our share of the first month's expenses, saying he was a little short at the moment, and I went for it. Ray was a good talker, smooth as silk when he wanted to be, and I figured he'd have it soon enough. He was doing a respectable nickel and dime business at the front door. He run the front door - that is, answer the bell, get the money, and run the baggies out to the customers. Now, while I'm no angel, I do have certain limits, and I made sure that Ray understood that I was in no way his business partner. I was just doing him a favor in exchange for his assuming an extra 10% of the expenses, and he assured me that his customers would know that I wasn't involved. I believed him.

Velma and I kept our food costs down by eating at the soup kitchens - Glide Church and St. Anthony's Dining Room - and so were slowly adding to our nest-egg, with an eye toward buying something that would carry us and our stuff away from the city. Ray and Angie were spending money on what I considered frivolities - eating out, having pizzas delivered, and toys-sex toys, porno films, trinkets, and so forth. My estimation of his net worth was in flux. He was either doing very well with his job and his drugs, or he was blowing his wad on the off-chance that the money would just keeping rolling in.

Towards Christmas, things started getting weird. First I hear Ray on the phone begging the landlord to give him an extension on the rent - the very rent to which I'd already contributed our share. Then we met Hawaiian Jimmy, an associate of Ray's to whom Ray owed some nebulous, but large, amount of money. The story Velma and I got was that Jimmy had done some work on Ray's truck, and Ray simply hadn't paid the tab yet. However from my own limited experience, I'd have to say that most people don't get that upset over a mechanic's bill. Something wasn't quite right about that story.

Then there were the customers at the door - a faceless procession of druggies who made noise about the bad count and the low quality. I could only say that I had nothing personally to do with Ray's business. I was just answering the door. Ray took to hiding whenever the doorbell would ring. His instruction to me was that I should tell all callers that he was out. And to add to the illusion, he took to parking his truck at a number of out-of-the-way spots, up to two blocks away. When Hawaiian Jimmy would show up, Ray would hotfoot it out the back door, down into the crawlspace behind, under or alongside the house. Angie would grab the baby, little Ray Junior, and hide in the back bedroom that Velma and I shared. It seems that Ray and Angie were more than just a little scared of the people with whom they did business. And to this day, I still don't know the whole story behind it.

Velma and I decided to leave right after Christmas. There was just no way we were going to stay in what was becoming a truly hostile environment. Ray wouldn't take any chances. Even when he wanted a pizza and couldn't get it delivered, he wouldn't show his face outside the house at night. I ended up going for pizzas with Ray paying me to run the errand. I've never seen anyone so nervous in all my life.

Ray and Angie were a persuasive pair if ever I met one. Between Ray's begging and Angie's sharing of her sexual favors, I was persuaded to stay just one week longer, over the New Year. Velma went along with it. I wish now that she'd held firm. If she had, we'd have left then and there. Then one week turned to two. Angie faked an illness and this time it was Velma who agreed to the extension, in order to take care of Ray Junior. Angie kept up our early-morning trysts, complaining that Ray wasn't up to it lately. Even after the death threats, even after the evening that Hawaiian Jimmy beat Ray over the head with the hard wood cane right in front of two other friends of ours, even after Hawaiian Jimmy swore in the presence of the neighbors to kill everyone in the house, we stayed.

The situation at the house was weird, but we stuck in there against our better judgment - biding our time, awaiting the chance to leave once Ray and Angie no longer needed us to baby-sit. Angie was going out more and more to turn a few tricks and hang out at the Jack-in-the-Box, and naturally, she couldn't take the baby with her. I knew we were in a dangerous situation. Any time death threats are involved, it's dangerous, so why didn't we leave? To this day, I kick myself for staying on. Hindsight is 20/20, so they say, and I'm forced to agree. If I'd had any sense, I'd have gotten Velma and myself clear of that place at the first sign of trouble. But the lack of a personal vehicle seemed an insurmountable obstacle. Leaving by bus, our other alternative, would entail selling or abandoning all the tools I used to my livelihood. I'd lost enough tools when the car was towed and I was loathe to go anywhere without some means of support.

Things came to a head in January of '82. Ray and Angie were spending more and more time away from the house, or else rushing in and hiding. Velma and I were terrified. We no longer cared much about what we took with us when we left. Then came the day when things went beyond weird, into a territory I'd never yet explored.

We awakened somewhat early and Velma and I made love. She went back to sleep while I went into the kitchen for a cup of coffee and a look at the morning news. As usual, Angie was propped up in front of the TV, and we had another one of our trysts, settling in afterwards to watch the news until her favorite cartoons came on. Velma and I followed a regular pattern during the day. We'd go walking until Angie woke up and got ready to hit the street, then we'd head back to take over the baby-sitting until Ray got home, usually around 5.00 or 6.00, when we'd usually go out again, staying away from the house until my hours at the door. This particular day, though, Velma wasn't up to walking. She'd had a tooth extracted and the painkillers left her feeling worn. So I rejoined her in bed and we relaxed until afternoon.

It was the last time we could afford to go to the connection where we got our pot. We'd set aside a small "smoke fund", and it was dwindling. Ray and Angie had taken to smoking ours. So after this last purchase, Velma and I deposited the remainder in our traveling expense fund. We took the long route both ways in order to avoid going back to the house for as long as possible.

We were there when some time around 4.00 p.m. Angie got a phone call. We've never been sure who called her, but phone records and a witness indicate it was Ray, calling from work. She dressed quickly and left with Ray Junior, telling us that she'd be right back, and if Ray came home before she returned, we were to tell him that she'd only stepped out for a minute just before he got there, and would be back soon. We never saw her alive again.

Ray came home at his usual time in a really agitated state. We passed along Angie's message, which only seemed to upset him more. He had a bite to eat then said he was going out to look for Angie. He asked us to wait by the phone in case she called. He made several trips, stopping back between each one to check, supposedly, for Angie - although it seemed more like he was checking on us. Then around 8.00 p.m. Velma and I were in such a state of nerves that we just had to get out of the house. We told Ray we were going to do a little searching on foot. He didn't seem too pleased with the idea, but he agreed. It was as though he wanted us to remain in the house, rather than help him look for Angie. So we left, wandering around, up Market, into the tenderloin, south of Market - just wandering, keeping an eye out for Angie - until we'd calmed down a bit and were feeling pleasantly tired.

We got back to the house around midnight. The inside front door was unlocked, which was unusual. Once inside the apartment, we noticed things out of place. Ray's work boots were in the middle of the floor, and his .22

rifle was off its rack, leaning against the wall. The TV was on with nobody watching it. The living room light was off, when normally it stayed on all of the time. We moved around the place carefully, tensed out, looking for whatever, and finding that fortunately we were alone. The cats were undisturbed, listening to the radio in the bedroom, and other than the few things out of place in the front of the apartment, everything seemed normal - with one striking exception, Ray and Angie and Ray Junior were nowhere to be found.

Ray made it a point to be in bed by 11.00 p.m. For him not to be in bed, let alone not to even be in the apartment, told us something was seriously wrong. I told Velma to load the rifle and shoot anyone or anything that come in range until I returned, and I left to check Ray's favorite hidden parking spaces, just on a whim. I found his truck one block from the house, catty-corner to the apartment. Ray had given me a set of keys back when I first started running for pizzas, and I unlocked the truck. I walked back around to the house and ascertained that Ray and Angie were still not there. Then I went back to the truck, fired it up, and pulled it around to the house. Velma had already started packing. So in what was no time at all, although it seemed like a lifetime while it was happening, we loaded up our things and drove away. We left a note for Ray, apologizing for taking the truck and offering to send him money for it if he would just call us in Florida, and citing the problems at the house as our reason for leaving. I don't know if Ray ever read that note, because the last time we saw him alive was around 8.00 p.m. that last night when we left the house to go looking for Angie.

The trip to Florida, while not uneventful, has little bearing on our story, other than the fact that we "ran up flags," as the police put it, proving our whereabouts almost hourly from the time we left Frisco. This would become very important later, as you will see. It took us quite a while to reach Florida. The truck broke down in Nevada, so we took a train to Salt Lake City and copped a ride from there to Green River, Wyoming. Finally we got a ride from there to Tampa, where almost immediately we got jobs at a resort motel in nearby Madeira Beach, a Gulf Coast resort next to St. Petersburg.

While staying with my adoptive mother awaiting accommodations at our new job to be readied, we received a call from the Frisco police. It was at this point that we learned that Ray and Angie, and even little Ray Junior, were dead. When they started asking questions about Ray's truck I got scared. What would have simply been a matter of grand theft auto was now suddenly the tie-in for a murder rap. So I lied through my teeth, hoping the cops wouldn't think of us as suspects. In leaving the place, we had not only taken Ray's truck, we had grabbed a number of Ray's and Angie's things as well. I had been so paranoid that I took Ray's rifle, so I knew that if the cops came sniffing around, they'd sure as hell consider us prime suspects. I ended up having two separate conversations with the Frisco cops on the phone. While trying to throw off their suspicions, I was also trying to seem helpful, but uselessly so. So I called them back to give them the registration number for the LTD that had been towed. They had requested it, saying they could verify my story by checking to see that it had actually been towed - and I fell for it. I couldn't see any reason not to co-operate. After all, while I might look a little suspicious, they didn't know yet that we'd ripped off Angie and Ray's stuff.

It was late April in 1982 when the Frisco cops came out to Florida to arrest us. We were at work when suddenly I found myself gaffed up, cuffed, and thrust into the back seat of an un-marked car. Velma was brought to another unmarked car, also cuffed, and we spent the next hour or so wondering what was going on. We weren't informed that we were under arrest or read our rights until we crossed the county line into Tampa. We later learned that the arrest warrants were improper, and that neither St. Pete nor Madeira Beach would honor them. Only Tampa would allow us to be arrested, and then it wasn't under the California warrants, but a federal "UFAP" warrant that the Frisco cops had cadged the local FBI office into issuing. If we'd been smart, we'd have just sat tight and fought extradition. I've been told that Florida wasn't going to give us up, but eternally stupid optimist that I am, I figured we'd waive extradition, go back to Frisco, clear it all up in six months time and maybe even sue them for false arrest.

Unfortunately, Velma had a lot less experience dealing with cops than I did. She made a statement, doing her best to keep us well clear of any involvement, going so far as to claim that we had hitched a ride out of Frisco, so as not to tie us to the truck, which we had junked in Nevada after it broke down. Her statement would come back to haunt us later.

So we left Florida, expecting to be gone less than a year. As of today, it's been eight years and three months, and it's going to be a bit longer. We're still waiting for our appeal to come through and a retrial to be ordered. Our wait for trial - four and half years in the Frisco County lockup - is a story in itself, as I will now relate.

Velma and I awaited extradition in the Hillsborough County Jail. The "you-fap" warrant - "Unlawful Flight to Avoid Prosecution" - was invalid, but by the time we realized that, we'd been in the Frisco lockup for over six months and it was a moot point. The Frisco cops are required by law to show a valid San Francisco arrest warrant in order to get the feds to issue the UFAP, and the one they had was irregular to the point of being invalid.

The arresting officers, Prentice Sanders and Napoleon Hendrix of the SFPD, are somewhat famous in their own right. They were written up in *Mother Jones* a number of years back on another case, a killing in the Vietnamese community. In this excellent article, entitled *Terror in Saigontown*, Sanders and Hendrix were noted for screwing up the case. But that wasn't their first screw-up. Out of three major cases that I've seen, excluding my own, Sanders and Hendrix have shown themselves to be both vindictive and inept - either totally unsuited for police work, or perfect for it, depending on your perspective. They have been censured rather strongly by the higher courts. The reference I remember right off is the Brock case, wherein they tampered rather heavily out of desperation for a conviction. To the best of my knowledge, the overwhelming majority of their cases are either lost in the trial court or overturned on appeal. Don't get me wrong; I don't take an automatic hard line against cops. My brother Steve has worked as both a cop and a prison guard, and my cousin Patty is married to a cop. I pride myself on taking everyone I meet as an individual and letting them show me how they want to be treated. However, my experience in this case, especially with Sanders and Hendrix, has left me with quite a bit less respect for "the law" than I had before.

For a first-timer, jail is a frightening experience. When you know you don't belong there, it's truly surreal. There we were, extradited to San Francisco, locked in tanks on the sixth floor of the downtown jail, neither of us having any idea of who to turn to or what to expect. With the exception of a few enlightened guards, the place was run like a sideshow. There was the female officer who removed an inmate from the jail at gunpoint and took him to a nearby hotel, where she cuffed him to the bed and raped him. My guess is that's the only way she figured she could get some. Then there were the attacks on inmates - one was strangled to death the day before he was to be released, simple because he refused to move into a cell with a violent nutcase. Another federal detainee was taken out of jail late one night to be gunned down while he "made an escape attempt." (This was after his girlfriend, who was also in the jail, brought charges against two jail employees whom she claimed had raped her in the infirmary.) But the prisoner was smarter than they thought. He refused to run. The cops chickened out, and settled for simply beating him and breaking his jaw, rather than killing him outright.

I know, I know, nothing is more boring that a convict recounting well-worn tales of police brutality. So I'll be brief and get to the more interesting stuff about my case...

It was now several months since the arrest, and I'd had to fire my public defender because he couldn't handle the case. I was now hooked-up with Mike "Mongoose" Burt, one of the hottest young lawyers running. We were set for the preliminary hearing to determine if there was enough evidence to bind us over for trial, and Velma and I were expecting to waltz right out of the courtroom with a dismissal of the charges. We were loaded for bear: the evidence gathered by the cops showed that the murders took place at two separate times, two weeks or possibly even a month apart, and that the bodies had been dumped at different times. By the cops' own evidence, Velma and I were well away from Frisco when the second dump was made. The witnesses all told basically the same story: Ray and Angie had received numerous death threats from a variety of people, and if anything, we were among the least likely candidates. As if that makes a difference.

The prelim went as planned: we proved that the evidence against us was at best questionable. We've never denied that we stole property, but the evidence that we had committed any murders was non-existent. How, then, did we end up being convicted?

Even though we did well at the prelim, we were bound over for trial. This was quite a shock, as the Assistant DA had herself taken off the case saying it was "too shaky" and even the magistrate didn't consider the evidence compelling. Since then I have learned that the prelim is more of a formality than anything. If you get arrested, 99% of the time you are going to face trial, no matter what. It wasn't until after the prelim that I learned we were facing the death penalty - a clever ploy by the new prosecutor - so the battle was joined and the stakes were raised.

Before we go to court, so to speak, I'll just tell you that I'm going to be quoting from the transcripts, so I won't have to clutter up the text with a lot of reference numbers. If you decide to look up the transcripts, well, happy hunting. But rest assured, you'll find the quotes all in there exactly as I am about to tell you. Ask for Case Number 109544a in the Superior Court of the City & County of San Francisco. While it's a bit of a long read at 20,000 pages, it's a juicy one.

The first obstacle to the case was the attitude of the new prosecutor. For whatever reason, Bill Fazio took a dislike to us from day one, and he got downright personal about it. Though the prosecutor is supposed to assume the innocence of the defendant and prove their guilt in a detached manner, without becoming emotionally involved, Fazio chose to literally radiate hatred toward me and Velma. Being on trial for your life is scary enough without having to absorb such concentrated negative hate-rays.

In the Frisco County Jail, male and female inmates are allowed to communicate via institutional mail, better known as "jailmail" or "kites". Velma corresponded this way every single day. She and I had enjoyed a very good, uninhibited sexual relationship, and being kept apart was sheer hell for both of us. We developed a code to use when discussing sexual matters, as well as private matters like our plans for when we regained our freedom. Bill Fazio actually had the guards photocopy our letters, and sent them out to the FBI for decoding. Velma and I were permitted weekly visits, separated by a sheet of bulletproof glass, talking over a telephone, which was tapped at the behest of Bill Fazio.

I had been briefly enroled as a teenager in a school away from home. It was a place for kids in trouble with the law that served as a dumping ground for kids with what were euphemistically called "family problems". I had been sent there for being somewhat asocial and was released before the mandatory two years' enrolment on the recommendation of my therapist that there was no real reason for me to be there. Bill Fazio used a forged court document to acquire my confidential records from this school, and even induced a psychiatrist, who had never met me because be didn't work there when I was enroled, to diagnose me as a sociopath. Although he was unable to use any of this "evidence" in court, the designation "diagnosed sociopath" became a part of my prison record.

Once we were arrested, our fingerprints were taken repeatedly. I couldn't believe how many times they pulled me out of my cell and took me back to booking to be reprinted. The police had lifted a set of prints from such a place that the person who left them *MUST* have been involved in dumping the bodies, if not in the murders themselves. The forensic evidence proved conclusively that the prints they found could not possibly be mine. The result of this revelation? The prosecutor promptly decided that the prints were unimportant. We actually had to file a motion to include them in evidence, and police have yet to match them with any prints on file -

mainly because they refuse to try. Bill Fazio actually said during the trial that fingerprints are not generally important as evidence. So if you're ever on trial, get your attorney to quote him. If your prints show up on a dead body somewhere, his position may prove useful to your defense.

Then there was the murder weapon. The police say Ray was killed with a .22 rifle, and that it was the same rifle Velma and I took from the apartment when we ran. When the bullet fragments recovered from Ray's head were first examined, not only was no proof available that they were fired from said rifle; the fact is, there was no way to be certain they hadn't been fired from a handgun. Then the forensics lab decided to alter the bullet by peeling it and bending it out of its original shape. Then, lo and behold, they found what appeared to be two parallel scratches they identified as rifling matching that of the firearm in question. No cause of death has ever been established for Angie or the baby, although they tend to believe she was strangled. Since Angie was pregnant when she was killed, an additional murder charge was added for the fetus, bringing the count to four.

The crime was prosecuted as a robbery-murder, and it was almost funny to see what we were accused of stealing. There was the van and the fire-arm, and some jewelry, although out of the sum total of jewelry we carried, only a couple of rings actually belonged to Ray and Angie. We'd been wearing most of the jewelry in plain sight for at least two years before going to Frisco, and some of it had been ours individually before Velma and I had even met. Then there was the stereo we'd had for at least a year before going to Frisco. Considering the attitude of the prosecutor, I'm surprised we weren't accused of stealing even more.

Inspectors Sanders and Hendrix provided the comic relief to the case each time they were called as witnesses. Why did they introduce into evidence a note book containing some mildly radical political writing that was found among my personal effects? "Because there was a picture of the President on it." I had taped one of those postcards of Ronald Reagan with a circle and a diagonal bar like those "no smoking" signs to the cover. Why did they seize a WWI issue bayonet that I used as a machete when cutting weeds? "It may have ben used to dismember the baby." Never mind that there were no indications on any of the bodies that any cutting had been done.

The witnesses were also a trip. Ron Ashley and Carol Scott lived in the front apartment on our floor. Ron told the cops at the very beginning about all the bikers and street people he saw trafficking back and forth to Ray and Angie's apartment, starting long before Velma and I arrived on the scene.

They both remembered quite clearly an individual known to them as "Hawaiian Jimmy" who visited the apartment regularly, and they testified that they saw and heard him threaten to "kill everyone in the house." Not only did Ron never hear any struggle or gunshots from the back apartment, but he also remembered quite clearly that Velma and I had left about a week before Ray and Angie disappeared. That is, before Sanders and Hendrix got ahold of him. After several visits from inspectors, their memory of the timing of these events suddenly became blurred. The same two individuals had no trouble coming up with new testimony, however. They claimed that I had threatened their young son, even though no mention of this had been made at their previous appearances. Other evidence indicates that they were dealing dope out of their apartment, and I would assume that Sanders and Hendrix had laid some heavy pressure on them. I just hope they realize that the penalty for perjury in a death-penalty case can be death.

The landlord testified early on that he had spoken with Angie by phone well after we had left the state, basing his testimony on his recollections as well as his records. Well, this is the sort of testimony the prosecution would dread. Somehow, by the time of trial, he decided that he'd spoken to Angie about two weeks before the date he originally remembered.

Statement by Michael Burt, Defence Attorney: "This is one of those rare death penalty cases where a reading of the preliminary hearing transcript leaves one with the uncomfortable feeling that two innocent people have been unjustly accused of the most serious of crimes after a preliminary hearing at which they were denied substantial rights."

From the testimony of Dr. Boyd Stephens, Coroner (paraphrased and abbreviated for clarity): On February 28, 1982, the body of Ray Boggs was discovered under an apartment building at 753 Webster Street, in San Francisco. Examination revealed the body to be in an advanced stage of decomposition, approaching skeletonization. Dr. Stephens stated that Ray died from a single gunshot wound to the brain, and that given this type of wound, one would expect profuse bleeding. It was Dr. Stephens' opinion that Ray had been shot at some unknown location and his body dumped where it was later found. Dr. Stephens found Ray had consumed codeine and alcohol before his demise.

On March 19, 1982, the bodies of Angie Boggs and Ray Junior were found under the same house, only ten feet away from where Ray's body had been found less than a month before. When Ray's body was discovered, the area in question was visited by an assistant coroner and a coroner's investigator, two homicide inspectors, a crime lab technician, and a total of approximately 20 members of the San Francisco Police Department. Photographs taken at the time clearly show that no other bodies were present. When the bodies of Angie and Ray Junior were found, photographs of the same area show that several boxes had been moved after Ray's body was found. One of the boxes was actually touching Angie's body in the crime scene photos. Not only does this show that Angie's and the baby's bodies were dumped at a later date, well after Velma and I arrived in Florida, but the aforementioned fingerprint, the one that could not have been mine or Velma's, actually shows up in the police photos on one of the boxes. Although the police claim that the murders took place on January 11, Dr. Stephens testified that the date of death could just as easily have been after that date; and all he can say about Angie is that she was probably killed some time before February 1.

The less said about the landlord the better, but one thing he did remember. When he called Ray's boss he was told Ray had skipped town because some people were after him. Ray's boss remembered that Ray had made a phone call home - the call Velma and I saw Angie answer - the day before we left Frisco. He also recalled that Ray had left work in a hurry that day, as though something were terribly wrong, or as if he were in a big hurry to meet someone, and was nervous about the circumstances.

When the landlord finally entered the apartment to clean it out, he found the note we had left for Ray and Angie. Too bad he threw it away. Even though the magistrate allowed him to testify as to its existence, it was never logged as evidence. I ask you, how many "mad-dog killers" leave notes for their victims telling where they can be reached? The landlord also testified that there were no bloodstains or signs of struggle inside the apartment, which is where the police claim we killed Ray and Angie.

Harvey Nelson, aka "Gypsy", was one of Ray and Angie's biker friends. Formerly a member of the Hell's Angels, Gypsy later skipped town when our defence attorneys started asking questions about his whereabouts at the time of the murders. The only interesting thing about his testimony, which was suppressed by the prosecution, was that Ray had told him back in December of '81 that he and Angie were planning to leave town. This would tie in rather neatly with the idea of their planning to leave us to take the heat for their actions - especially since we both resembled them to some extent.

One witness who absorbed more than her fair share of abuse was Anna

Caquias. On the first day of the prelim, she really spilled the beans, telling of an incident she witnessed between Ray and Sonny Barger, the head man of the Hell's Angels. She testified as to Ray's drug dealing, even as to where he kept his records - although the records were never found. She mentioned hearing other death threats made by Hell's Angels and others to Ray regarding drug deals gone bad. Then came the second day, her face was nearly caved in and she was "physically unable to continue her testimony." At every appearance she made on our case from that point on, two big bikers were observed in attendance. Funny how the police weren't interested in how her face had been practically pureed.

Juanita lived upstairs at 753 Webster. Velma and I had visited her in the presence of Ray and Angie. She testified to having seen Angie leave the apartment in a taxi with two other women - about the time we were supposed to have killed her. She was able to place the incident on the day in question because Ray came looking for Angie that same night in a rather agitated state. This evidence, too, was suppressed as hearsay.

Statement by Michael Burt, Defence Attorney,: "As a matter of logic, it would seem virtually preposterous to suggest, as the prosecutor apparently does, that the Hendersons murdered and then carefully disposed of their friends and housemates in order to steal two cheap rings, a parrot and a cage, a broken-down truck, and an inexpensive rifle. Not a single witness testified that any of this property was stolen. The Hendersons and the Boggs were friends and housemates, and it is entirely conceivable that the property legitimately came into the Hendersons' possession. The property was worthless, and more valuable property was found in the apartment and on the bodies of the victims. It is significant that the property was innocently disposed of under circumstances that virtually guaranteed that it could be traced directly to the Hendersons."

Statement by Michael Burt, Defence Attorney: "..presence at the scene of a crime, even coupled with false statements and other incriminating evidence, does not (under California law) establish reasonable or probable cause. In this case, there is not even proof the defendants were present when the crime was committed. There is only evidence of access to a crime scene prior to the crimes, coupled with evidence of false or misleading statements and evidence that one or both of the defendants openly possessed and openly sold certain property. It is clear that a combination of these facts do not mysteriously become imbued with an aura of guilt merely by viewing them in their totality. Three times zero, in a court's arithmetic, still equals zero.

Facts identical to those relied upon in the present case are too speculative to support a criminal charge."

So how the hell did Velma and I end up doing hard time? A death penalty case is a prosecutor's dream. The law requires that juries on these cases be "death-qualified" -a process by which all those who would automatically vote for or against death are theoretically excluded from serving. In practice, those who support the death penalty keep their attitude to themselves, saying they will consider the question fairly. Those who oppose the death penalty seem compelled to say so, and so they are excluded. This practically guarantees the jury will be stacked in favor of the death penalty.

My jury was a real winner. An ex-cop. A handful of gay boys, two of whom fell in love during the trial. The court clerk, who was gay himself, brought it to the attention of the court that one of these gay boys wrote a note to the other about a nightmare he had had about me, and how he had decided he was deathly afraid of me. The judge - may his testicles rot off his crotch, slowly - was made aware of this, and refused to do so much as relieve the juror in question of his duties. One of my very worst jurors was the bored wife of an attorney. There was a fetching Thai girl, wet dream material for sure, and a black guy who was obviously very taken with Sanders and Hendrix. An older white guy was proven to have spouted off about everything he knew about the case at a party, and the judge did relieve him of his duties, even though he obviously didn't want to. Anyone in the jury pool of almost 200 who showed any signs of fairness or decency was systematically excluded by the prosecution, if not by the judge himself. That included folks who didn't consider the cops one step below God, people who lived in the neighborhood of the crime, and two girls in their early twenties who, regardless of how they might have voted in the case, appeared to be rather taken with me personally. And so it goes.

I took the stand during my trial. Naturally. I hadn't killed anyone. All I had done is abscond with a few pieces of property that belonged to someone else. And by the time I finally came to trial, I'd already served the maximum sentence for theft and auto theft, and then some. So why not get up there and tell the jury myself that no matter how ugly, unkempt, and radical I might appear, I was still not guilty of murder? I spent two or three days on the stand and I did rather well, I think. I told the truth so far as I knew it. My testimony, however, was of no consequence to the death-qualified jury. Death qualification tends to sensitize a jury to the point that they're no longer thinking in terms of guilt vs innocence, but rather death vs. life without parole. Which is what I got.

The penalty phase of a death-penalty trial comes after the finding of guilt. By that point, having already decided that the accused is a mad-dog murdering fiend, the jury rarely goes for anything but death. It was in this phase that my attorney decided to present my character witnesses. Smooth move, Mike. If he had presented them before, they might have swung the jury in my favor. As it was, all the jury got to hear about my character was Bill Fazio using the phrase "murder and madness" twenty or thirty times.

A very special prosecution witness was never called to the stand, but made her statement every day of the trial. Ray's mom, who was a bag lady, showed up every single day dressed all in black with a single red rose (provided by Bill Fazio, I am sure) pinned to her lapel. We were certain that she tampered with the jury, expressing her opinion that I was guilty at every opportunity. We canvassed the jury after the case, and made the mistake of calling the foreman first. She was the attorney's wife, a take-charge type, and when she realized we were curious as to Mrs. Boggs' behavior during the trial, she immediately accused us of trying to get a mistrial - which is what we were *SUPPOSED* to do - and promptly called all the other ex-jurors and told them not to talk to us. The only one who would talk was a Chinese gentleman. While he was reticent to say anything, he did admit that after hearing the character witnesses, he had begun to doubt the propriety of the conviction, and asked why we didn't present them during the trial, when they would have done some good. Just like I had asked Mike to do all along, and which he has subsequently promised to do in the retrial. Once again, smooth move, Mike!

I don't hold a grudge against Mike, or against the previous defender, because I know that when I do go back for retrial, Mike will waltz me right out of that courtroom with no sweat. However, I do confess to being tempted occasionally to lodge my size eleven sneaker in his butt for not listening to me!

High point of the trial: Mike shoves the photos of the bodies under Fazio's nose and dares him in open court to explain how those boxes got moved. These are the photos that prove the bodies had been dumped there long after Velma and I had left town, and clearly remove us from the list of suspects. "Maybe some cats moved them. Or maybe some rats moved them. Or maybe a bird flew under the house and moved them." Right, Bill.

You can check out any time you like, but you can never leave..
(artwork by the author)

As industries go, it does well: one of the few true growth industries in the state of California. The stock-in-trade stands at roughly 440,000 units, requiring minimal upkeep. An average of about $28,000 changes hands, annually, on each unit in stock, and a supply of new units, handled by a string of related companies set up to service the main industry, is constant.

Welcome to one of the largest industries in the state of California. Welcome to the California Department of Corrections (CDC).

The last annual budget of which this author is aware allocated somewhere in the neighborhood of $5 billion to change hands in the course of normal, day-to-day operations of the CDC - but this is only the budget of the largest segment of the prison industry itself, as another $20,000 per unit, per year must be factored in for each occupied bunk in the state's extensive - and overloaded - system of county jails. Accurate figures for this entire network are hard to come by, but the best estimates, with a margin-of-error not exceeding 5% overall, would break down as follows :-

in primary CDC facilities:	110,000 +
in outprograms: (includes parole, probation, work-release, drug & alcohol programs, etc)	225,000 +/-
in CYA (Calif.Youth Authority):	10,000 +/-
in youth versions of above-listed adult programs:	10,000
in county jails, awaiting trial or official CDC intake: (divided between 55 counties: more than 6,000 in Los Angeles alone)	20-25,000

incarcerees in "mental hospitals" & medical facilities: 70,000 +

According to the latest published estimates, the total number of incarcerated persons in the United States comes to 1.2 million - in other words, California alone supplies approximately one-third the total number of prisoners currently incarcerated in the United States.

The county jails that feed the burgeoning "stock" of the CDC warehouses do so at an alarming rate; as prisoners are released back into the community, a high rate of recidivism is maintained by what is touted as the most unbalanced parole system in existence, as well as the policy of the CDC to not only refuse to actively rehabilitate prisoners, but indeed a policy of actively opposing attempts by the prisoners themselves to rehabilitate, at their own cost. The parole system guarantees that even those fortunate few that turn their time behind bars to self-improvement will likely be returned to prison; a person on parole in the state of California can have his or her parole revoked, and be returned to prison for at least a one-year stay as a "parole violator" for the "crime" of "having contact with a police officer" - literally, being stopped without reason for a routine ID check. Once parole has been officially "violated", the parolee *WILL RETURN* to prison, even in the absence of any actual criminal wrongdoing.

With such a high amount of guaranteed income generated each year, and protected (if not expanded) by governmental mandate, the CDC correctional officer is among the highest-paid uniformed state employees, the average pay per annum coming to $58,000; they are matched only by the California Highway Patrol, for high pay - and this doesn't take into account the even higher rates of pay for officers of rank and tenure. Rather than guaranteeing a high degree of professionalism, the majority of CDC employees are essentially glorified stockboys, and the educational requirements at the CDC training program and 1) a high school diploma or FED, and 2) the ability to count as high as "20". No, this is *NOT* a joke, *NOR* an exaggeration! The average CDC guard is undereducated, from a position of social disadvantage in the community, generally exhibits emotional instability, and receives training from the CDC that is skilfully designed to inculcate an "Us vs. Them" mentality, reflecting that of police and sheriff's officers. They are encouraged, both by CDC rules/policy and by their higher-ups, to regard the prisoners as less-than-human, the official term "inmate" being in less use than the term, "body" (as in, "This is S & E (search and escort)4, we have three bodies en route to AdSeg (administrative Segregation, the "hole") under escort, be advised"), and infractions of both Federal Law and internationally-recognized human rights against prisoners are, at best, ignored, if not outright encouraged. While the CDC guards are taking the actual risks (albeit, small risks) in working in a prison environment where they are outnumbered by the "bodies" by a ratio of roughly 20:1, their $58,000/year paychecks are a bargain for the higher-ups; the *real* money is pocketed by those higher on the totem pole, capped by a "Good Ole Boys" network of wardens and administrators, inexperienced but well-connected and generally free to live the high life on their share of the profits generated by the system; a prime example is the warden of Folsom, who was hired because of his prowess on the handball courts in Sacramento (handball fanatics seem to abound in the hierarchy of the CDC). In all fairness, it must be admitted that he is, if not suited to the post, at least less damaging in it than the previous warden, who used Folsom as a private slave-labor camp and source of jobs for his family - roughly two-thirds of the paying positions at Folsom prison and its various related facilities were held by members of the Campo family, and all purchases of appliances (TVs, radios and the other personal property allowed to prisoners with money to spend on them) were purchased through a Campo-family owned and operated company.

As stated before, simply being released from prison is by no means the end of the nightmare; even those fortunate prisoners who are paroled (prisoners with certain of the longer sentences are discriminated against in the granting of paroles) must run the gauntlet, so to speak, of their parole officer and the local police. As previously stated, any contact with a police officer guarantees a revocation of parole, even a simple request to produce identification. Even though the CDC facilities, state-wide, are currently operating at 175% of capacity, California returns more parolees to prison, alone, than the other forty-nine states combined; the figures for 1989 (the most recent figures available to me) indicate that California returned 39,976 persons from parole to prison, as opposed to 33,235 for the rest of the country, combined.

A brief trip through the system might be instructive; all the scenarios below are taken from actual cases, and can be verified easily:

First comes the arrest: Police in the state of California, from the lowest traffic cop to the well-connected and somewhat flamboyant inspectors with the various metropolitan police departments, are expected to fill a monthly quota - for traffic cops, a minimum number of tickets issued per month (this is the reason for the massive number of tickets written during the final week of each calendar month), for other officers, a minimum number of arrests, whether for murder or walking a dog sans proper dog-license. To fall below quota incurs penalties, hence every officer, no matter what his relative position on the pecking-order, makes certain to fill (if not exceed) his or her quota.

So you've helped the nice police officer maintain position on the totem pole; you've entered the system. First up, there is the intake procedure: a humiliating strip-search (even for such "crimes" as the above-mentioned lack of a dog license), followed by a laughably-brief "medical" examination, generally done by a less-than-qualified Medical Technical Assistant (MTA), asking a standardized list of questions regarding medical history and known current infections, and administering a recently-instituted AIDS test, mandated years too late. This is followed by a meeting with an intake officer; more questions, and a brief check of your epidermis for gang-oriented tattoos. Once intake is completed, you are ungently escorted to the holding cells; very few counties actually boast "cells", most now use what are called "tanks" - cramped rooms, roughly the size of the average living room in middle America, containing bunks for anywhere from eight to twenty or more prisoners, and filled beyond capacity as a matter of policy.

These dorm-style living arrangements - where non-violent offenders are nestled check-by-jowl with those arrested for drive-by shootings and bloody sex crimes, where quite often one can find juvenile offenders sleeping side-by-side with seasoned professional criminals - will be your home between day-of-arrest and day-of-trial, whether this period is but a few days or several years (this author personally awaited trial in a twelve-man tank in San Francisco county, without any access to the outside, even an exercise yard, for four-and-one-half years while awaiting trial, and my tenure in the county facility is *NOT* the longest on record).

For many arrestees, the stay is brief; they've been arrested before, done time in prison at least once or twice, and whether they're actually under arrest or simply detained for a parole violation, the incarceree will be offered the chance, in most cases, to accept a plea-bargain (if an arrestee) or agree to the violation in question, thereby transferring to one of the far more comfortable prisons.

For the first-time arrestee, however:

Prosecutors and police departments fear the first-time arrestee, as he or she is an unknown quantity; people with a criminal record can at least be second-guessed, their behavior predicted. Worst of all is the first-time arrestee who might well, judging from the state of the evidence in the case, be innocent of the charges - someone whose guilt, though assumed by the prosecution, is at worst questionable - this definition actually covers a minimum of 25% of all arrestees in the state of California, according to work published by the American Civil Liberties Union. By no means can the innocence of a person be admitted by police or prosecutors, once an arrest - let alone a conviction - has occurred; witness the statements of Daryl Gates regarding the release of Messrs. Chance & Powell (both of whom were met, in prison, by the author), recently released with much fanfare, through the assistance of Centurion Ministries' Rev. James McCloskey, after serving seventeen years in the CDC for a murder they did not commit.

Convicts, whether in prison or out on parole, have a statistically lower life expectancy than the general population, hence the number of innocent people arrested will, indeed must, always rise, in order to feed the gaping maw of the CDC.

County jail and the trial-by-ordeal process generally pigeonhole the newcomer quite handily. A willingness to implicate others, especially those that the investigators mention during questioning, or a willingness to take a deal without putting the courts through a lengthy trial fraught with work for all involved is generally taken as an indication that the arrestee qualifies for a shorter prison term, or placement in a better (lower custody level) prison, perhaps even to have some of the charges dropped. It is frightening, how easily the investigators can fill their quotas just from the information gleaned from one first-time arrestee. More insidious is the system of "jailhouse snitches" employed by the investigators; professional prisoners, people with extensive criminal records, who are arrested regularly and allowed to "plead out" to a series of offenses that net only extensions of their parole, in exchange for giving false testimony at particularly "hard" trials, most notably those involving patently-innocent defendants who, in the eyes of the police and prosecutors, must be convicted "at all costs", in order to save face. Simply being innocent of the charges is no guarantee that one will not have one or more "informants" show up for trial, claiming that you displayed intimate knowledge of the facts of the case and in many instances "confessed" your wrongdoing to them in the confines of the county jail. Those uncooperative arrestees who demand their right to a jury trial can also look forward to increased harassment in the county jail, by both guards and "pet" prisoners, and can generally expect to have the charges against them enhanced, or new charges added - I personally saw the charges against me raised from four to seven in number, and the severity of the case increase tenfold, after my preliminary hearing, solely because I was so "uncooperative" as to refuse to take a deal for twenty years - and harassment of one's friends and family outside - persons not at all involved in the process - is standard operational procedure. In my own case, friends who would come to visit received threatening phone calls, warning them to "stay away from people and cases that don't concern you"' and one fellow-occupant of the county jail had his home literally burglarized by police officers who stole, among other things, more than $10,000 worth of furnishings, including a prize Persian rug, as well as seeing his son seized and placed in a foster-home outside the state.

Prosecutors, no less than the police, operate on quotas - called "percentages" in the various District Attorney's offices. To fall below a certain percentage of convictions brings penalties. If it is necessary to "fudge" the facts a bit, to have police inspectors return to various witnesses and counsel them to change their testimony, or to tell outright lies during the prosecution of the trial, then that's the price a prosecutor must pay to keep filling quota, to maintain his or per position in the office pecking-order.

Normally, however, county jail is itself enough to pressure a pre-trial detainee into taking a deal. In Los Angeles county, the staff of the county jail system relies on brutality; in San Francisco, the tool is a combination of unhealthy conditions and dehumanizing treatment. Each county has it's speciality. Each county jail administrator expects the pretrial detainee to show the good sense to take a deal and leave quickly for a more comfortable cage in the station prison system; after a period spent sharing a twelve-man tank with seventeen other prisoners, all too many detainees are only too happy to comply, regardless of their lack of complicity in the crimes charged against them.

The majority of defendants are provided with overworked, underpaid and thoroughly apathetic Public Defenders, most of whom aspire to a better-paying and more prestigious position in the District Attorney's office, and jockey endlessly for the few available positions by cooperating as far as possible with the prosecutors against whom they're paired in court. Trading on cases is rampant. "You let me get a criminal Trespass on this burglary, and I'll get this Rape to plead to Grievous Assault by Friday" - never mind that both the alleged burglar and the alleged rapist are, in one-quarter of all cases, innocent of the charges. The lives of defendants in criminal cases are often sold out for as little as a "power lunch" that might provide an introduction that could, possibly, advance the defense attorney's career. Worse yet are the attorneys in private practice - primarily low-budget ambulance chasers and divorce attorneys - who specialize in handling court-appointed cases to take up the slack for the public defenders, or to represent one of two or more indigent co-defendants. Handling the bottom of the legal food-chain, the court-appointed attorneys do even less work than the worst public defenders. Attorneys in the Public Defender's office are required to prepare and file all their own paperwork - sometimes amounting to a staggering mass of motions - all that is required of a court-appointed private practice attorney involved in the same case is to show up in court, "join" in the motion of the public defender, then split... the court-appointed attorney bills the taxpayers for an unreasonable amount of money just for putting in a brief appearance and mumbling a sentence or two. Defendants saddled with court-appointed counsel are regularly "dumped" by their attorneys, usually for refusing to plead out and make the job even easier (as was the case with my co-defendant), and it is a well-known fact that even a really apathetic public defender can get you a better deal than a court-appointed attorney.

In four and a half years in the San Francisco county jail and courts, I only

rarely saw a defendant win a case - the political careers of judges are also
built on percentages, this time with reference to convictions.

Intake into the CDC is essentially a repeat performance of that at the
county jail... the bored MTA asks the same old questions, another strip-
search for tattoos denoting gang affiliation, the AIDS test - again instituted
years too late - and the visit to the classification committee. Committee is
an annual thing, but the initial interview sets the tone for all those to follow;
the classification committees are CDC employees who are set to the task of
determining the appropriate place of your incarceration, deciding on
placement in one of the myriad state prisons based upon such relevant data
as whether you've ever served in the military, whether you are married, and
whether you exhibit any "questionable" tattoos or have been sent to
associate with "known gang members," referring, for inspiration, to such
paperwork as the parole officer's multipage recommendation, the comments
of the assistant district attorney on your case, and whatever commentary
might be forthcoming from the investigators and/or arresting officers. Be a
prisoner seated before them who refused to take a deal, on one of their bad
days, and your placement will be in the CDC's current version of hell, either
Folsom New Facility "B" yard, or "C" or "D" facilities at Pelican Bay
state prison, the equivalent of the infamous Soviet Gulag. I myself currently
sport a total of 25 security points, making me technically eligible for
placement at one of the more progressive facilities - one where efforts at self-
rehabilitation or self-education are actually permitted and in some cases
encouraged, such as the California Men's Colony - but, because I refused
to take a deal, I am currently a guest of New Folsom "B", up until recently
the most violent facility in the state (only recently supplanted by Pelican Bay
"C" and "D" yards).

Within the CDC system you become, for all practical purposes, a non-
person, an un-person, the property of the state. Your mail, and quarterly
"care packages" (if you are lucky enough to have friends outside willing
to send them) are opened, and anything that appeals to the guards is
"confiscated" - anything, that is, ranging from nude photographs of/from
your lover/wife/girlfriend, particularly tasty or valuable items in your care
package, or checks/money orders, whenever possible (I myself have lost all
three of the above categories to "confiscation"). You are eligible to be
pressed into service as part of the convict slave labor force, at jobs paying
a maximum of 93c an hour, reaping large profits for the main CDC office
in Sacramento. You are also subject to be exposed to all sorts of interesting

new diseases; we are just now coming out from under an outbreak of tuberculosis, and with the AIDS confinement units at CMC and Vacaville medical facility now housing infected persons only if they request it (AIDS patients cannot be required to enter quarantine, thanks to the legal efforts of a very-badly misinformed Gay Rights group), the average number of active AIDS cases housed at Folsom alone averages out to approximately 70 to 80 per cellblock at the present time, and large signs, in both English and Spanish, now greet visitors to the facility with the information that they are entering an environment detrimental to their health, and to take whatever precautions are necessary... the information on the number of AIDS cases currently housed on mainline, by the way, was provided by a Lt.'s clerk, who saw the actual list of AIDS cases (made available to staff) and passed the information on to one of my co-workers. The clerk was found out and is currently "in the hole" (if he is still alive!) for having shared "confidential" information.

Exchange of bodily fluids - be it via a shared cigarette, a shared cup of coffee, or a shared joint, is endemic in prison; here, one might consider the risk of contracting AIDS the great health risk in this environment. However, the greatest threat to life is from inter-prisoner violence; since sometime in the late 1960s, the CDC hierarchy, via the guards, have cultivated a number of prison gangs, divided along racial and territorial lines, by which they keep the prison population in a constant state of turmoil and through which they accomplish most of their hatchetwork. All that is necessary to kill a particular prisoner, is for one of the guards to inform one of their pet snitches (there is a care group of snitches at every facility in the state) that such-and-such inmate is incarcerated for child molestation - the snitch passes this tidbit along to the appropriate gang "shot-caller", and the inmate named is very quickly stabbed, usually on the exercise yard, by one of the gang members. In return for this sort of dirty work, the guards allow the gangs to make and maintain an arsenal of weapons (mostly handmade knives, ranging from 4 to 6 inch slicers to 36 inch "bonecrushers") and control the prison drug trade; drugs cannot enter a prison without the explicit knowledge and consent of the guards. The snitches - at least the staff's pets - are maintained comfortably, generally receiving a share of the personal goods confiscated from quarterly "care packages" and being allowed to possess items normally considered contraband; here at New Folsom "B", the main snitch is a watch-officer clerk who has been "busted" repeatedly for possession of folding money, a felony - and yet, there are never any repercussions, even though the possession of actual currency by prisoners is classified as evidence of an attempted escape.

A further threat is from outright murder by the guards themselves; in one instance known to this author, an individual was pulled from his cell and ordered to report to the cell block office; upon arriving, but before he had a chance to enter, the block officer tossed a homemade weapon out into the rotunda, at the feet of the prisoner, and the gunner overhead opened fire, on cue. The incident was witnessed by several of the inmate workers in the block - fortunately, the shot prisoner survived, though the round that hit him caused extensive damage to his skull and obliterated one eye entirely. In another instance, one of the more humane guards had to walk through the field-of-fire and shield the prisoner with her own body in order to extract him from the cell block alive; the gunner in the control booth intended to kill the prisoner for associating with one of the gunner's enemies from outside the prison. One other incident would sound like a partial plot from a badly-written old movie, if it were not documented, and evidence already presented before the court: one prisoner, who had the bad taste to win a rather embarrassing lawsuit against the prison, was removed from the prison grounds entirely at about 2.30 a.m., taken to a relatively remote area of Sacramento County, and ordered by the guards - all S & E officers - to "run", so that they could shoot him in an "attempted escape". Had the prisoner in question not stayed stock-still, and had the incident not been witnessed by a person not a party to the exchange, the man would've been murdered outright whether he ran or stood his ground. Each of these prisoner-victims has, since the incidents in question, received the benefit of "hardship transfers" to prisons away from New Folsom - had there not been factors operating in their favor, they would never have lived to tell their tales.

Worse yet was the practice, ending only recently when the Federal authorities' attention came to bear, of arranging gladiatorial contests at Pelican Bay state prison, in "C" and "D" facilities, among the prisoners serving a term in the hole. Late at night, the control officers would open two cells on the same hall - each containing a member of a rival gang, or two men known to be enemies - and the nightshift guards would place bets on which would draw blood first, and whether there would be a death or merely a wounding. There are entirely too many credible witnesses for this merely to have been a story someone cooked up, and the families of those prisoners murdered in this fashion will gladly supply evidence to any interested parties.

If you can avoid the violence, the next-worse aspect of California prisons is the mind-numbing, dehumanizing way of life. First will come a wait of up to 3 or 4 years to be placed in a prison job; then, the majority of prison jobs are either unpaid, or pay between $19 and $24 per month - less than a dollar a day for what amounts to slave labor. Then depending upon one's assigned job, there are the dangers of working with a non-uniformed prison employee, especially with those women who fill positions as work supervisors. Several of these employees delight in teasing prisoners sexually (even worse are the conditions at the women's prison, where the Protestant Chaplain was recently led off the grounds in handcuffs after it was discovered that he was sating a number of rather perverse desires with the women prisoners); those non-uniformed women employees will use suggestive language, skimpy clothing, semi-discreet exposure of their genitalia, and even outright physical contact to arouse men who have been, in many cases, incarcerated for years without female companionship, simply because the women know that the prisoners dare not do anything about it. Even those women who work as guards tend to be sexual teases, many of them stopping the same few prisoners, over and over again, for "pat-down" (contact) searches, using the opportunity to linger in the area of prisoner's genitals with their hands, enjoying the pressure thus placed upon the prisoner. It is not so amazing that this happens - the occupational title of "prison guard" seems to draw some of the worst elements of society - but rather that so few of the prisoners have actually succumbed to the pressure and attempted to respond; while there are occasional rape charges filed by non-uniformed female employees against prisoners, roughly three-quarters of the charges that are filed are without any basis in fact.

While it may sound trite, the food provided for prisoners is literally unsaleable; most of the meats are in the primary and secondary stages of spoilage, the vegetables are of the poorest quality, the fruits must be pared of rotted segments in order to be eaten, or else thrown away outright, and the nutritional value of the meals, as they are prepared, just barely meets subsistence-level; those prisoners who are unable to supplement the meager diet with purchases from the inmate canteen suffer from constant low-grade malnutrition.

The litany of abuses could go on and on. While it is bad enough to consider that the guilty are treated this way (remember that the overwhelming majority of them will, eventually, be released back into society, carrying a massive load of rage and resentment), more horrifying is the knowledge that, of the 440,000 men and women currently incarcerated in California, fully 210,000 are innocent of the charges against them.

As I state in another context, to accept what I say would upset many people's conceptions of reality' better to assume that all prisoners lie like dogs, and ignore what I say. Nonetheless, your life may one day in the hands of someone recently released from a California prison... how lucky do you feel?

At one point during my extended stay at the San Francisco county jail, the administration learned that the Grand Jury was intent upon investigating the jail living conditions; at the time, the average 12-man tank held fifteen incarcerees, a motley assortment of pretrial detainees, Federal detainees (who were housed by the county due to problems at the city's Federal detention facility), and convicts awaiting transfer to prison. The jail was filthy, the conditions cramped and intolerable - and the violations of Federal law rampant and obvious. The day before the Grand Jury were to take their inspection tour, facility administration had a massive number of prisoners moved to various surrounding counties - bringing the per-tank population down to about 75% of capacity; a particularly good meal was served to the inmates, the jail received a major cleaning, and several prisoners - myself included - were warned in no uncertain terms that any attempt to speak to the Grand Jury - even if they themselves initiated a conversation - would cost our lives. After the Grand Jury inspection, conditions at the jail returned to normal.

At that same jail, in the months prior to the inspection, the following incidents occurred: one prisoner, who repeatedly had his attorney call the administration out on the carpet for the violations of Federal standards, was taken from the jail late at night and beaten by several of the off-duty guards, resulting in a broken jaw, several cracked ribs, and numerous lesser injuries. After the beating, he was made to understand that his next complaint to his attorney would sign his death-warrant. Another incarceree, a female, was taken from her cell in the women's section of the jail to the infirmary, where at least two guards and one MTA raped her repeatedly. When she told her attorney what had happened, one of the Medical staff - who held a minor degree in psychology - added a notation on her record to the effect that she was emotionally disturbed and suffered from frequent hallucinations. The damage to her mouth, vagina, and anus must've been caused by a *VERY* powerful hallucination. Two other prisoners received beatings in the hallway of the jail itself, one of them near-fatal in that the prisoner suffered a rather bad concussion from repeated kicks to the head administered by one of the guards, after he had already been "subdued" - this author was one of the witnesses to this event, as it happened within scant feet of the tank in which I was housed. When an investigator from the ombudsman's office, an adjunct of the country sheriff's department (and hence just another branch of the same authority that runs the jail in question) came around to question possible witnesses, the guards pointedly mentioned to several witnesses, myself included, that the ombudsman's office could offer no protection to those who talked, as anyone who co-operated with the investigation would be housed right where they were in the jail, easily accessible and at the mercy of the guards against whom they gave evidence... needless to say, no witnesses came forward. In one other incident, a detainee who was scheduled to be released - the case against him, a very questionable rape charge, having fallen apart (there was no actual evidence against him, he had been a "suspect of convenience", charged in the absence of an actual rapist - not an uncommon occurrence) - was moved from the "mainline" (general population) to one of the side-hallways, where "problem cases" are housed, and was told that he would have to share a five by eight foot two-man cell with another prisoner, one who was admittedly dangerously insane and had to be housed alone, for safety considerations. When the man about to be released refused to enter the dangerous cell, two guards proceeded to attack him physically, one pinning his arms to his sides and the other cutting off the prisoner's air by applying a choke with his baton. The prisoner resisted, and the guard with the baton increased the pressure across the man's throat; needless to say, the prisoner died, with less than 48 hours to go before he would be released, free, to file suit against the authorities for wrongful arrest. Aside from a brief hunger strike by detainees at the jail, and a one-inch notice in the back pages of the local papers, his death accomplished nothing... and the guards who killed him remain employed at the county jail.

The pattern of brutality and abuse is ongoing; the machinations whereby these abuses are hidden is a conspiracy of statewide proportions. The men and women who are remanded into custody might deserve punishment, but punishment such as this serves no reasonable purpose; it simply makes worse an already-untenable situation. Those who exhibit tendencies to antisocial behavior should be removed from society and their tendencies corrected, not made worse, yet the current system seems custom-made to be precisely that - to release the prisoner, worse than before, into a society already in the throes of near-collapse. That fully one-quarter of the people receiving this treatment are patently innocent makes the nightmare more intense; better we should release ten guilty parties than put one innocent person behind bars, particularly in such conditions as obtained in the CDC.

You can read these observations of mine and take them in any way you desire; you can decide that, since I am myself incarcerated, I am obviously just another of those unbelievable prisoners, lying through my teeth, and what I say here can be discounted as a fabric of rhetoric - to make this assumption leaves one's worldview, the paradigm in which one moves and breathes, more liable, as to assume otherwise would imply a responsibility to take action, to expose the abuses further, to combat the abuses at every level; you might as well assume that I'm lying, and allow these brief pages to be excluded from your comfortable little world...

... except that, someday, you may find yourself face-to-face with a recently-released victim of this system; you may find yourself depending upon the good graces of someone who has truly experienced the depths of man's inhumanity to man.

How lucky do you feel?

"A judge can only wonder if anyone tells the truth. Many lies are patent and intentional... two witnesses take the stand, each swears to tell the truth, each looks the judge squarely in the eye and tells a diametrically opposed story. The judge and jury are supposed to observe the demeanor of the witnesses on the stand and determine who is telling the truth, but one can only guess...

"Few trial lawyers or judges find that truth emerges from the process; on the contrary, they find that perjury and falsehood are as commonly heard from the witness stand as truth. All too often the truthful litigant loses and the liar wins..."

- *Judge Lois C Forer, Phila. Court of Common Pleas, in*
"The Death of Law", publ. by David McKay

Perjury occurs in: 50% of contested civil actions
70% of criminal cases
90% of divorce and custody litigation

How lucky do you feel?

3
MARK DEFRIEST
by Sondra London

The Homicidal Houdini

Among Florida prison officials, one name is always mentioned in awed tones: Mark "Houdini" DeFriest, a young man who has truly become a legend in his own time. It was right before this book's deadline that I heard from the man they call "The Most Dangerous Convict in Florida".

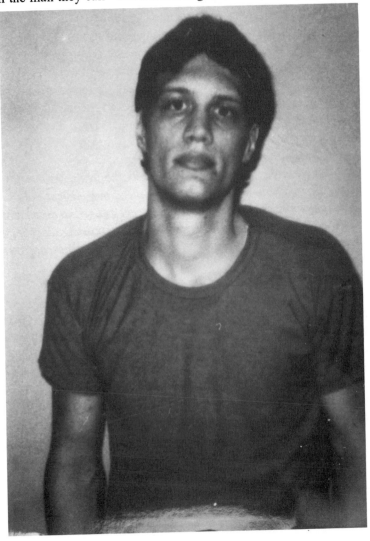

Mark DeFriest

MARK DEFRIEST

The word moves in mysterious ways through CBS - the Convict Bullshit Hotline - but it never takes long... and as soon as he heard we were publishing the stories of maximum security inmates, he wanted to contribute. I had read a newsletter he put out a few years ago, and had been impressed with his extraordinary personal story, and the enterprising spirit portrayed through his publication. Though I was intrigued, still I had never contacted him, as it seemed we were both up against the same institutional monster, and there was no use associating my name with his, thus bringing down more heat on myself than I had already incurred with my own prison publishing projects. Even though I would never have written to him, I was pleased that we had finally been introduced to each other, just in time for his story to be included here.

Joe O'Dell observed that the first thing a man does when he gets into prison is try and find a way to get out, and the next thing he does is look for signs of weakness in people that he can use to escape. Mark DeFriest has applied his formidable talents to both of these ever-popular pursuits. A prison publisher and escape artist extraordinaire, he has used his writings to obtain cash contributions, which along with an alleged quarter million dollars in profits from his prison drug trade, he claims he has secreted away in stocks, bonds and money-market accounts all over America.

DeFriest is considered so dangerous that he lives in an escape-proof cell especially constructed for him. As Florida's most closely-managed inmate, he is not allowed exercise privileges, media interviews or any visitors such as other inmates might have. He may not even have a toothbrush, nor will he be allowed to receive a copy of this book.

It's not the savage strength of his macho muscles that has the Florida Department of Corrections so impressed with Mark DeFriest. "He is very creative in thinking of ways to outwit the system - that's the key to his danger," said Assistant State's Attorney Rick Replogle, who prosecuted him in a 1989 contraband case.

Psychiatrist Robert Wray called DeFriest "extremely disruptive, homicidal, psychotic, anti-social" and recommended hospitalization and medication. However FSP Prison Superintendent Tom Barton said that DeFriest has been unresponsive to counseling and will receive no mental health care. "He's sharper than you and I are".

DeFriest's IQ testing reveals a score of 130, and while that is on the high end, it probably does not accurately reflect the full extent of his uncanny ingenuity. He can pick a lock and make a key from nothing more than a toothbrush or a scrap of aluminium, and can fashion a weapon from a piece of paper or a ball point pen. Handcuffs, leg manacles and straitjackets can't slow him down, and prison officials are hand-pressed to outguess him in the ongoing struggle to keep him confined. One might well speculate on the myriads of socially-redeeming projects this talented man could have accomplished, if his interest had been channeled that way. But the way it's been going, "Houdini" DeFriest will be looking for ways to escape for the rest of his life: indeed, he once predicted he'd be shot dead in an escape attempt.

Walking Out of Prisons

The 1989 contraband conviction resulted from a strip search with a metal detector, which revealed an astonishing array of escape supplies stashed up DeFriest's rear end in a 6" aluminium cylinder: 34 razor blades, seven hacksaws, six handcuff keys, solder, drill bits and padlock keys, twenty hundred-dollar bills, $19 in postage, gold jewelry and a set of keys with interchangeable teeth. "If he knew all the patterns, he could have probably walked out of the institution, with the exception of the last gate," said investigator Brian Gross.

Mark did know the patterns, and he still does. He produced for reporters of the Gainesville Sun a copy of the twenty key codes for the Foldger-Adams system, that could get him through any lock in the prison. But once he gets through the locks, what about the razor wire surrounding the prison? "Well, the razor wire isn't so much of a deterrent as it looks" says the lanky 6'1" man with the word DEATH tattooed on his upper arm. "I've went flying through that stuff quite a few times. It doesn't really slow you down."

And how does DeFriest obtain the valuable knowledge he needs to perfect his escapes? He sums it up: *MONEY.* "The money involved in cocaine sales would corrupt a saint. The monthly salary of a Florida State Prison guard is insufficient incentive in my opinion to keep them from participating." Court files reflect that DeFriest has used guards to smuggle in everything from drugs to guns.

The 32-year-old New York native was initially sentenced to serve four years in 1980, but as of 1993, he is doing life plus 45 because of an accumulation of charges related to his relentless escape attempts. Having escaped from two state prisons, a county jail, and a state mental hospital, he stands convicted of those escapes, as well as grand theft, burglary of a home, possession of cocaine, marijuana, and paraphernalia, and being an inmate in possession of weapons, firearms and explosives.

In his first escape attempt, he simple dismantled a cell door, rolling it back with his bare hands. "The door was kind of like a can of sardines," he grinned.

He escaped from Appalachee Correctional Institution in 1980 by climbing a fence on his way back from Bible study. He was arrested in Bay County in 1981 and sentenced to life for burglary with a firearm, along with two additional years for the escape from ACI.

In the Bay County Prison, he made over a half-dozen escape attempts, used a toothbrush to dismantle three cells, was caught with numerous hand-made weapons, and shot at an officer. "Half the personnel may quit if DeFriest returns," said Captain Jerry Girvin.

Then he was at Polk Correction Institution. where he was found with a home-made gun. At that point, he said he wanted to plead guilty to his crimes, because he wanted to go to Florida State Prison, so he could escape and be gunned down by guards. Instead, he was declared incompetent and sent to the Corrections Mental Health Institution at Chattahoochee, where he promptly escaped by removing his handcuffs and firing a home-made gun at the employees.

Arrested and incarcerated in Leon County, he sawed through the bars of his cell, climbed down knotted bedsheets, crawled over a chainlink fence, and escaped in a truck-tractor taken from near the jail. It cost him a broken arm and leg, as well as charges of escape and attempted murder.

Back in Leon County while awaiting a competency hearing in 1982, he was handcuffed, stripped, and locked up alone without any known tools in the so-called "Bundy Cell", where he managed to reduce his restraints to fragments of scrap metal within ten minutes.

Cruel and Unusual

In 1982, DeFriest sued Girvin and Bay County alleging cruel and unusual punishment, claiming that for eleven days in 1981 he was kept naked in a bare cell, cut, sprayed with mace and doused with buckets of cold water. He claimed further that he was given no treatment for his wounds, was denied the use of toilet paper and a shower, and that the water to the toilet in his cell was turned off so he couldn't flush it.

Girvin replied that DeFriest was kept naked in a small cell without a mattress because officials found that to be the best way to prevent another escape attempt. "We knew Mark had the ability take apart almost any locks or doorways we had." He also admitted using mace and cold water, but excused his actions by explaining, "We'd gone to every other effort we could think of verbally to calm him down," to which Judge Roger Vinson replied wryly, "Did you think to calm him down by giving him a mattress?"

DeFriest testified as to the circumstances of his second Bay City escape attempt. He and two other inmates armed with pipes had escaped from their cells but were trapped in a locked hallway. They kidnaped an officer, who locked himself away from them in a cell. DeFriest fired a double-barreled zipgun as another officer tried to telephone for help. He said he had aimed it at the telephone, but it misfired, and when he realized he couldn't escape, he threw the weapon on the ground and waited for the officers to arrive. More than ten officers then threw him to the ground, and one cut his clothing off with a knife, gashing his arms and legs in the process. "They split my meat open when they hanged me into the elevator door," he said. "They said, 'Whoops, the door ain't open!' "

Sheriff's Sergeant James McArthur, who admitted removing DeFriest's clothing with the use of a knife, denied cutting or wound him, and testified that use of force was necessary because DeFriest refused to co-operate when ordered to get on the floor. "There's never nobody hit him or nothing. It was a wrestling match, was what it was."

By this time, Florida prison officials were understandably at their wits' end, and as a last resort, had DeFriest transferred to the Federal prison at Marion, Illinois, which since 1963 has replaced the infamous Alcatraz as America's top security prison. As an incorrigible, DeFriest was confined in the Behavior Control Unit, where the theory and practice of brutality is unsurpassed in modern times.

In 1984, he tried to escape, and was shot in the chest and abdomen. "At that time the pain of the bullets ripping through my body was minimal, compared to the emotional pain I experienced during recovery," Mark reflects. "My wife picked that difficult point in my life to leave me."

After spending several months in a hospital, DeFriest was returned to Florida, where he first entered his new custom-made home: a steel cage within a cage, it was designed to protect Florida State Prison from it's most dangerous inmate. But "Houdini" was not done yet.

Busting Out Bundy

Soon after his return to Florida State Prison, DeFriest was sentenced to five more years for possession of contraband: seven .22 caliber rounds, two used .22 caliber cartridges and one home-made ice pick.

And in 1984, several FSP guards went to prison for their part in yet another of DeFriest's escape attempts, this one involving the notorious Ted Bundy, who had already twice escaped from other state prisons himself. DeFriest testified in court, "My plan was simply to take control of Q-wing one night and saw out the bottom floor... What I wanted to do was take control of the wing with firearms and go through all the grill gates downstairs and saw the windows out."

He explained it in a little more detail to me:

"What happened was, I sold Bundy some sawblades and stuff when he was on R-wing in 1984. Then someone snitched him out for trying to cut his bars out, so they moved him to Q-wing and put in him Q-2-W-3... right next to me in Q-2-W-2. So I involved him in my plan and made a key for his cell door from a print I bought off one of my guards. I turned his radio into a VHF receiver, so we could listen to the cops on the radios. Everybody seems to believe he was a fag and I used to let the whole floor into his cell to fuck him, but this is all lies, and nothing like that happened. I just involved him in my own plan to escape, that's all."

Can't Take a Joke

"DeFriest loves to brag - that's just the way he is," said FSP inspector Brian Gross, who remembers when DeFriest challenged FSP officers to find several items of contraband hidden in his special cell. After they searched his cell a number of times, DeFriest showed them a tiny slit over the cell door, and, taking a long piece of wire, fished out a cell key he had fashioned out of a toothbrush. "We wouldn't have found it otherwise," observed Gross, "but he likes to brag that he can beat the administration any time."

DeFriest is unrepentant. "The persecution, depersonalization and humiliation I suffer is compounded by the frustration of doing life on close management in solitary confinement. My contempt for the tyranny of prison officials has no bounds. To me, any act or action is justifiable."

Though his activities may be severely curtailed, DeFriest has no intention of giving up his fight with the system that controls him. "I'm going to spend the next 20 years of my life on close management, no matter what I do or how I act, so it really doesn't matter if I continue my covert operations," say DeFriest. "Since I am bored to death in solitary confinement and have nothing better to do, I may as well continue on my merry way and screw them if they can't take a joke."

The subtle humor of Mark's jokes might have escaped Leon Circuit Judge Charles Miner. After Miner sentenced DeFriest to 45 years for burglary with a firearm, plus another 35 years for grand theft, and possession of firearms and drugs, the shackled prisoner shuffled to his feet and told the judge, "I'll see you later," then let out a big laugh, "I'll send you a postcard from Bermuda the next time I escape."

The United States Mail is an excellent avenue of escape, as Mark DeFriest has demonstrated. He buys mailing lists from religious publications and mass-produces letters that have gained him hundreds of pen-pals and thousands of dollars. For example, when he was put on the prison's "special management loaf" for a few days, he circulated a copy of the memo ordering it, after first altering it to make it appear the change to the execrable - but edible - cuisine had been permanent. His 1989 newsletter preached the spirituality to be gained from writing to prisoners, and the raising of consciousness that comes with assisting them. And the donations came rolling in.

He had set up a network of various bank accounts across the country so that donations to the newsletter could be kept in his name without the knowledge of the prison officials, who promptly shut down the paper because of regulations against inmates "operating a business." DeFriest says he then returned $15,000 to people all over the world. "I don't steal from my friends or turn on people who trust me, so I didn't accept the money," he said, "I make most of the money I need to finance my operations from drugs."

The Deep End

Now Mark writes to me from what can only be called the Cell from Hell, the only one of it's kind anywhere. It's interior dimensions are 6' x 8' with five sides constructed of solid concrete. The front wall consists of steel bars covered by a metal screen, with a sliding barred door. Another concrete wall with a solid steel door stands outside the front of his cell. Only when this outer steel door is locked can the inner barred door be opened. There is one air vent. "Only five feet under my cell is the worst the prison offers... the electric chair. I am forced to hear, through my air vent, the pleas for help and the somber cries of those souls leaving their earthly bodies through prolonged execution." Since Mark entered this cell, he has involuntarily witnessed over two dozen executions. He will never leave this cage-within-a-cage except for a weekly five-minute shower in handcuffs, during which he is accompanied by three guards.

I asked Mark how it all started, and he replied :

"It's really ridiculous! My father and I were very close, and I quit school to go to work for him in 1974 when I was 14. He had a shop that repaired trucks and heavy equipment and we worked together until I was 17 and got married and moved to Dothan, Alabama, where I opened my own small repair shop. In 1979 my dad died of cancer and I returned to Florida for the funeral in Clearwater, where he lived with my stepmother, whom I never got along with.

"My father told me before he died that he wanted me to have all his tools from the shop, and that all the money would go to my stepmother to live with, and there was a will to this effect. Since I was down in Florida, I stopped by my dad's old shop and picked up the tools before the will was probated. This was a big mistake. As it turned out, my stepmother had some plan to sell the shop tools before the will was probated. When she found out I picked up the tools, she called the cops and had a warrant taken out against me for stealing them.

"To keep it short, after all the legal hassles, the judge turned all the tools over to the rightful owner, *ME*. I got four years for B & E... but not for taking the tools. It seems I used my set of keys to go in the shop and my dad was not around to testify that I had his permission to go in the shop with him or without him, as we still did some repair work together at times. That's why I still had my set of keys. Of course, my stepmother got up there and told them she never said it was OK for me to go in the shop.

"So you see why I say this is a ridiculous thing, to take four years of a man's life. I know it's no reason now, but maybe you can see why I went off the deep end with all my escapes, and destroyed my whole life."

Yeah, Mark, now that you mention it... maybe I can.

ON A HIGHWAY TO HELL
by Mark DeFriest

I am a white male prisoner incarcerated at Insanity State Prison in Nowhere, USA. Today, I have decided to do something I have never done before. I will in great elaboration make an honest attempt to summarize a typical day here in this hostelry, and to document the behavior of my fellow prisoners as well as the guards.

Because I recently spent several months on the disciplinary wing for conduct unbecoming a model prisoner (namely actively promoting peace and world healing within the prison) I will formally introduce you to the tribulations of "Mad Monday" through a nostalgic chronology of events on the great disciplinary wing of this hostelry...

MONDAY MORNING

6.03 a.m. After a stone cold breakfast I lie back down to contemplate another sleepless night, sleepless because of the screams and banging of my fellow prisoners which never cease. I rub my temples and sit up in a lotus position for 25 minutes of subconscious meditation. I get up and spread my blanket on the floor for 30 minutes of Hatha Yoga. I lie back down and try to relax for a few minutes. It's now 8.00 a.m. and the shift has changed, but I'm not really in the mood to face the constant agitations, so I lie there hoping that somehow they won't start but knowing they already have. "What's the use?" I say out loud. So I push the covers back, momentarily halting before placing my feet on the floor. You see? It's my own ritual to keep my sanity, which basically motivates me to somehow endure the day. I'm sitting on the corner of my bunk. I say, "Thanks for the opportunity of waking up to do battle with life again." I realize that a lot of people won't be waking up this morning. I say, "Good morning world," followed by, "Good morning, Insanity State Prison".. While there's life, there's hope. I walk approximately three steps to the steel toilet and sink. My toiletry practices completed, I go to the cell door to see what guards fate has brought me today. I see Smith and Sgt. Jones, so I know things will not be too bad. I listen to obscenities that are exchanged, as if profanities are common courtesy. No one seems to be seriously offended, as if immune to being insulted or cursed. I once read that sailor's mouths are filthy. Apparently the creator of that saying never stepped inside a state prison. Since Sgt. Jones is on, I hang a towel over my door bars as a curtain in an attempt to forever alienate myself from the environment. It takes courage to face the daylight which has surrendered the privacy of night, and most times I don't have it, so I hang a curtain when I can. It's 8.27 a.m...... and awakening are some of the worst undesirables humanity has produced. I walk and pace my cell to fully wake up. I stop at the door again, and pull my curtain back to peek up and down the corridor. The first and loudest voice that I hear is a guy known as the Dictionary of Worthless Information. He arrived at that nickname by very simply being almost always inaccurate. Today he's talking about relativity. Can you believe that? Relativity in a state prison. He's talking to some guy named Oh-Wee, whom they say arrived at this name by being so ugly that his mother was unable to name him at birth. All she could do was say "Oh-Wee, Oh-Wee." They are arguing about who advanced the theory. The Dictionary says it was Louis Pasteur, the guy who was famous for the pasteurisation of milk, while Oh-Wee says it was Jonas Salk, the polio vaccine originator. I want to call out and say, "You're both wrong, it was Albert Einstein," so that the screaming would stop, but I learned long ago that it's futile to attempt to correct them. All they want to do is argue to pass the time, so I stop expecting the normal from the abnormal. Keeping silent, I recite in my mind the words to a song I know. "Welcome, my friends, to the show that never ends." I'm just going with the flow.

It's now 8.58 a.m., which means it's almost time for disciplinary court. I'll give you somewhat of an explanation of what D.R. Court stands for. All last week and over the weekend prisoners are moved to the disciplinary wing pending court, for infractions of the prison rules and regulations...if you're a lucky prisoner and live in the general population, a D.R. is a serious thing as you are physically locked up in solitary pending court. To a prisoner like myself, on close management status, it's not so serious. What can they do to you? Your normal status is 24 hour lock-down. Close management is long-term solitary confinement for behavior and security risks. They say close management is not punishment. I will let you, the reader, be the judge of that. There is only one difference from close management lock-down and disciplinary lock-down status, which is punitive in nature. The difference is that they take all of your personal belongings while you are being disciplined and store them in the property room until such time as you get off of disciplinary confinement.

The court itself is composed of three supposedly unbiased individuals who hear charges of infractions brought against a prisoner. You're allowed witnesses whose statements, it seems, only count if they are detrimental to the defence. The kangaroo court, as it's called, is probably the closet thing to communism in America. On every disciplinary sheet, no matter what the evidence presented on your behalf, it will 99.9% of the time read, "We the team find guilty based on the officer's statements and sentence you to 30 or 60 days disciplinary status time," or "hole time," if you will. "But, Sir..." you scream when your classification specialist cuts you short by saying "That's all, prisoner number so and so. Have a good day." And the guards usher you toward the door. Talk about tyrannical!

At 9.07 a.m. the first "victim" is lead down the corridor to face "Fidel Castro's Communist Panel of Three". He's a guy I recognize as "Half Dead". They call him Half Dead because his motor is wide open when he's moving at a snail's pace - too many years of having taken Horizal and Thorazine. A few minutes later he's back screaming, "I had four witnesses and they found me guilty!" He curses the guards and then almost as if nothing had occurred starts his snail pace back to the cell. The 2nd victim enters and exits so quickly it's hard to believe he went. His partner is a dude named "Parking Lot" and he asks what happened, and the guy says "I plead guilty so they'd take it easy on me like my classification officer said he would. But I guess he lied because he gave me the maximum 60 days." When I heard that last statement I just had to step back to gain my composure. How could he allow them to trick him like that? The stir, or pen, (in convict argot) is a training school for philosophy. No prisoner can survive years of it without having had burst his fondest illusions and fairest metaphysical bubbles. "The truth lives," we are taught. "Crime and injustice will be found out." "Bah!" I say. I heard more doors slam again. I didn't know if it was someone going or coming because I was looking elsewhere at the time.

Suddenly, I heard someone say, "Pick it up on one!" which is a red alert. "Pick it up on one" means pick up any personal property laying on the floor because someone is about to stop up their toilet and flood. In most cases it's never much to pick up because on disciplinary status you're only allowed the barest of necessities... one bar of soap, one toothbrush, two t-shirts, two pairs of underwear, one towel, one cup, one pen, one writing pad, ten envelopes, a Bible and bedding... and, if you have a court order signed by a federal judge, your legal property and supplies. So imagine using one bar of soap for 30 or 60 days at a minimum. Some people stay on disciplinary for years. I know two prisoners who have been on disciplinary status since 1979 and 1983, respectively. As another song goes, "They just don't care anymore."

Well, anyway, a code red alert was sent out, to "pick up on one," so I obliged, picking up my legal stuff. Shortly thereafter, a trickle of water started seeping slowly under the cell door, and it grew to about 1/4" covering the cell floor before it was detected by the authorities, who in their pursuit to pick up another casualty for disciplinary court spotted the water. As luck would have it, the perpetrator of this crime was dumb enough to call the guards to his cell and scream, "Row, row, row your boat, assholes!" This was fortunate, as normally they turn the whole first floor's water off, not being able to tell who did it. So they cut his cell water off.

It doesn't take long for the chaos to start now. It's 10.03 a.m. and it seems like the whole wing is beating on their cell doors and screaming for one thing or another. All the deafening noise seems to be unheard by the guards and it goes on and on... an ear splitting roar which is nothing new. It's a 24 hour cycle. While one group sleeps another group beats, so forth and so on.

Well, court is over with, so I know that the culprit who instituted the flood will now have to deal with the authorities. Sure enough, at 10.09 a.m. I hear the stampede of what sounds like elephants, only it's 15 urban guerrillas known as the prison goon squad. Their usual attire consists of steel toe cowboy boots which usually do as much kicking as walking, brown pants with a black stripe down the side of the leg, a brown shirt with bullet-proof flak jacket, a helmet with plexi-glass eye shield, a billy club with a metal ball on the end, a plexi-glass riot shield for the leader of the gooners to rush in a cell once the door is open and the prisoner is smashed up against the wall or floor. The lead man usually weighs about 300 pounds, and was specially hired for this reason, although the state will deny it. It looks bad on their record of integrity. The rest of their apparel consists of handcuffs, leg irons, waist chains, and tear gas or mace. Let's not forget a mouth full of tobacco juice, and one of the most disgusting and indifferent looks one could want to see. The only thing missing to make them real Nazi storm troopers is HK MP5 sub-machine guns and a few "LAWS" (light anti-tank weapons). But never fear, they have all that and more, an arsenal of the latest weapons, in the gun tower. I know of six occasions when they came armed into the prison... one time they shot a man down in a wing. This is how the 15 man team comes to take a 150 pound man in a cell to another wing. They are at his door now. I hope he goes peacefully so that he won't give them an excuse to maim him severely. I might note that it's one time the wing is quiet, when a prisoner is being beaten by the urban guerillas. I guess it's because some prisoners are quiet only to hear the sickening sounds of another's miseries. In any event, the guy exits the cell automatically without trouble.

I now recognize him as being a guy I've noticed who walks to the shower with a towel tied up around his chest as a woman will do to hide her breasts. But the way it's done in here, it bares the buttocks, which is a sure sign of homosexuality. When he steps out into the hallway the whistles and cat calls start. I notice that as he walks down the corridor in the midst of the urban guerillas there's a smile on his face and a swing in his walk like a girl, as if to say, "Look at me, guys. Aren't I the mean little girl?" Yes, this one definitely has a lot of sugar in his, or her, tank... as the saying goes. Observing this guy, I note that it must be one of his first encounters with the urban guerillas. As if out on a lark, he isn't taking any precautions. The goon squad is known to have one member whose speciality is accidentally tripping you down a flight of stairs or prancing on you like a wild animal to wipe smiles and arrogant looks off your face. You're always handcuffed behind your back when this occurs, and a use of force report is filed, fabricated to the effect that you resisted or kicked a guard. The guy is taken from the wing and I don't know what happens to him.

Shortly, lunch will be here, which will bring matters to a climax. The whole shebang wakes up and eats. Then it's really confusion, and so "Mad Monday" proceeds. 11.01, lunch time. One guard comes around and opens the feed flaps on the doors. The first trustees usually follows the guard with a keg of juice, which we call "red tide" because it's such a strong chemical solution that homosexuals use it to dye clothes they make. After the solution is emptied from the cup, if not washed immediately it dyes the cup. Powerful stuff, that red tide is. So powerful, I pass daily. The tray man is next on the scene. I'm a vegetarian with a specially approved religious vegetarian diet to comply with the tenets of my faith (which took an act of Congress to obtain). So it would appear that I wouldn't have any problems obtaining the correct authorized nutrients, as my tray is specially made up in the separate diet kitchen with my name tag and "Vegan Diet" written on it. Plop goes my tray on the food slot. So much for etiquette. The first thing I see is a big piece of what has to be a rare cooked piece of meatloaf. It looks mean and nasty, like it came straight out of the packing to be thrown out and placed on my tray. Yes, you're correct. Somebody forget to cook it, which is common. Since another guard immediately follows the tray man to close the flaps, I brought this dietary problem to his attention. It's Smith, I notice, so I explain my problem and show him my dietary slip stating I'm a vegetarian, and that there was a slight mistake. Man, he was a good listener. He didn't interrupt or say a word. When I finished I attempted to hand him my tray back to return to the kitchen for the right one. He closed the tray flap so quickly that half of my meal was splattered to the floor to mix with the yet-to-be-cleaned-up flood water. He looked me in the eye and smiled, and said, "Looks like you have a problem there, good buddy." I smiled back and said, "Sure enough, there, good buddy. He, he, he!" He didn't like my attempt at wit, so he moves on without a word. I stepped to the toilet and flushed the whole tray. Coincidentally, it was my small portion of vegetables that fell to the floor. I told myself, "Maybe next time." The premise that tomorrow will be better helps to keep me sane. And, I reasoned that I had been eating too good as of late, anyway, with all the contraband food I obtain through clandestine means. So, I go to my stash, namely an 8 1/2" x 14" legal size envelope. I open it and remove two slices of bread. I open a flattened plastic baggie of peanut butter, and build a sandwich. I also remove a contraband "Snickers" candy bar from the envelope, seal it back up, and stack it back in my legal files box. Before I can eat my clandestine lunch, a few cells down I heard a guy I know by voice named "Fat Jack" hollering about his tray. Apparently Fat Jack is expecting a special high protein diet and they gave him a "Vegan" tray. What I believe happened was, either accidentally or by design, the tray labels got mixed up and he had my tray while I had his. He was preparing a cup of coffee to drink with his meal when given the "Vegan" tray with no meat. The coffee was very hot because he saved it from breakfast in a milk carton and tied a long three foot string to the top, then rolled toilet paper around his hand to make a "bomb" as it's called in convict argot, which you light on fire and hold the milk carton of coffee over it. If done right, there is no smoke and in four minutes you have a cup of nice, hot coffee. Fat Jack started his coffee when they first came on the floor to feed so that by the time they got to him with the trays he had it all ready to drink with his meal. When Smith refused to take the tray back, he threw the hot coffee in Smith's face to burn it.

So the war begins. While we are waiting the return of the urban guerillas, I'll describe Fat Jack. He's 5'4" tall and at least 425 pounds of pure bad understanding about food. He's the fattest man in the prison and they use leg irons on his hands to cuff him. He must turn side-ways to get in a cell door. The man resembles a "weeble wobble but don't fall down" type. But today, I wasn't so sure he could stand. I know he might weeble, or even wobble for awhile, but we all knew he'd fall in the end. But Fat Jack seemed to think he'd stand. We waited and waited, and I attempted to warn him because violence isn't necessary, but he was beyond reasoning. He told me to mind my own fucking business. And from that point the issue appeared moot, so I watched destiny occur. Shortly thereafter I could hear the stampede of a herd of elephants again. They came to Fat Jack's cell and ordered him to back up to the food hole to be handcuffed with leg irons and go easy. As the lead gooner was saying this, old Jack gathered mucus and saliva from the pit of his stomach and spat in the leader's face. So it looked like he was going down fighting, and I might add, he put up one heck of a fight. The cell door was popped, and the first two gooners to enter his cell charged with the riot shield. The Jack literally smashed them back in the hallway. It was one of the first times I can ever say I saw fear in the faces of the 15 man squad. Again they charged, and the Lieutenant was saying "Get him, boys, get him." The Jack howled like a mad grizzly bear and flung them back out into the corridor, and followed them out, escaping the cell to make the spectacle public. The gooners stopped, momentarily puzzled, and The Jack laughed an hysterical laugh, and this time it was The Jack who charged. The Lieutenant is standing back like a commander in Vietnam, screaming: "Get him, boys, get him!" The fight continued until somehow, Jack was knocked down, and once off his feet that was the beginning of the end.

My dear reader, have you ever seen 15 grown men attempt to beat up a 425 pound egg? Like a bowling ball in a bowling alley, The Jack rolled around the floor knocking down gooners like bowling pins. If the situation were not so serious, it would be a great comedy. Finally, subdued by the weight of many gooners, a nurse was standing by and moved in with a hypodermic needle to administer a strong tranquillizing drug, likely Prolexion. The gooners stayed on top of him until the drug took effect, and he was hauled off to the wing which houses mentally ill prisoners, and has it's own house of horrors. They call it behavioral control, where camouflaged as modern penology they have the art of torture and suffering down to a scientific art. Fat Jack is now on the "rack", an infamous steel table where stripped nude the man is chained out in four point restraint. This will last eight hours if he behaves and suffers in silence. If not, it's sixteen hours, and twenty-four, and so on. One is not allowed to eat on the rack. If you're still a problem after twenty-four hours they will feed you with a needle in the arm.

If one must urinate, it must be done on the steel table, and you lay in it. In the winter months one freezes, also. Not that it matters much to the victim, as mind-altering drugs take all the life out of a man, namely Prolexion, Horizol, and to a lesser degree, Thorazine and Mellirit. They call Prolexion "Liquid Strait-Jacket" and they are not wrong. I took a trip down this road myself back in my wild days, and one shot of Prolexion was enough to teach me the errors of my ways. Like Custer, Fat Jack had his last stand.

After seeing this, I decided to lie down and put my radio together, and listen to some music to black out the returning chaos. *"STOP RIGHT HERE!"* you say. Did he say "radio"? Yes, my dear reader, a radio! I call it my Ferrari after the sports car. I obtained it from an enterprising trustee who either bought it cheap or stole it in population and smuggled it back here to sell for a profit in the best of capitalistic tradition. I have a reputation as a wizard of electronics, so the trustee bought it to me first. For $20.00 I am now the owner of a little baby walkman style FM only radio with headset, and believe me, I love it like a mother loves her newborn infant. For as long as it lasts - days, weeks, or luckily months - before being confiscated in yet another shakedown of the cells, and me disciplined yet again for an illegal contraband radio, I am able to keep up with the news of the world, the new songs, and the changing culture of America. It's literally my life's blood to the outside world, and knowing it won't last long, I enjoy it to the fullest. Being adept in electronics has allowed me to make a small radio even smaller and easier to control. I have cannibalized it so it doesn't even resemble a radio anymore. It is also constructed now so that only I can make it function again. It's now the size of a pack of cigarettes. To conceal the headset I wear a bandanna in the way a woman does to cover her hair, which is another sign of the prison homosexual. To attempt to look more like a woman they wear a bandanna over their heads. I do not care. It conceals my headset with the wires running along my back and a battery pack in one pocket, and radio in another. At close look I seem like the Bionic Man with wires all over the place. But it allows me to pace my cell and drive my Ferrari unnoticed by passing guards. The constant roar of noise is cover for any sounds escaping the headset.

I know you are thinking that today in the good ole USA, even prisoners are allowed radios. This is not always the case. At this prison security or behavior problem prisoners are not allowed any type of electronic entertainment devices. The penological reasoning behind this is: if a prisoner is not allowed radios or TV to buy his mind he is quicker brought to heel, and the desired behavior control is reached. It works just the opposite. Believe me, I know. I have been to more liberal prisons where there is not half the problems that I have described. The wings are a lot quieter, and the prisoners are off into their radios and TV sets. In further proof of this, here on Death Row at Insanity Station Prison, you almost never hear of floods, acting out, and other undesirable behavior problems, as they are given TV sets and are allowed to buy their own radios.

In fact, the matter of a TV set is so serious that I will pause in my narrative of "Mad Monday" to tell you just how serious it is. It's a killing matter. Prisoners murder their fellow prisoners for the sake of a TV set. In the convict argot these murders are called "TV Killings" or "TVK's" for short. Of all of the prisoners on Death Row I know of 37 who are "TVK's". They did five or ten years on close management, and gave up all hope. They then murdered someone to obtain an active death sentence. Now, are you thinking, "How can a prisoner in solitary murder someone?" It's done easily enough. In each cell there is a sink. One dismantles the bottom that controls the cold water and obtains a 14" rod of brass, 1/4" in diameter. It is then filed on the stone floor to a point, and makes an ice pick type of weapon. It is then tied on the end of a broom stick, or if not available rolled up newspapers to make a pole, tying the ice pick on the end. Then, a trustee is stabbed while pouring red tide or passing out a tray. Once given an active death sentence by the court, the prisoner then comes under Death Row. There he is allowed a TV and a radio in his cell, four hours of outside exercise in a small yard, in the sunlight. He is further allowed to buy all types of food from the canteen legally, and he is allowed one to six hours of contact visits per weekend. That's 312 hours per year, providing he has someone willing to visit him. By comparison, when he was on close management, he was not allowed to legally order any food items from the canteen... this means a bag of potato chips and a candy bar were contraband in his cell! He was allowed only one visit per 30 days, or 12 hours per year. He was not allowed any out-of-cell exercise whatsoever. Now... was this incentive to behave or cause murder? Of course, I must confess that TVK's are rapidly growing out of fashion in direct proportion to the growing body count. One realizes he must pay for his *Bugs Bunny and Road Runner Show* with his life. Still, 7 or 8 lives are lost this way each year. Not all killers automatically receive the death sentence... I know of one that it took four murders to get it.

Are you wondering, "How about you? Have you considered murder as a relief?" In all honesty, I have. I will be confined on close management for perhaps another ten years. But there are two reasons that I cannot do it: first and foremost, it is an affront to my spirit and to my sense of justice to commit such an act. Secondly, it would be giving in and admitting defeat... letting the system win, so to speak. Quite literally, killing two birds with one stone.

I now return to "Mad Monday". After Fat Jack left, I put together a mosaic of peace and turned on my radio. I then laid down, and listened to a few songs, before sitting up to write letters until 4.00 p.m. I enjoyed the peace and music while it lasted. However, it was short-lived. It's now 4.04 p.m., and fate has brought me one of the most inhumane guards here. Sgt. Brown is working, and it never fails. Brown brings out the beast in the most gentle man. I once read that someone asked Napoleon in the early 1800's, when setting up the French penal system in French Guyana, "And who, Sir, will you get to watch over these hard cases? Napoleon replied, "Why, still harder cases, still." Napoleon did not lie, and the same holds true 150 years later. Our dearest Sgt. Brown is one of the "harder cases, still" that Napoleon spoke of. I carefully picked up all property, hid all contraband items out of sight, and secretly hoped for the best, but prepared for the worst. I knew in my heart of hearts that trouble with a capital "T" was on the way. Chow was served without too much hassle. I was even given the correct tray.

Following the evening meal, mail is supposed to be passed out. But it's a standing practice with Brown to do anything to disturb tranquillity. He delays the passing out until the last minute. At 8.01 p.m. here he comes down the corridor. I am expecting trouble, and I am not wrong. Brown reaches cell 5 across the corridor, passes a letter under the food flap, and moves on down the hall.

I heard an exchange of words in heavily accented English. I knew it was the two Cubans in cells 5 and 6, who have been arguing and going through problems for a week now. The Cuban in cell 5 had been delivered the other's letter; taunting, he says, "He, he, Brown give me your letter," and reads of the address as proof. "He, He, I write your mother and tell her you homosexual, ha, ha, he he!" So the other Cuban is going nuts. He calls Brown when he walks back down the corridor and says "You gave him me mail. Get me mail. Get me mail." Sgt. Brown comes to his cell with a look of total indifference and shrugs his shoulders as if to say, "So what?" It was the wrong thing to do, as the Cuban was holding a container behind his back full of do-do. Yes, reader, human faeces. Before Brown realizes his mistake and can run, it's splashed in the intended target - the face of our dear Brown. Latins are notoriously famous for allowing faeces and urine to brew for weeks in a closed container, to throw on individuals. It's the ultimate insult, to the macho Latin mind. And, I must confess, they have the art down to a science. They brew an almost napalm-like substance that sticks to everything. Sgt. Brown came running by my cell with faeces in his hair, face and mouth. He's gone for the next hour to the guard station for a shower and change of clothes, and is back before 9.00 p.m., count time. The Cuban is gone now, another casualty for you know where.

9.01 p.m., master count time. Sgt. Brown goes by each cell as we stand at attention on the cell doors and recite our number. "123456", I say as he passes by. As I continued to journey visually through the perilous escapades of this "Mad Monday" I found myself in a somewhat animated state, almost facetious in nature. Not that anything about my present living situation is facetious, but in order to maintain sound facilities one has to occasionally be humored by the enigmatic cycle of sporadic occurrences of a typical "Mad Monday". The proximity of mass catastrophe is always a certainty. Considering the fact that it has always been my nature to be as prudent and knowledgeable in all matters as comprehension will allow, I stand on my door now - not to indulge or participate in any fashion but merely to analyze the un-analyzable, so that I may write this narrative and be able one day to ameliorate these dreary surroundings.

While I'm standing on the door, my nostrils have been assaulted by what smells like a poisonous odor. It's soon recognized as the burning of a mattress, and other flammable articles in a cell, which seems to be coming from the third floor. Talk about brightness, here's a classic example through written illustration of the oddity of some people. It's my understanding that some guy upstairs allowed Sgt. Brown to confiscate a pack of cigarettes from him, and in order to retaliate against Brown, the prisoner blocked off his cell bars and door by covering them with a blanket. He then ignited his remaining bedding and mattress on fire. Needless to say, shortly thereafter the fumes and smoke forced him to change his mind. So he quickly opened up his cell by snatching the covering off the bars. But it was a fraction too late to realize he needed air to breathe, because air also intensifies fire. In order to breathe, he wet a towel and placed it over his face, which didn't work either. His last attempt was to place his head in the toilet and flush it, but that was as futile as all his prior efforts to obtain oxygen. Of course, the entire third floor was literally held in darkness from black smoke. It was a haze down here on the first floor. People were beating on the doors, screaming "Fire, Fire, Fire!" Of course, Sgt. Brown knew. How could he not? But as usual, he remained indifferent to the matter. From his reactions and responses it seemed he kept looking and viewing his watch to have things happen in the 1/100th of accuracy, because he waited until the last possible second before summoning help, then slowly proceeded to the third floor with two of the fire extinguishers from the guard's office, and putting the fire out.

The cell door was then opened. The man had collapsed and was unconscious. He was dragged out of the cell and down the stairs to the second floor and was treated with oxygen and all the scientific gadgets to revive a victim suffering from smoke inhalation. So, to reinforce my opinion that Sgt. Brown did in fact have the art of inflicting undue punishment down to a science, after the medical personnel removed the perpetrator of the fire from the wing to his ultimate fate (of which I know not), I started to wonder if they really took the right one? It seems to me they left the basket case supervising the wing.

All during this sporadic chain of events, guys were asking, almost pleading with Sgt. Brown to cut on the air vent, exhaust fans in the pipe alley to clear the wing of smoke. Again, he went back to his old indifferent self. It's funny how he picks the weirdest times to go deaf. The smoke was nauseating on the first floor, so I know it had to be suffocating on the third. The enmity that Brown subjects us to is somehow always exculpated by reports written to his superiors. The chants have now started, and vulgarities have been and are being poetically spoken. Faeces are running down the third floor. I hear somebody scream, "Forget the fans, grab the mop buckets!" A red alert is issued. "Pick it up on one, two and three," which means the third floor is going to flood. I do not like floods because the water also comes down the walls inside my cell. Whoever built the building forgot the cement sealer. Sure enough, my walls start leaking and raining water, which indicated the third floor was flooding. There are 34 cells on the third floor. It was no isolated flood, as at least 25 cells had stopped up their toilets. Before the third floor water could be turned off, an ocean of water and floating particles and debris start raining down over the catwalk tier like the waterfalls of Niagara, all coming to rest on the first floor. I hear, "Pick it up on one and two." The second floor has now joined the chaos, then spreading like wildfire, the first floor joins in. Before the water supply can be turned off on the whole wing, they must go to each individual cell pipe alley to turn off the water. That's 102 vales they must turn off. The whole wing is an ocean. It's one of the biggest floods I have seen. I am standing in three inches of water on my cell floor. It's so big I know they will work all through the night and it will be well into Tuesday before things are cleaned up and order is restored. As I stand on the cell door and gaze out upon my fellow prisoners acting out their fantasies, I look down at my feet as I stand in my flip-flop shower shoes, and look for the non-existent rubber duck that should be swimming around in the debris. I gaze back out upon the corridor. I look from door to door and see some insane-looking faces behind chicken-wired cell bars smile away, having a great time. Squirt bottles filled with urine are held at the ready to fire, looking like soldiers protecting a fortress. One thing about them, they don't hesitate to fire at passing guards and trustees alike, now that the zoo is in full swing. I gaze upon the corridor, and it reminds me of photos I have seen of the bombing of Beirut - all types of floating refuse particles and debris are floating by my cell. Pieces of the old burnt mattress from the third floor fire pass by, and I also notice what has to be a piece of meatloaf from lunch. I think of Fat Jack, and bet he'd love to have that! And now, dear readers, brace yourself for the final irony of "Mad Monday". As I stand on the door with the bandanna over my headset driving my Ferrari, the rock music is blaring away in my ear...and I hear AC-DC's song *On a Highway to Hell* come on. With lyrics to this song in my ears and mind, I close my eyes and wonder what this Highway to Hell had in store next.

I realize the irony of my situation and the depravity of myself and my fellow prisoners. It was too much to bear. I slosh my way two steps to the bunk and get ready for bed. My daily practice of 30 minutes night-time Hatha Yoga, and two hours of physical exercise was now not possible due to the three inches of water in my cell. As I lie down and re-arrange my electronics gear for night-time Ferrari cruising, I thought, "No one could possibly believe the events of this 'Mad Monday'." Ten years ago I would have laughed in the face of anyone who told such a story. And as I write this narrative, I look back on this "Mad Monday" and realize a man must be greatly the philosopher to survive the continual impact of such brutish events and deprivations upon his psyche as experienced here in this mad house labelled a state prison. Through the years I have become such a philosopher, and have endured nine years of this torment. I turn up my Ferrari and drift off, trying to forget the tribulations of this "Mad Monday"...

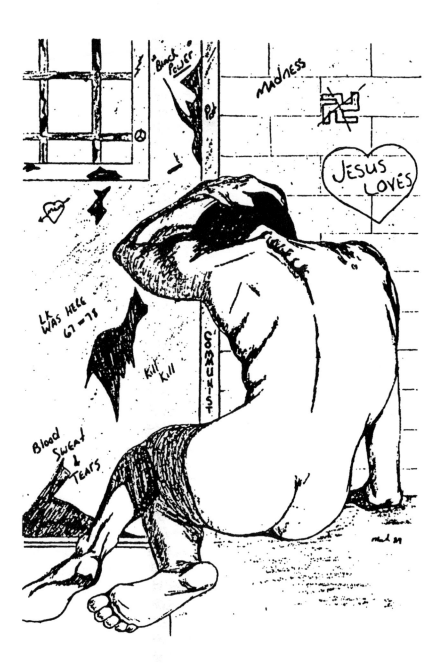

Artwork by Mark De Friest

Part Two

Charismatic Psychos

"In America it has always been popular to follow mass murderers, crooks, killers of all stripe. America cultivates violence in everything it fashions, even people... the people fashioned by its vast, complicated, governmental administration. *The Executioner's Song* should speak to America; should tell Americans that if the story of Gary Gilmore entertains them, if they thrill to the violence done to (as well as done by) Gilmore, then they should always be prepared, always have a gun or a cop within reach, because it will happen again and again, as long as the American traditional system of violence stands above the use of reason.

"For Americans to be shocked and disgusted at senseless murders and at crimes of extreme violence against the innocent is exactly identical to an old, worn-out prostitute expressing moral indignation at the thought of premarital sexual relations. Tell America that."

Jack Henry Abbott, **The Belly of the Beast**

1
THE STORY OF CARL PANZRAM

Reform School

"I would not reform if the front gate was opened right now and if I was given a million dollars when I stepped out," wrote Carl Panzram from Death Row in 1930. "I have no desire to do good or to be good."

Panzram was an early prototype of America's most predominant dark folk hero, the modern serial killer. Calling himself a "piker" for only killing 21 people, he was the specter that haunts everybody's worst nightmares: an unstoppable psychopathic monster, deadly, dark and menacing, unrepentant to the very end. Yet Panzram remains paradoxically a source of wonderment and fascination, if only for the outrageous extent to which he took his campaign to "reform people who try to reform me."

His memoirs, which were later extracted in *Killer, A Journal of Murder*, by Gaddis and Long, foreshadowed prison literature like *Starke Stories* and *The Rolling Papers* by a good sixty years.

Born in 1891 to a "hardworking, ignorant, and poor" Teutonic family on a Minnesota farm, his father left home when he was seven. Later, Carl, his size seeming to exceed his eleven years, set off to seek his fortune in the wild west. Stealing a cake, a few apples, and a big pistol, he hopped a freight train. But the aspiring Jesse James didn't get far.

When they brought him back, he was sent to the state reform school, which was run by a couple of religious fanatics. At the Minnesota State Training School at Red Wing, Mr. Moore and Miss Martin shared their love for Jesus with the little boys in such memorable lessons as The Paint Shop, where "they used to paint our bodies black and blue." Panzram learned to love Jesus "so damn much I'd like to crucify him all over again." Instead, he burned down The Paint Shop in an act of faith which was shortly followed by a touch of Christian poisoning in Mr. Moore's rice pudding.

But Panzram's two years at Red Wing did teach him something useful after all: "... stealing, lying, hating, burning and killing. I had learned that a rectum could be used for other purposes than crepitating... I made up my mind that I would rob, burn, destroy, and kill everywhere I went and everybody I could as long as I lived."

He returned to a chilly welcome. His mother was grieving over the drowning of her favorite son, and Carl was shunted straight off to a Lutheran boarding school. When some of the boys got in his face about coming from reform school, he beat them up. The preacher corrected his bad behavior with a beating. Carl promptly pulled a Colt .45, said his goodbyes to the preacher, and hopped the next westbound train.

The west was wild enough to be sure, but not quite as much fun as the little blond thirteen-year-old hobo might have hoped. He was soon gang-raped. "I cried, I begged and pleaded for mercy, pity and sympathy, but nothing I could say or do could sway them from their purpose. I left that box a sadder, sicker but wiser boy..."

He got as far as Butte, Montana, where he was picked up for petty larceny and sent to another reform school. Once again brutalized, he fought back, braining a former prizefighter with a piece of weighted lumber. This time, he was reformed in a new way. The process included not only beating, but forced circumcision.

This walking time bomb finally escaped from Montana State Reform School and drifted from town to town, aimlessly robbing and burning churches for a couple of years.

Joining the Army at 16, he was soon incarcerated for three years at Ft. Leavenworth, Kansas, for theft. Leavenworth made the young Carl Panzram into a man, filling him with "stinking codfish, greasy stew or moldy and wormy rice or beans." The formation of his character included having his 16-year-old leg shackled to a 50-pound iron ball for six months straight. What would have broken men twice his age only fueled the rage that drove him on. "The worse the food was and the harder they worked me, the stronger I got."

A Little Sodomy

Upon discharge from the Army, he drifted through Kansas, Missouri and Illinois, working odd jobs as a railroad guard or strike breaker, or as a roustabout with a traveling carnival. Between odd jobs, short stretches of time and petty offenses became a way of life. He remembered one 40-day term on a Texas roadgang in particular, having escaped and, upon being captured, been whipped and sentenced to more time. Escaping again, he came upon a large fire in Houston, and looted a few burning homes along the way.

Panzram later described a memorable moment from those days. He was traveling with an Indian in 1911, when they attacked a railroader, robbed him of $35, bound his arms and legs, and stuffed a sock in his mouth. "I figured that as I had such a good chance as that, I would commit a little sodomy on him... He is still there, unless the buzzards and coyotes have finished the last of him long ago."

Later that year, Panzram gave the military life another try, this time enlisting in the Foreign Legion of the Mexican Army. One month later he had deserted, riding his horse to death before he hit the border.

He had learned how to ride the rails early, but this big burly hobo wasn't going to take the raw end of the stick anymore. Now that he was a *man*, he could force his will on any hobo he pleased. "Whenever I met one who wasn't too rusty-looking, I would make him raise his hands and drop his pants."

Prisons all over the wild west provided Panzram with outstanding opportunities to advance his education and refine his social skills. "I learned more about sodomy than old boy Oscar Wilde ever thought of knowing... I was so busy committing sodomy that I didn't have any time left to serve Jesus as I had been taught to do in those reform schools."

While he was awaiting sentence for highway robbery, assault and sodomy in The Dalles, Oregon, he learned how to blow up safes from a con named Cal Jordan. Panzram knew how to apply that lesson: he blew up the prison and escaped. But then he came back to break his partner out and was caught. "The thanks I got from old Cal was that he thought I was in love with him, and he tried to mount me. But I wasn't broke to ride and he was, so I rode him."

Incendiary Commentary

By 1915, the 23-year-old Panzram "had the look of the road in his clothes. Prison, violence and roustabouting had hardened him into a silent, strange-eyed man with broad-muscled shoulders and a hairline that was already beginning to recede."

Using the name "Jefferson Baldwin", he was arrested in Oregon for stealing some jewelry, a watch, and $130 in cash. He copped a plea to the watch, in return for a dismissal of the other charges. But the state reneged on their side of the deal and gave him a maximum sentence. Panzram reacted in character. He "tore loose all the radiators and steam pipes, smashed all the electric wiring, took the cook stove, all the dishes, all the food, all the blankets, mattresses and clothing, all the furniture, benches, tables, chairs, books and everything that was loose or could be torn loose or that would burn. Then I piled it all up and set fire to it."

This incendiary commentary on the judicial process netted Panzram seven years in the state pen under the regime of the infamous Warden Harry

Minto. Though prison reform movements had long since succeeded in banning the beating and firehosing of prisoners, Oregon had somehow managed to defy all nationally-recognized standards for their civilized treatment.

Inmates of the Oregon State Penitentiary were compelled to remain silent at all times, walking lockstep with one hand firmly on the shoulder of the man in front, eyes submissively drawn down. Moving out of line or talking drew an instant clubbing from the guards.

In 1915, the most common method to reform an inmate of this wild west gulag was handcuffing him and hoisting him onto a pillar by his cuffs for an extended lashing with a cat-o'-nine-tails. But there were creative variations on the theme. He could be prescribed "a dose of salts", a brutal whipping while being held down by a handful of other prisoners. If he got jumpy, he might have to be restrained with "the jacket", a variety of straitjacket that almost completely cut off his circulation. Of if that wasn't enough to settle him down, they might move him to "the restraint machine", a cold, damp concrete floor where the naked prisoner would stand cuffed behind his back to the iron-barred door, for eight hours at a time. The *really* hard cases required a more aggressive form of rehabilitation: "the hummingbird", a sadistic combination of steel, wire, sponge, water... and a little *electricity*.

Panzram was undaunted. The first to be issued a "hornet suit" of red and black stripes, he wore the ostentatious uniform of the troublemaker with pride, and strove to live up to the expectations that distinction placed upon him in the minds of his fellow cons. He attempted again and again to escape, and was stripped, flogged and thrown in the Hole more often than not.

Panzram masterminded one escape involving a prisoner named Otto Hooker, and in that jailbreak Warden Minto was shot dead by Hooker, who got away. When John Minto came to take the place of his slain brother Harry as the new Warden, he took a particular interest in reforming Carl Panzram.

Panzram undoubtedly took some heat from the Warden, but he kept to his reformation program. He stole some lemon extract and brewed it up, got all the cons drunk, caused a riot, and burned down most of the prison workshops. This jolly little bonfire did not go unnoticed by the Warden, and netted him bread-and-water in the Hole for sixty days. Another trip to the Hole became necessary after the prison's flax mill suddenly burst into flame. It was said that it was the way Panzram *roared* from the Hole that particularly aggravated Warden Minto.

After another escape attempt, Panzram and another prisoner were stripped, chained and firehosed. "At the end, I was out and hanging by my arms. When I came to, I was near blind, all swelled up, black and blue all over the front of my body, my privates as big as those of a jackass .." Panzram describes how he was rehabilitated by this experience. "Many a man has paid for what those men did to me that Sunday morning. Maybe that hose did wash a lot of dirt off me, the outside of me, but it also washed a hell of a lot of dirt inside me too."

Carrying the Flag

The injuries sustained by Panzram and other inmates were so severe, Warden Minto was fired. His replacement was Charles Murphy, a liberal humanitarian, of all things. Panzram didn't get it. "I thought he must be a punk or some kind of fruit. But damned if that wasn't wrong."

The next time Panzram was caught sawing his bars, Murphy asked how many times this inmate had tried to escape (eight), and how many times he had been severely punished (eight). Observing that experience wasn't teaching Panzram much, Murphy ordered him extra rations and reading material.

When Murphy heard Panzram boasting of being the worst con in the prison, he astonished everyone by offering to open the prison gates and let Panzram go anywhere he wanted, so long as he'd agree to come back at suppertime. Panzram took him up on it with no intention of ever returning, but he came back for supper nonetheless. And when Warden Murphy let the cons form a marching band, Panzram carried the flag.

He was responding to the humanistic treatment to some extent, but after two short months, he got drunk, overstayed his leave while rejoicing in the arms of a pretty nurse, and then hopped a freight train. After shooting the sheriff of a small farming town, he was captured and brought back to prison in chains.

Warden Murphy, humiliated and enraged over his star prisoner's defection from his innovative program, reverted to type. Panzram got "the restraint machine" for eight hours a day, three days in a row. Murphy wrote to the judge who presided over the trial for the crimes Panzram had committed while on escape, "I know for certain I will never trust him again, but what steps to take towards reformation, I do not know. I am inclined to think it is hopeless."

In 1917, Panzram finally escaped from the Oregon pen for the last time, calmly walking off while three other escapees were shot down. He became a new man. "John O'Leary" was the merchant seaman who embarked on a worldwide murder spree described so frankly by Panzram in his memoirs. The excerpt published here gives a few of the highlights of those years in his own words:

EXCERPT FROM THE MEMOIRS OF CARL PANZRAM

"Back in New York in the summer of 1920 I think - June or July but maybe August. Five days after I got back broke on the Manchuria I went up to New Haven, Connecticut. There I robbed the home of someone in that place. I got about $40,000 worth of jewelry and some Liberty Bonds. They were signed and registered with the name W.H. Taft and among the jewelry was a watch with his name on it, presented to him by some congress or some senate while he was the Governor General of the Philippine Islands. So I know it was the same man who had given me my three years in the U.S. Military Prison when he was Secretary of War about 1906. Out of this robbery I got about £3,000 in cash and kept some of the stuff, including a .45 Colt Automatic. With that money I bought a yacht - the Akista. Her initials and registry numbers were K.N.B.C., 107,296.

On my yacht I had quarters for five people but I was alone for a while. Then I figured it would be a good plan to hire a few sailors to work for me, get them out to my yacht, get them drunk, commit sodomy on them, rob them and then kill them. This I done. Every day or two I would get plenty of booze by robbing other yachts there. The *Barbara II* was one of them. I robbed her and a dozen or so others around there. I was hitting the booze pretty hard myself at that time. Every day or two I would go to New York and hang around 25 South Street and size up the sailors. Whenever I saw a couple who were about my size and seemed to have money, I would hire them to work on my yacht. I would always promise a big pay and easy work.

What they got was something else. I would take them and all their clothes and gear out to my yacht at City Island. There we would wine and dine and when they were drunk enough they would go to bed. When they were asleep I would get my .45 Colt Army Automatic, this I stole from Mr. Taft's home, and blow their brains out. Then I would take a rope and tie a rock on them and put them into my rowboat, row out in the main channel about one mile and drop 'em overboard. They are there yet, ten of 'em. I worked that racket about three weeks. My boat was full of stolen stuff, and the people at City Island were beginning to look queer at me so the next two sailors I hired I kept alive and at work. One was named Delaney and the other was Goodman or Goodwin.

The three of us on my boat pulled out one day and went as far as Graves End Bay, New York, where I robbed another yacht. They knew it but I figured on killing them both in a day or two. But we only got as far down the coast as Atlantic City, New Jersey, where my yacht was wrecked, with everything on her lost. The three of us got ashore alive. The other two I paid off and where they went I don't know or care. I was sick at that time and a Dr. Charles McGivern took care of me there at his home for a week or so. Him I gave a few pieces of jewelry of Old Man Taft's. I also gave him the .45 Colt Automatic that I done the killing with. I left his home and went back to Connecticut looking for another $40,000, but I got six months in the can at Bridgeport, Connecticut, instead for burglary. I done that six months and while there I borrowed $100 from my doctor, Charles McGivern. When I got out of the can I went to Philadelphia. There I got my Colt .45 back from the doctor.

Then I joined the Flying Squadron of the Seamen's Union who were on strike at that time. A few days later I got into a gun battle with some scab sailors and the cops. The cops won. I got pinched and held for the grand jury under the charges of aggravated assault and inciting to riot. I got out on bail and immediately jumped it. I went to Norfolk, Virginia, got a ship to Europe and robbed and jumped her when I got there. From Europe I went down to Matidi [Matadi] in the Belgian Congo, Africa. From there I went to Luanda, Angola, Portuguese West Africa. There I went to work for the Sinclair Oil Company, driving niggers, and I sure drove the hell out of them too. I wasn't there long before I decided to get a nigger girl. I got one. I paid a big price for her. I bought her from her mother and father for 80 eschudas [escudos] or about $8 in American money. The reason I paid such a big price for her was because she was a virgin. Yah, so she said. She was about 11 or 12 years old. I took her to my shack the first night and took her back to her father's shack the next. I demanded my money back because they had deceived me by saying the girl was a virgin.

I didn't get my money back but they gave me another and younger girl. This girl was about eight years old. I took her to my shack and maybe she was a virgin but it didn't look like it to me. I took her back and quit looking for any more virgins. I looked for a boy.

I found one. He was our table waiter. I educated him into the art of sodomy as practiced by civilized people. But he was only a savage and didn't appreciate the benefits of civilization. He told my boss and the boss-man fired me quick, but before he did I licked the hell out of him. They chased me out of the jungles of Quimbazie where that happened and I went back to Luanda. There I went to the U.S. Consul, a Mr. Clark, but he had heard all about me and my ways and he would have none of me. I left his office and sat down in a park to think things over a bit. While I was sitting there, a little nigger boy about 11 or 12 years old came bumming around. He was looking for something. He found it, too. I took him out to a gravel pit about a quarter mile from the main camp of the Sinclair Oil Company at Luanda. I left him there, but first I committed sodomy on him and then killed him. His brains were coming out of his ears when I left him and he will never be any deader. He is still there.

Then I went to town, bought a ticket on the Belgian steamer to Lobito Bay down the coast. There I hired a canoe and six niggers and went out hunting in the bay and backwaters. I was looking for crocodiles. I found them, plenty. They were all hungry. I fed them. I shot all six of these niggers and dumped 'em in. The crocks done the rest. I stole their canoe and went back to town, tied the canoe to the dock and that night someone stole the canoe from me.

To some people of average intelligence, killing six at once seems an almost impossible feat. That is because of their ignorance of the full details. It was very much easier for me to kill those six niggers that it was for me to kill only one of the young boys I killed later and some of them were only 11 or 12 years old.

In Africa there are bull buffaloes that weigh 2,000 pounds and have enormous strength, yet a crocodile 12 or 15 foot long can kill and eat a buffalo. Any of these six niggers that I killed could kill and eat one of those crocodiles. Armed with no more than some small sticks and a bit of grass and a piece of rotten meat they do that trick every day all over Africa. I was forearmed with the knowledge that I had gained and also a nine millimeter German Luger automatic pistol and plenty of bullets. The seven of us were in the canoe, the other six in front of me where I sat in the stern. The canoe was about 22 feet long, four-and-a-half foot wide, two-and-a-half foot deep.

The niggers expected nothing. They all had their backs turned to me. I am a crack shot. I fired a single shot into each nigger's back, and then reloaded with a new clip and fired another shot into the brain of each one as they lay dying or dead in the bottom of the canoe. Then I threw them all over board and the crocodiles soon finished what I had left of them. This canoe was registered and licensed. It must still be in existence. If it is, there are two bullets imbedded in the wood, one in the bottom near the stern and one on the port side near the middle. These niggers were all full grown men with families who must be still alive and who still remember me as dozens of people saw me at Lobito Bay when I hired them and their canoe.

The pistol with which I did that killing, I brought back to the States. There is a record of it at the Maxim Silent Firearms Co. at Hartford, Conn. where I sent it in the winter of 1922 and 1923, from Yonkers, N.Y. under my name of Captain John O'Leary. Under that name and address, 220 Yonkers Ave., I sent the pistol to them and they sold me a silencer for it. All of this must be on the books of that Company's records. The Port Police and Belgian Consul at Lobito Bay can verify the rest of the Lobito Bay end of it. I thought that the pistol wasn't deadly enough as it was so I got a silencer for it to be able to do a bigger and more efficient business in the murder line. And, believe me, if that heavy calibered pistol and the silencer had only worked as I thought it would, I would have gone into the murder business on a wholesale scale instead of being a piker and only killing 21 human beings. My intentions were good because I am the man that goes around the world doing people good.

Next I bought a ticket on that same Belgian steamer and went back to Luanda where I again went to Mr. Clark, the U.S. Consul, and bummed him for a ticket to Europe, but he gave me the air and set the cops after me. That night I went to the house of a Spanish prostitute and robbed her of 10,000 eschudas. She also set the cops after me so I beat it. I couldn't get out of there by rail or by ship as the cops were looking for me so I hiked out. I hiked north for the Belgian Congo, 300 miles away, through Ambrizett and Ambreeze, up to the mouth of the Congo River at San Antonio. There I hired a canoe and paddlers who took me across to Point Banana. There I bought a ticket on a French ship to Boma and from there up to Matidi. There I stayed about a month. Then broke, I couldn't get a ship. I stowed away on a U.S. ship, the *West Nono*. They carried me as far as Axime on the Gold Coast and dumped me there. I walked to Secondee (Sekondi) and there robbed some lime juicers and bought a ticket on the *S.S. Patonie*. On her I got as far as Las Palmas (Canary Islands), and there the U.S. Consul didn't know me and I gave him a lot of bull and he bought me a ticket on a Portuguese ship to Lisbon, Portugal.

When I got there I at once went to the U.S. Consul to try to get a ship out but I got hell instead. He knew all about me. A Mr. Crandall, director of the Sinclair Oil Company, had been there a few weeks before me on his way from Luanda, and he told the Consul all about me. That afternoon I stowed away on an English coal carrier that took me to Avenmouth, England. A day or so later I signed on a U.S. ship as a consul's passenger to New York. This was in the summer of 1922.

Just as soon as I got to New York I took my old license as captain and owner of my bill of sale which had been given to me in the Customs House in New York City for my old lost yacht, the *Akista*, that I went and saved all of this time from 1920 until 1922. I got a new license and set of papers by turning my old ones in to the Customs House in New York City. I kept these new papers and began looking around for another yacht of the same size and kind so I could steal her, take her name and number off and put mine on.

In July at Salem, Massachusetts, I murdered an 11 or 12 year old boy by beating his brains out with a rock. I tried a little sodomy on him first. I left him laying there with his brains coming out of his ears. [*The victim was 12-year-old Henry McMahon.*] Went down towards New York - robbing and hell-raising as I came. That same summer and fall I went through Philadelphia to Baltimore where I bought a ticket to Jacksonville, Florida, on a boat. At Jacksonville, I signed on a ship and went to Baton Rouge, Louisiana, paid off there and went to the Marine Hospital at New Orleans. I stayed there a month or two and when I left this hospital, I robbed their drugroom of two suitcases full of drugs, cocaine, morphine and opium. Sold some in New Orleans, some in St. Louis and the rest in New York. In January or February 1923, I got a job as a watchman at 220 Yonkers Avenue, Yonkers, New York, for the Abeeco Mill Company. While there I met a young boy of 14 or 15 years whose name was George and whose home was is in Yonkers. I started to teach him the fine art of sodomy but I found he had been taught all about it and he liked it fine. I kept him with me until I left that job in April 1923.

A month or two later I got a job as watchman and caretaker of boats at the New Haven Yacht Club at New Haven, Connecticut. I took very good care of their boats, so much so that I robbed one the next night. The name of the yacht I don't know but the owner of it was the Police Commissioner of New Rochelle, New York, or some place near there. Part of my loot was his pistol, a .38 Colt double-action side-break gun.

A few weeks later about May or June I stole a yacht at Providence, Rhode Island, and sailed it up as far as New York. I was alone until then. At New York I picked up a kid about 18 or 20 years old, took him on the yacht with me as far as Yonkers. There I let him go back to New York. At Yonkers I picked up my other kid, George. I took him along on the yacht to Kingston, New York. There I painted the yacht over, changed the name and numbers to correspond to my papers. I tried to sell the boat there. While doing so, I met a fellow who said he wanted to buy my boat but instead of that he got out on the yacht with me where we were laying at anchor. There he tried to stick me up but I was suspicious of his actions and was ready for him, and I shot him twice with the same pistol I had stolen from the Police Commissioner's yacht at New Haven a short time before.

After I killed him I tied a big hunk of lead around him with a rope and threw him and his gun overboard. He is there yet so far as I know. Then I sailed down the river, stealing everything I could as I went. I got as far as Newburgh, New York. There the kid, George, got scared and I let him go home to Yonkers. When he got home he told the police all he knew about me which wasn't much but was enough for the cops to come looking for me. They caught me and my yacht at Nyack. They took me, boat and all my plunder to Yonkers in jail there. Charged with sodomy, burglary, robbery and trying to break jail there. I got a lawyer there, a Mr. Cashin. I told him the boat was worth five or ten thousand dollars and that I would give it to him if he got me out of jail. He got me out and I gave him the boat and my papers. When he went to register the boat he lost her because the owner from Providence came and got her.

A few days later I went to New Haven where I killed another boy. I committed a little more sodomy on him also and then tied his belt around his neck and strangled him, picked him up when he was dead and threw his body over behind some bushes. [*The identity of this victim was never definitely established.*] Went to New York then and got a job as a bathroom steward on the Army Transport, *U.S. Grant*, going to China, but instead of me going to China I got fired for being drunk and fighting. The next night I robbed the express office at Larchmont, New York, and got caught in the act, put in jail and indicted at White Plains, New York, for burglary. I at once saw that I could be convicted so I immediately saw the prosecuting attorney and with him made a bargain. He promised me that if I would plead guilty and in that way save the county the expense of a trial, he would agree that I would get a very light sentence in return. I kept to my side of the bargain but he didn't. I pleaded guilty and was immediately given the limit of the law, five years. At once I was sent to Sing Sing."

Kill 'em All!

After the law finally caught up with Panzram for good, he found himself in Dannemora, a dead-end prison for incorrigibles in Clinton, New York. In his first few months here, he kept up a steady pace, as he made a time bomb; tried to burn down the shops; tried to club another inmate to death; broke both legs and ankles, fractured his spine and ruptured himself in an attempt to drop 30 feet to freedom; and finally was thrown out of the hospital for trying to sodomize another prisoner, "to see if my sexual organs were still in good order."

Discharged from prison in New York in June of 1928, he was imprisoned in Washington, D.C. by late summer. Upon being found sawing his bars, he was pinioned by a rope to a post 18 inches around and nine feet high, so that only his toes could touch the floor. Virtually crucified, he was suspended in that agonizing position all night. Bellowing curses at his mother for bringing him into this world, Panzram swore to kill her and everything human. By dawn of the next night of torture, the hate-crazed prisoner was openly boasting of murders in Boston, New Haven and Philadelphia.

Henry Lesser, a sensitive young Jewish guard, saw Panzram dragged back to his isolation cell, covered in bruises and dried blood, and unexpectedly felt angry and ashamed. He took pity on the tormented man and took steps to befriend him. As he began to gain Panzram's trust, Lesser was surprised to uncover in Panzram a sophisticated thinker, a reader of Nietzsche and Schopenhauer, or as Dr. Benjamin Karpman would say, "a mass murderer who clearly expressed a philosophy of hate." Panzram had found a friend. He resolved to put his life story on paper, to answer all of the guard's questions and then to leave him to do what he wished with the manuscript.

After conviction on a burglary charge, Panzram was transferred to the federal pen at Leavenworth. While there, he kept in touch with Lesser by letter, and Lesser soon had enough material to submit a sample to H.L. Mencken. Thanking him, the famous editor returned the manuscript, assuring Lessor that no magazine or publisher would ever handle it, concluding, "I can't recall reading anything more shocking."

In June of 1929, Panzram bludgeoned a prison employee to death, and his autobiographical project was abruptly terminated. At his murder trial in 1930, Panzram told the judge that he didn't need a lawyer, he wanted to plead innocent but let the state prove its case unhindered. Upon due consideration, he was found guilty and sentenced to hang on September 5,

1930. Panzram was pleased, and admonished the Society for the Abolishment of Capital Punishment for trying to save his life.

"I prefer to die that way, and if I have a soul and if that soul should burn in Hell for a million years, still I prefer that to a lingering, agonizing death in some prison dungeon or a padded cell in a mad house... The only thanks you or your kind will ever get from me for your efforts on my behalf is that I wish you all had one neck and that I had my hands on it... I have no desire to reform myself. My only desire is to reform people who try to reform me, and I believe that the only way to reform people is to kill 'em. My motto is: 'Rob 'em all, rape 'em all, and kill 'em all!'"

Panzram's execution went as scheduled. Walking briskly and willfully to the gibbet that had been specially constructed to hoist his powerful 210 pounds, he spotted two priests. "Are there any Bible-backed cocksuckers in here?" he roared, and the clergymen fled aghast. Asked by the hangman if he wanted to make a last statement, he snapped, "Yes, hurry it up, you Hoosier bastard! I could hang a dozen men while you're fooling around!"

Carl Panzram -
the original "psychokiller-author"

2
GERARD JOHN SCHAEFER
by Sondra London

The Classic Case

The phrase *serial killer* was coined by Robert Ressler, who helped form the FBI's world-renowned Behavioral Science Unit. In his book ***Whoever Fights Monsters***, Ressler cites a classic case: "In our road shows, when I used to display the slides and give the lecture about the organized offender Gerard John Schaefer, someone in my audience would accuse me of having taken the characteristics of that sort of offender right from the details of Schaefer's case. That's not so, but it is true that the patterns associated with the organized killer are starkly apparent in this instance."

Even though he uses the Schaefer case to illustrate every salient feature of the organized type of serial killer, Ressler recently confided to me in a personal conversation, "I cannot say Schaefer actually is a serial killer, as we go by the record. By my own definition, a serial killer commits at least four murders, in four separate events, precipitated by fantasy, and separated by an emotional cooling-down period. Now, by law, Schaefer has only been convicted of two murders which were done at the same time, so technically, he doesn't fit the definition. But everything else fits - the background, the fantasies, the psychological characteristics, the additional crimes he's suspected of - and so far as I'm concerned, the only thing that keeps Schaefer from being labeled a serial killer is the inability of law enforcement to catch up with him."

It is significant that Ressler selected Schaefer among thousands of convicted felons as the classic case to illustrate every distinguishing feature of the organized serial killer, as no one knows the subject better than its originator. However, neither Ressler nor any other agent from the Behavioral Science Unit knows Schaefer as well as I do, because they have never even met him. I have gone much further than that.

A Real Lady Killer

At a high school dance in 1964, right before my eyes, appeared a virtual teen dream - a tall, blond smiling Adonis in a dazzling white jacket that set off his deepwater tan, and a ruffled blue dress shirt that complimented his brilliant blue eyes. Who is that guy? I wondered, as he flirted with me across the proverbial crowded dance floor.

At 18, John Schaefer was a year older than me, and even though he lived nearby, I had never seen him before that night, because he went to the Catholic School. He came to the dance with someone else, and so did I, but he was interested enough to find out my name and then go through the Ft. Lauderdale phone book and call every Stuart or Stewart [*Ms London's maiden name*], until he found me. That was the first time I was pursued by an alleged serial killer, but it was destined not to be the last.

I found Schaefer to be a very well-mannered Catholic boy whose family belonged to the local yacht club. His previous girlfriend had been a debutante and he had learned all the social graces. Besides being tall, blond and handsome, he was bright and sensitive, and he treated me exceptionally well. It wasn't long before he became my first lover.

My parents were glad I had met such a nice boy, and invited him to go along with us on our summer vacation. Out on my grandma's old porch swing, we whiled away the hours with the old ladies who adored him. I remember him patiently holding up his hands for my aunt to wind her knitting yarn and laughing good-naturedly at her jokes, shucking peas and shooting the breeze, good-ole boy style.

After supper we might ramble through the old graveyard, philosophizing about the ancient dead before making love amongst the tombstones. There was nothing abnormal about our youthful sexual affair - my sweetheart was a gentle, sensitive and enthusiastic lover. I will always remember him that way - how well he treated me, how beautiful he was, and how sincerely we loved each other. Many times he held my life in his hands, as he took me into the wilderness of the Everglades, and out on the high seas in his boat. But after a year, as young lovers will, we went our separate ways...and I thought I'd never seen him again. Then in 1972 came the screaming headline "**6 Dead, 28 May Be**" and the ghoulish stories about the smiling cop turned sadistic killer and corpse-loving fiend, hoarding the teeth, jewelry, and ID of his mutilated victims, and writing it all up in feverish prose. Absolutely unbelievable! First, I was appalled that crimes like this could be committed by anyone. Remember, those were the days before we ever heard the term "serial killer", and before Ted Bundy, John Wayne Gacy and Hannibal Lecter so graphically defined it. In the early seventies, the crimes Schaefer was accused of committing were not only unheard of, they were unthinkable.

And then, much more insidiously, it began to soak in... could the same sweet boy I had held in my arms and trusted with my life really be this depraved homicidal maniac whose picture is all over the papers? Frightened by what had become of my baby-faced dream, *I had to wonder: Did I lose*

GERARD JOHN SCHAEFER

my virginity to a real lady-killer?
As shocked as I was by the news, I'd always wondered about my first lover. Gentle and sweet, smiling and polite, John was unfailingly eager to please - yet as I searched my mind for clues to what he had become, I recalled that like many men I have known, he was haunted by violent desires and powerful, ambivalent emotions. I still don't know the whole truth about my first lover, but I can't say I disbelieved the headlines.

I will never forget how he told me of his urge to kill a woman he said was flaunting herself at him. Years later, I confirmed that he apparently did assault her. Even though he didn't kill that one, the way he looked and the words he used when he described his intentions are engraved indelibly in my memory: "I'll take her out to the Everglades and shoot her in the head, and she'll be alligator meat by morning. No body, no crime".

People say all kinds of things, and violent imagery crops up in many everyday conversations. I didn't take him seriously, but frankly, having my friend break down in anguished tears over his homicidal urges was too much for me. After all, I was just a kid, and we girls really do want to have fun. I wasn't afraid of him, but I grew tired of being drafted into the battle with his demons. I was eighteen in 1965 when I left him, turning my back on his tears. He called me a few weeks later to let me know how much I had hurt him, and swore that he would "get me back". I thought I knew what he meant at the time, but later I wondered.

I didn't see or hear from him again, and for many years, I put him as far out of my mind as I could. But as hard as I tried, I could not escape the somber knowledge that while so many of the women he had encountered were dead, I was alive. I found myself scrutinizing the faces of certain blue-eyed strangers, wondering, "Is that him? Is that how he's changed over the years? Is he out of jail already? Has he come looking for me? Is he still mad at me for leaving him?" I'd be on edge until I could determine that the stranger didn't recognize me, because I knew that if it really were him, he'd know me instantly.

A Day at the Beach
It was a blistering hot Saturday in July of 1972, and two teenage girls planned on hitting the beach. The blond, Nancy Trotter, 18, came from Illinois, and the brunette, Paula Sue Wells, 17, known as Sue, came from Texas. They had been vacationing in Stuart, Florida for just two days, and they wanted to catch some rays so they'd have something to show for their

141

trip when they got back home. Sue and Nancy were getting a ride to the beach with the smiling young sheriff's deputy they'd met the day before.

When Nancy and Sue first met Jerry Schaefer, the uniformed cop had been driving his squad car. He told them he'd give them a ride to beach if they'd meet him at the bandshell at 9.30 a.m. the next day. But when he pulled up to the bandshell on Saturday, July 22, he was driving his old Datsun and wearing Bermuda shorts and striped shirt, telling them he had been switched to plainclothes duty that day and was just doing observations. Because he was a cop, they jumped right in his car, never stopping to wonder what he planned on observing.

Marion County Sheriff Richard Crowder was using his day off to mow the lawn, when his wife called him to the phone. It was Deputy Sheriff Jerry Schaefer, and he said it was important. "He said, 'I've done something terrible. You're really going to be mad at me this time,'" Sheriff Crowder told me one day in his office. "I asked him, well, what was it, and he told me he had arrested a couple of girls and had tied them up but they had got away. So I told him to come on in and report to his shift captain, and I got in my car and went out looking for the girls. I found both of them still in handcuffs. One of them was swimming across the river, and the other one was walking along the road. Schaefer came on in and turned himself in. Now, he was convicted on that one, and he went to jail for it, but while he was out on bail, it looked like he got ahold of another couple of girls and this time, he killed them."

The next day Nancy and Sue, covered with bruises, scratches and insect bites, talked about their ordeal. The authenticity of their statements is unchallenged and the immediacy of their experience is best conveyed in the victims' own words as they told State's Investigator Littman about their day at the beach with Schaefer.

Nancy told how it all began. "Well, he started driving towards Jensen beach, and he asked us if we wanted to see an old Spanish fort that was on the river, and we said OK, you know. And so he was driving down, and then he pulled in this dirt road, that's when I started getting worried. He kept going back further and further..."

Sue continued, "I got worried, because he had told us the day before when he picked us up, not to tell anyone, you know, he emphasized it several times, not to tell anyone a policeman was taking us out there. I got worried when he turned down that road, because it seemed awfully suspicious."

Nancy described how Schaefer parked the car at the Spanish fort and they all got out. Schaefer thoughtfully sprayed the girls with insect repellant before escorting them around the fort. "Then we went to get back in the car and, uh, we just sat there, and then he looked at us and he said, 'Why did you girls lie to me yesterday?' And we were shocked. And we said, 'About what?' and he started, 'Well, I checked up on you in Juvenile Court' and he said he had called up there and that we were runaways."

After explaining to Investigator Littman that it wasn't true, Nancy continued, "We both started laughing, you know, runaways, it sounded kind of funny. And when I told him, I said, 'I'm not a runaway, my mother knows where I am and I'm eighteen and it wouldn't matter anyways...'".

She picked up, "Then he asked us if we wanted a free ride home, and we said, 'We're not ready to go home, we want to stay another week.' And he said, 'Well, I'm sorry, but you have to go home anyway. Your parents are worried about you, and they want you to come home, and you're runaways. And if you resist, I'll put you under arrest.' And so we figured, well we don't want to be put under arrest, you know, a free ride home, OK, you know? So then he said, 'Do you have any dope on you? and we said 'No' and he said, 'Get out of the car.'"

The girls described how he made them stand outside the car while he went through Nancy's purse. Then, Sue continued: "He asked me if I had anything on me, and I said I do, then he said, 'Well, what do you wear?' and I told him, and he said, 'Do you wear any underwear?' and I told him no. So he said, 'Well, I can't search you because that's illegal, but there's one thing I can do,' and he got in his car, and that's when he got the handcuffs out."

When he asked Nancy what she was wearing, she told him she had on a bathing suit underneath her clothes. "So he said, 'Well, I'm placing you two under arrest for runaways,' and he handcuffed us behind our backs."

Then Sue described how she told him, "Well, may I laugh? This is really funny,' and he said, 'Sure go ahead and laugh,' so we just started giggling and then he said, 'Y'all think this is a big joke, you just don't know how serious it really is.'" But they were soon to find out.

Schaefer made Nancy and Sue get back in the car, still handcuffed behind their backs. They thought he was going to take them back to the police station, but he told them they were going to sit right there. He asked them numerous questions about the halfway house they'd given as an address, and he wanted them to tell him all they knew about Stuart, with particular emphasis on where they were getting their dope. They told him they'd only been there two days and they didn't have any dope. For 45 minutes, they sat handcuffed in the back seat of Schaefer's dingy Datsun in the sweltering midsummer heat, listening to him rant about dope and related topics.

"And then he started talking about white slavery," said Sue.

"He asked us how we'd like to be sold into white slavery," explained Nancy. "He said it ought to be a nice experience, you could really see the world, go to South America or South Africa and be a white slave... then he said, 'Would you screw me for $150?' and I said, 'No, not for all the money in the world' and he said 'If you were a white slave, you'd be doing it for free.' Then he goes, 'How would you like that, Sue? How would you like that?' So we just quit talking to him."

"Then he started estimating how much he could get for us", said Nancy. "And he started asking about our parents, if they knew where we were, and did we think they'd put up a ransom for us."

"And I told him my parents would try to scrape up the money, I mean, they're not that well-off, but..." Sue hesitated, then continued, "And then he started in about the while slavery again, and he kept saying he had a friend he could sell white girls to."

Then Nancy Trotter mentioned the same theory Schaefer had described to me seven years before. Even the wording of her statement was similar. "He was telling us about how people disappeared, and there's no crime without a victim, it's just a missing person when they don't have a body." Simple as that. "No body, no crime." All these years, it seems the same sinister refrain had been running through his mind. I wonder how many other women have heard Schaefer recite his grim motto, and what must have happened to them.

Paula Sue Wells was almost certainly still in shock, and her memory had already begun the healing process of suppressing parts of her ordeal, but as she and Nancy relived it for Investigator Littman, the worst parts began to come back. "Yes, now I remember. I hadn't thought about it till now, but he said he'd kill us and bury us in a hole real deep and cover us up and nobody would ever find us."

"And all we'd be was a missing person," said Nancy. "I thought all this was to scare us into telling who had the dope in the city, but we were both confused. We couldn't see what it was all for."

But the confusing chat in the car was drawing to a close. It was time for action now.

A Good Scare

"He had us get out of the car," Nancy said. "We were still handcuffed, and he got my blanket and made us go over in the field."

Sue continued, "He went to his car and got the key to his trunk, you know, and I saw everything then. He had a bunch of ropes and rags and stuff to tie us up with, and he said, 'We're going to go out in back here in the bushes, and y'all don't run away.' and, 'Can I trust you to stay here while I go get my friend?'"

"Yes, and he wanted us not to scream, too" interjected Nancy.

"So then he took us back in the bushes and laid the blanket down, and gagged both of us, and he told me to lay down on the blanket, but I didn't lay down. I just stood there. And then he tied my legs up and said he was going to separate us and tie us up in different places. And he told me not to try to get away because if I did he would kill me, he'd catch up with me and kill me. And then he told me not to scream, because he said if I screamed, he'd come back and wrap the gag around me so tight I would shit in my pants."

There you have it. Sue had mentioned Schaefer's signature. His fantasies consistently revolve around the moment when the female victim is so terrified she defecates... if she doesn't do it before her death, then hopefully she can be made to do it in the course of being killed. The whole subject holds an endless fascination for him to this day, and there was bound to be some reference to it in any crime he committed. In serial killer parlance, this "signature" would be the highlight of Schaefer's "ritual", since its sole purpose is his own personal gratification, rather than carrying the pragmatic focus of the highly-organized "M.O." he used, when qualifying his potential victims beforehand and carefully disposing of their corpses afterwards.

Sue went on to describe how Schaefer had gagged and bound her hand and foot as she stood there handcuffed in the trees.

Meanwhile, Nancy had been standing there waiting, gagged and cuffed. "Then he took me over to the river and had me stand up, and he tied my feet together with the rope, and then he redid my gag, cause it was falling off. And he had me stand on the root of a tree and he made a noose around my neck, put a rope around my neck, and hung it over a branch of the tree, and he tied the other end down onto a branch, a stub that was sticking out. Then he started, like you know, a scene. Like, please don't do it here, there's too many mosquitoes, and I was crying and he didn't do anything. And then he started, he pinched me, you know. And I got real disgusted, and I said 'Don't' and he said, 'I could just take your pants off right here' and he started..."

"Where was he pinching you?" asked Littman.

"On the butt" Nancy replied. "And then he started to go for my zipper, but I turned around. And he just laughed, and he didn't do anything. And I started to fall off this root. If I fell off this roof I would have hung. I started falling off and choking, and he just, he pushed me back up and sat me on there, and he warned me not to scream. And then he left me."

Nancy described how she chewed the noose around her neck, then crawled up the root and untied the rope from the stub. After that, she had to do a backbend to untie her legs, as she was still handcuffed, but she did manage to get them undone and escape.

Meanwhile, Sue had maneuvred her way out of the ropes restraining her legs, but she still had the gag in her mouth when Schaefer came back. "He said, 'I'm going to tie you up to a tree now, so that if you try to get loose, you'll hang yourself.'" Then Schaefer helped her to her feet, and picked up the blanket. Carrying a long rope and the blanket he set off for the river. "I couldn't walk very fast cause of the stickers, and he kept saying, 'Hurry up, hurry up!' and I kept saying, 'Well, I have stickers in my feet, wait and let me try to get them out.'"

Apparently Schaefer couldn't wait, because he picked Sue up and threw her over his shoulder, carrying her to a tree, where he trussed her up much like he had Nancy, except this time it wasn't a root she stood on, it was a slope. "He tied my legs up, then he ran a rope up from behind, from my ankles up, and tied it to the handcuffs. And then I had to spit the gag out, and he said 'How did you do that?' And he put it on real tight, and I felt like I was going to black out. So I said 'Loosen it, it's hurting me,' so he loosened it up a little, and he tied me to the tree and all, and then he said, 'Do you have VD?' And I said, 'No' because I was afraid. I really thought he was going to sell us, and I was afraid if I told him I had VD, he wouldn't, and he'd have no use for me, so he'd kill me... Then he picked up my shirt and looked down my pants and he just laughed. Then he said, 'Don't scream, and don't try to run away cause I'm not going to be very far down the road, I'm just going down the road to meet that man that's going to buy you,' and I said, 'Why do you want to sell us?' and he said, 'For the money, I'd do anything for money,' and I said, 'Well, that's wrong,' you know. And I was going to talk to him, that's before he gagged me, when I was trying to talk to him. He said,

'Don't lecture me, sweetheart. I didn't bring you here for a lecture.' Then after that, he tied me up, and before he left he said, 'Don't try to run away,' and then he walked off, and I started getting loose. And I found Nancy walking down the road..."

Nancy cut in, "Yes, I had gotten loose, and..."

"He didn't come back to check on you then?" Littman asked Nancy.

"No," she explained, "I went up on back of that Spanish fort and I saw his car still there. So I ran back by the river and I saw Sue in the trees, and she was calling, 'Nancy, Nancy' but I thought he was there making her call me, I thought he saw I was gone. So I didn't say anything. I started going faster down by the river, and it sounded like someone was following me, so I started running, and I took upon land, and hid in this overgrowth for about a half an hour...I got eaten alive by mosquitoes..."

Nancy told of struggling through the underbrush and the woods, and then picking her way along the river until she saw a road on the other side. Handcuffed, she managed to swim across the river to the road, where Sheriff Crowder picked her up.

"After I saw Nancy, I was afraid to hell for her again," said Sue, "because I was afraid he had just left a couple of minutes ago, and I still had the noose on my neck and part of the rope on my feet." After she got free from the ropes, she ran through the woods and the river, still gagged and handcuffed, her arms bound with a scarf. "I found a dirt road, and I ran down it and I was crying, and this man stopped in a pick-up truck and then the policeman came".

Robert Ressler analyzes Schaefer's crime: "Before going further with the story, let me point out the attributes of the organized offender that are present so far in the narrative. The abductor personalized the victims by talking with them, used his own vehicle, and conned the women into his car by means of his verbal skills. He brought his own threatening weapon to the scene and took it away with him, had a rape kit, and was plainly planning to complete sexual acts with the women prior to torture and murder. After the murder, he was going to hide and dispose of the bodies. He displayed mobility and adaptive behavior during the crime when he left the women tied up and went to pay attention to some other aspect of his life, telling them that he would return and finish them off later."

Schaefer avoids discussing this potentially lethal assault case, because he dislikes the inevitable conclusion that the similarities between the double assault and the double murder are both numerous and significant. Still, when pressed by a reporter in 1991, his eyes sparked for the camera as he smirked, "It was an emotional intimidation type of a thing," and then he laughed out loud, "Oh, it gave them a good scare, no doubt about that."

Physically painful torture wasn't necessary to gratify his sadistic urges on this occasion. Just from knowing the fear these girls suffered, he derived a certain measure of the desperately twisted feeling of sexualized power he could experience no other way. Of course, with Schaefer, it goes without saying that if those two girls hadn't escaped, the psychological terrorism might well have escalated up to and beyond the death of the victims.

In *Beyond Killer Fiction*, Schaefer persuasively describes the pleasure his fictional persona derives from experiments in terror like these:

"My own preference was in the preliminaries, and the increasing terror generated by the woman's awareness that she was in the hands of a homicidal maniac. I was entranced by the various ploys that the captive women would use in order to save their lives. Most of them would try something, and I made it a game to see how long it would be before the victim would request to be killed.

"This entertainment varied from one victim to another, and it might take the form of physical or psychological torture. If and when the lady decided to say she'd had enough, I was quite willing to put her out of her misery...if she asked nicely.

"This sort of experiment is perfect for a person of sadistic tendencies, since we sadists do not consider our victims to be genuinely human. Ted never thought of the women he killed as persons, but only as objects. I did the same and found it an excellent way to avoid any human feeling for them. I guess one would consider that a sociopathic quality, but what the hell, we all have our faults, and I am no different than anyone else in that respect."

Doing Doubles

These days, Schaefer's sweating it out in the big house, with a parole date of 2016. He's twenty years into double life terms for killing two teenage girls, the blonde Susan Place and the brunette Georgia Jessup, who were chopped into pieces and buried some time between July, when Trotter and Wells were assaulted, and January 1973, when Schaefer finally went to jail for that assault.

Schaefer continues the hypothetical speculations of his fictional persona, as he compares his crimes, of which he claims innocence in real life, to those of his arch-rival, Ted Bundy:

"Ted was, of course, a tyro when he nabbed Ott and Naslund; when I nabbed Jessup and Place I had been in the ghoul game for almost ten years, so I knew what to expect from these young juicy creatures at the end. By then I was into doing double murders and an occasional triple when the opportunity arose, whereas Ted at the same point of time was only able to handle singles. He was playing at copycat and doing a poor job of it at that.

"Doing doubles is far more difficult that doing singles, but on the other hand, it also puts one in a position to have twice as much fun. There can be some lively discussions about which of the victims will get to be killed first. When you have a pair of lively teenaged bimbolinas bound hand and foot and ready for a session with the skinning knife, neither one of the little devils wants to be the one to go first. And they don't mind telling you quickly why their best friend should be the one to die.

"Giving the victim false hope is always fun. For instance, say you have the Jessup and Place girls and you decided that one will live and one will die. But which will be the lucky one? Ask them and they will tell you in great graphic detail why each is the best of the litter for you. Sex? You cannot imagine how companionable such a little teenaged vixen can be until you have one at your complete mercy. My, how they do ask for the privilege of doing whatever might please your amorous interests. Anything at all they are agreeable to.

"Take the Place girl, Susan. She was a heroin addict and was without any means of legitimate income. How do you think the girl earned the money to support her narcotics habit? Yes, with her sex; so she was quite knowledgeable and skilled for a young lady of 17. The other bimbo, Crystal as she liked to call herself, was a veteran of the beachfront hippie pads and skilled in her own right as well. I ask you, what does a fella do when confronted by so much agreeable young flesh? One does the best that one can and asks questions that would make a Tangier whore blush."

Not a Serial Killer

Though his nineteen appeals have been consistently dismissed or rejected, still Schaefer continues relentlessly pushing his case through the courts - insisting that he did not get a fair trial, that he's guilty of nothing more than writing realistic fiction, and that he's never been linked to the scene of any murders anywhere - not even the two he was convicted of. His Writ of Certiorari is before the US Supreme Court now, and if they, too, dismiss his plea for a new trial, that will finally mean the end of the appeals process for him. I expect he will continue developing his writing skills within his current twin specialities; nuisance lawsuits and terroristic threats.

I won't go into Schaefer's frame-up story here; he can tell that one on his own time. Suffice to say, it has all the elements. It's the perfect picture of an innocent man victimized by corrupt public officials in a convoluted plot to frame him for heinous crimes he knew nothing about. Makes a lot of sense, if you follow his logic. Except that kind of logic only makes sense as yet another example for the textbooks.

Sure, it's a plausible story. If you ignore his obsession with sexualized violent fantasies featuring himself as the homicidal maniac. And his pursuit of the perverse status his infamous crimes convey. Whether or not they were ever actually committed anywhere but in the twisted theater of his own mind, still he trades on his reputation as "a real good ticket to the society of fiends."

And it's easy to sympathize with his plight. Except for the way he continues to show the same disregard for the rights of others that got him locked up in the first place. It becomes much harder to maintain a posture of Christ-like tolerance when the rights he ignores are your own.

His statements are perfectly reasonable and coherent. It's only when you put them all together that the whole pattern emerges of a personality at war within itself: simultaneously reveling in and denying his crimes, seeking and fleeing from their infamy. He runs the gamut from gleeful boasts of one-upping Ted Bundy to deadpan denials: "I've never killed anyone, period." It's a classic case, right down the line, to this very day.

As someone in a unique position, with knowledge no one else has, I can only say that I have learned much more than I ever wanted to know about my first lover - but after giving due consideration to all of his conflicting statements, I do not call Schaefer a serial killer. Even though he manages to display enough characteristics to justify his appearance in most catalogues of the serial killer genre, still he is not technically in the Ted Bundy league. It doesn't really matter whether the experts categorize Schaefer's killings as serial or not; such anecdotal commentary is meaningless in a criminal court, and much more than that is required to convict someone of murder. The correct categorization of Schaefer's criminal career is understandably of interest only to him. But his feelings are so easily hurt, and while it most often pleases him to be known as "The Greatest Mass Murderer of Women This Century", at other times it pains him. And I'd hate to catch him on a bad day.

GERARD JOHN SCHAEFER

In all fairness, I must allow that I have no first-hand knowledge placing him at the scene of any murders. There were many questionable aspects of his 1973 trial. I must agree with Schaefer that regardless of what he might have done, he still has a right to a fair trial, and I sincerely hope he gets one. If he does, I am quite certain the truth will come out.

Otherwise, his record speaks for itself. It's not so much the two assaults and two murders he is convicted of, it's the personal things that were found amongst his possessions: the jewelry, the birth certificates and driver's licenses, and even one gold tooth, that were traced to a string of dead and missing girls. And then there are "the unnamed ones" - women who came to Florida from everywhere, and just vanished, whose bodies will never be found. The State doesn't have enough evidence to bring charges on all these unsolved cases, but twenty years later, their ghosts still linger around Schaefer's dungeon door. I've heard their voices, and you can hear them too. The voices of his victims ring through his prose even as they ring through his mind - the known ones, the unknown ones, the made-up ones, and the ones that got away. Like me - I know he hears my voice, and it's not singing his songs. Not any more.

As I sat and talked with Schaefer in prison during a series of personal visits in 1989 and 1990, I found he resembled no one so much as John D. MacDonald, the Florida novelist who wrote so hard but looked so soft. He no longer has those movie-star good looks that dazzled me when I first saw him. He's a nebbish: portly, pale and balding, and half-blind without his specs. He looks no more like a killer than he looks like a cop. Maybe a nearsighted, deskbound lawclerk. I remember when Detective Kelly, a veteran homicide cop out of Miami, told me he found Schaefer "intimidating." I got a good laugh out of that one.

I had always known Schaefer to be well-spoken and pleasant, funny and smart, a cultivated man with many fine qualities. And incongruous as it may seem, he still has those qualities, along with a certain class consciousness, always setting himself a cut above his neighbors, whom he calls "nothing but a bunch of ignorant niggers and white trash." But in addition to the refinement he has retained from his background, he's also become a convict, a career criminal in his own eyes.

Even though his demeanor is perfectly civilized, still at times he can be quite chilling. It's not the man himself, as his physical presence is utterly non-threatening. It's the very idea of the shadowy entity lurking out of sight, hidden by the superficial appearance of this nice, normal-looking guy, reminding me of what Hannah Arendt, the Israeli historian, called "the banality of evil." It's not what he's doing, it's what he's thinking that keeps you wary as any snake-charmer. A self-acknowledged con man and manipulator, he works with words, creating a constantly changing wall of confusion, making every imaginable outrageous statement, and contradicting himself all the while. I had the feeling he was trying to keep me perpetually off balance, and like a paralyzed puppeteer, to manipulate me into doing his will.

In studying him like a wild beast in his cage, I've caught more than a glimpse or two of his hidden, dark side. I've seen it in his threats and his cruelty, his self-deception and his self-destruction. Then there's the ambiguity of his all-purpose smile. I've learned how that cheery facade covers a sinkhole of pain, and holds back a cannonade of hate. And I've come to understand what he calls the "puritanical rage" he feels when a woman shakes her naked assets in his face.

Killer Fiction

The work that appears in *Knockin' on Joe* began when I addressed a letter to Schaefer on February 8, 1989 in his maximum security cell in Florida State Prison, asking if he remembered me. "How could I *NOT* remember you?" he replied. "A former great love of my life, but then I always burn with a blue flame when it's a romance. Did burn. Sure ain't no romance to be had in here."

I told him I was a writer now, and asked if he'd like to work on a book about his life with me. "I've been approached by about a dozen writers; a few of them I've even talked contract with, but in the end I've never concluded a deal. My position is that any book about my case or life must be truthful and accurate as to facts, and none of this "police sources suspect" bullshit. In plain words - no hocus pocus." He continued, "The story about my case has not been done. It's virgin territory, a virtual terra incognita." And he allowed, "Naturally, I'm favorably disposed toward someone who has known me intimately."

I wanted to know if he was still mad at me for breaking up with him. As Neil Sedaka used to croon, *Breaking Up is Hard to Do,* and I have some painful emotional memories about us, but nothing you'd classify as hostile. He mentioned the names of a few people we knew from high school, and then concluded, "Social stuff can go on the back burner. You want to write a book and I'm uncommitted as yet, so to get things going in the right direction, sit down and give me your pitch on exactly what you have in mind." My proposal persuaded him I was up to the job, and thus the project began.

To me the most intriguing aspect of Schaefer's case was that in 1972, writings seized from a closet in his mother's house were introduced as evidence and used to convict him of murder. While it was never claimed that these fragmentary notes actually described the crimes in question, they were introduced into evidence on the legal principle of *mens rea*, or the guilty mind. In other words, they portray his murderous intent with chilling accuracy. Indeed, one of the jurors stated flatly that it was these closet fantasies that persuaded him to convict Schaefer for murder.

I asked Schaefer, "Do you still write those nasty stories?" In reply, he began firing off a series of searing scenarios of sexual homicide that went so far over the top, I didn't know quite what to make of them. For a while, I was simply reeling.

Then I received his account of shoptalk with Ted Bundy, describing how Ted has seen the news stories about Schaefer and recognized his face from the pictures in detective magazines. After describing a discussion of techniques and preferences, Schaefer wrote that Bundy "couldn't get enough of conversation like that. It was like he felt I knew for sure there was a real boring side of Deathwork, and it wasn't all raging sexual release, as the media likes to portray it."

"That's *IT*!" I literally jumped up and raced to my office, without even finishing the letter. I didn't know what else he was going to write, but from that moment on, I knew I had to publish it. That was the first time I felt the dread publisher's plague... an irresistible urge to share a story with the world... An intoxicating experience that I came to indulge rather frequently over the next few years.

I critiqued, edited and typeset Schaefer's stories, sending them back for his approval. It was a mutually creative process; seeing his work professionally laid out gave him more pride and confidence, and having his work so attentively studied and presented made him flex his writing muscles that much more. More than once, a story that started out rather skeletal, so to speak, was brought to life in a painstaking rewrite.

So between March and July of 1989, Schaefer sent to me the stories included in the first two sections of *Killer Fiction* (some of which were the original *"Starke Stories"*). Selections from the original manuscripts of the stories and drawings used as evidence in his 1973 murder trial were included in the section entitled *"Actual Fantasies"*.

This project was the beginning of an adventure I could never have foreseen: a long, strange journey into some of the darkest criminal minds of modern times. Although I now have an impressive collection of fiction, non-fiction, interviews and artwork from high-profile criminal figures all across the United States, I must say that publishing this one limited edition book affected me in a way nothing else could; it was what you might call my baptism of fire.

"I'm not writing non-fiction. It's killer fiction: a new genre, where the writer takes violence as an artistic medium and, instead of glorifying it, makes the Reader see it as the cruel and horrid act it is in reality. I don't represent violence as good or bad, merely as it is. I let the Reader conclude that violence is a socially negative force, not to be revelled in".

The Edge that Cuts

This horror-filled excursion into the domain of the sexual psychopath can easily be taken for a mere superficial thrill, rather than the painstaking attempt of an accused serial killer to expose exactly how his mind works. Far from provoking the admiration and delight of its readers, *Killer Fiction* more often provoked shock and revulsion, along with a certain grim fascination. That was the whole idea.

The difference between *Killer Fiction* and its closest approximation, *American Psycho*, is that the glossy Madison Avenue version is nothing but synthesized exploitation, word-processed in a penthouse by a wannabe wunderkind of the literati... while *Killer Fiction* was the real thing, a lethal weapon forged in the hellfires of the heart of a convicted madman with a number instead of a name, and a sentence instead of a life.

But the *"Starke Stories"* portion of *Killer Fiction* goes beyond the fantasies accompanying the crime itself, and brings to life the supercharged reality of its aftermath, punishment in a maximum security prison... giving us a close-up inside look at the atrocities committed in the name of Justice by the State. Most of the objections to *Killer Fiction* voiced by the State referred to it as "pornography", thus apparently putting the onus of their disapproval on the sexually explicit portions of the text. However, since *Playboy, Penthouse*, and every other X-rated magazine is allowed into the prison, it is more likely that the sordid descriptions of the prison itself were what got their shorts in a wad. I could understand that. I got kind of worked up over them myself.

I had been calmly editing these hair-raising narratives for about three months when Schaefer finally threw me. He sent me a story that seemed calculated to offend every possible sensibility. I hadn't reacted when he wrote of slicing and dicing many a woman just like me, of degrading her corpse and her memory; I'd managed to maintain my equanimity when he waxed anti-Semitic, anti-Catholic, and anti-gay; but I had taken him to task over being a racist. Having fought racism for years, I have many black friends, and adamantly object to his racist tirades. So he send me this story that absolutely radiates hatred, perversion and racism. He called it *Nigger Jack*, and I hated it.

When I first read it, I scribbled, "This is *DISGUSTING!*" on his manuscript, wadded it up, and sent it back to him. Schaefer was thrilled.

"I was *SO PLEASED* with your reaction to *Nigger Jack.* Honestly, I never thought I'd be able to gag the Media Queen! If I can make someone as jaded as yourself squirm with distaste and revulsion, there is yet hope for me as a horror writer... move over, Clive Barker! I may retire on that effort. I still think the idea of enclosing a barf bag with the book would be a boon... I've never been bland, indifferent, or predictable. I *ALWAYS* managed to generate a reaction... of course it's not always a favorable reaction. But I do not write these stories to degrade the reader. I'd like to strike a blow against Capital Punishment by showing how it degrades all the parties involved, and thus Society as a whole. The validity of the scene goes to the basic truth of the event: *DO* women pop when electrocuted? *(YES)* Now we are dealing with *FACT* - a fact people would rather not be confronted with. I believe it has a greater impact on the reader to present such a matter as a visual so that a mental picture is formed of what is being done by the representatives of the People. Who are the People? The People is *YOU*, Kiddo. All the college cuties out in the field hopping up and down with BURN TED signs never once thinking they could end up on the same griddle, just like Andrea. To give the College Cutie the benefit of the doubt, let's say she's acting in ignorance of what *REALLY* occurs. *Nigger Jack* will let her know in graphic sequence what she condones but does not see. It is a slap across the face of pro-death penalty society. Even the jaded Media Queen is taken aback! *GOOD.* Because if it can get *YOU* upset, and in upsetting you causes you to *THINK*, then imagine what it can do to the ladies of the Ft. Pierce Bridge Club, most of whom vote for pro-CP candidates. The hoi polloi have always loved a good execution - so long as they read the socially acceptable version in the paper. In *Nigger Jack*, people will get a little different slant on it, and I think that's a good thing. I do want to make the point here that gratuitous grossness is not intended, but I *DO* strive to offend your social consciousness to the point where you say, "I refuse to allow this to be done in my name, I am the People!"

As I caught myself over-reacting, I wondered how I could be so disturbed. After all, I kept telling myself, it's only a story. But I found these particular stories almost palpably assaultive. Schaefer seems to relish the shock waves his writing can create, and the more negative the reaction, the better it pleases him. It's almost as if, upon being physically restrained in prison, he has merely found a more psychological, subtle way to perpetrate the same type of sadistic acts that he can no longer physically perform.

Eventually I had to admit that Schaefer was right - if it could upset even me... there had to be some kind of art to it. It's not a matter of it being pleasant or uplifting. This stuff doesn't come from the aesthetic of loveliness - this is from the aesthetic of ugliness. It succeeds as art, not in spite of its hideous impact, but precisely because of it. It's the power of the forbidden, the repressed, evoking the dismay that we feel as the gritty texture of life continues to shred the fabric of our enchanted dreams in this post-modern, apocalyptic age. This not the *so-called* cutting edge, it's the edge that really cuts.

I began to sense that any story that could make its own editor react so powerfully must have some sort of significance... and that made it all the more reason to carry on, continue the work, and publish in. In 1991, shortly after Loompanics ran the entire story in their Catalogue [*having 5000 copies confiscated at the Canadian border for their pains*], Schaefer wrote, "I had a fan letter saying **Nigger Jack** was 'a hilarious and entertaining prison insider story.' I had never seen it as pure comedy. The fans all want *MORE*. Are they crazy or what?"

And so I set aside my own personal distaste for the ugliness of the work, and focused on presenting it in all its twisted glory for exactly what it is.

Pornographic Filth

In 1989, prison guards called **Killer Fiction** "pornographic filth," confiscating it from Schaefer, and claiming it was "unsuitable for a prisoner," only returning it after verifying with the attorney general that Schaefer's fiction did pay an integral part in an appeal he had before the court. By virtue of its introduction into the public record by the State of Florida, in theory Schaefer's possession of **Killer Fiction** is protected as a testamentary document. However, he is still not allowed to have it in prison, even though that's where he wrote it. He has only held the bound volume in his hands once. In September of 1990, while Schaefer was temporarily housed in a less-restrictive institution, two copies were allowed in for autographs by sympathetic prison guards, one of whom admitted to being a fan. (One of these exceedingly rare book belongs to a reporter; the other belongs to me.)

Later, Schaefer suffered renewed attacks by the Florida Department of Corrections. Starting in March of 1991, mail between him and Media Queen was confiscated and destroyed, and he was sentenced to 30 days in "The Hole" for "conspiracy to conduct a business." The incriminating evidence consisted of a letter describing the continuing adventures of Detective Dan Kelly, Rogue Cop. The Disciplinary Report States, "At 9.30 a.m. on May 16, 1991... I opened a letter in front of Inmate Schaefer and discovered the envelope contained two letters discussing new stories to be written and their intended characters and plot. The letter and contents were turned over to Institutional Inspector Brian Gross and this report was written."

On April 4, 1991, Inspector Gross had warned Schaefer, "It is overtly apparent that these documents are part of an agreement with Media Queen, although they may also be part of a lawsuit. Sending these documents back and forth through the mail to Media Queen is considered a business transaction and you will not be allowed to continue doing so while incarcerated. You have already received a written order to cease conducting business through the mail, and any further attempt may result in disciplinary action."

While no money was ever received by Inmate Schaefer for **Killer Fiction**, this did not deter the prison from interpreting his writing as a business activity, according to their singularly curious definition. When Schaefer filed a grievance regarding the sanctions placed upon him, Gross replied, "You have no authorization from the Department and for this facility to engage in the act of having books, texts, novels, short stories, and/or any other form of printed information, be it fiction or non-fiction, printed for you. Engaging in a business constitutes an agreement between parties for the exchange of real properties, thoughts and/or ideas, or other remunerations, to include recognition and notoriety."

Although the investigator stated that Media Queen was conducting a business with Inmate Schaefer, he maintained that there was no such entity... even though I had previously furnished the Warden's office with copies of my corporate papers. The prison's response to Schaefer's Request for Administrative Appeal still managed to conclude, "There is no Official Record of any media business or enterprise by the name of MEDIA QUEEN in Atlanta, Georgia." I love it! Schaefer stands convicted of exchanging ideas for recognition with an entity that does not exist! If it weren't so serious, it would almost be funny. I must admit I'm not sorry that the investigator and the Warden both subsequently lost their jobs after the state investigated them.

Books Won't Burn

Censorship by the ad hoc Prison Guard Literary Guild is not the only form of repression that has been encountered by *Killer Fiction*. De facto censorship of the marketplace determines what works achieve wide distribution. Publishing, after all, is not an art... it's an expensive, high-risk business. Protests, boycotts and lawsuits cost money. What attracts the few repels the many, and the weight of the numbers rule. This dynamic tends to squeeze out those who publish alarming or disturbing work, and makes this kind of material extremely hard to come by.

Marketplace censorship exerts economic pressure, but that's fair play in the free market of ideas. The dangerous form of censorship comes from those who would give the power to decide what may be read to any government agent.

Censoring a painfully realistic work of art is like killing the wicked messenger, or taking dope so you won't feel the pain of your foot in the fire. That is information the body desperately needs so that it can yank the leg out of the fire, before the heart and soul are lost too. These voices are our early-warning system. If we can bear to listen to their pain and outrage, perhaps it will in some unforeseen way modify the choices we make as we create our lives.

Works like *"Starke Stories"** are like vivid, disturbing dreams that carry vital information from our unconscious to our conscious, and just as with our dreams, these urgent messages from the underbelly of our society are informing us of things that we might prefer not to face, but really need to be aware of for our own survival. And just as my critics claim it is dangerous to publish this unique work, I say it is just as dangerous to allow it to be repressed.

As Alfred Whitney Griswold says, "Books won't stay banned. They

*Footnote: *Killer Fiction*, a limited edition anthology, is now out of print - *Starke Stories*, its most important and disturbing section, is preserved here.

won't burn. Ideas won't go to jail."

The End

It started because I loved the young Schaefer, but that should be no surprise. I only knew part of him, and that proverbial mask of sanity can be quite charming, while it lasts. But eventually all that talk about wanting to kill turned me off, and I left without looking back. For the next seven years, I never thought about my first lover... until the headlines about the murders forced me to re-evaluate my impressions of him. I wished the whole thing would just go away. But, of course, our past is a pattern etched into the fabric of the present, and woven into the future. And as it once ended long ago, so it was bound to end again.

During the next seventeen years, I tried to avoid the uneasy memories of my extended close encounter with Ressler's archetypal serial killer. It was as if a repellant, noxious cloud obscured his image in my mind. But once I endeavored to resolve my own unanswered questions, to overcome my fear and confront the reality of the man himself, I found he was simultaneously less powerful than I had feared and more complex than I could have imagined.

I found myself having more than one relationship with him at a time, a curious experience to be sure. I noticed that we had a *multiple interface -* an involuntary adaptive response that develops in a relationship with someone with multiple personalities.

There were so many different facets to what went on between us. There was love, of course, but not the romantic kind. This time around, it was the kind of compassionate love you might have for a brother who has been disfigured by some terrible disease, and even though he no longer resembles his true self, he's still your brother.

Whether Schaefer's criminal career only took place in his own overheated imagination, or whether he really did take the lives of as many helpless victims as he boasts, still it was fascinating to work with him long enough and closely enough to take a few snapshots of his thinking. Schaefer set out to take me on a hair-raising trip into the mind of a homicidal maniac, and by mixing fact with fiction, that's just what he did. It wasn't exactly a pleasure cruise, but I wasn't bored. *It was always something.*

Obviously, there was fear. There was also anger. And disgust. There was frustration. Manipulation. And counter-manipulation in turn. But we had a lot of fun too. And there were plenty of laughs. He has a wicked sense of humor, he's well-read, and he can write some real hot stuff. He had a lot to teach me and for a few years, I was there to learn.

There was a certain professional dimension, but because we had been so intimately involved in years past, our relationship was also intensely personal. I teased, I scolded. He blustered, he sulked. On Monday I stalked him like a media-hungry reporter, and on Tuesday I babied him like a mother. I even tried to protect him from himself. He'd come up with bright ideas that were bound to get him in trouble, and I'd try to stop him. When he misbehaved, instead of reporting it to the authorities, I asked his mom to reason with her son. Through it all, we did get a lot of work done, and produced some significant material, much of it included here. It wasn't all that bad. I have loved Schaefer, hated him, laughed with him and cried with him.

I grew accustomed to being offended by the depravity he revealed in his letters and interviews, but I was *concerned* when he began to issue death threats. Though it's always disconcerting to receive threats from convicted killers, still I attempted to negotiate with Schaefer, even as he escalated his misbegotten attempts to manipulate me to work for his release.

With his lurid boats of rape, sodomy, torture, murder, even necrophilia ... and his manifest fury at every living being in the world, especially his arch-enemy, himself ... somehow I had managed to tolerate his noxious presence and withhold judgment long enough to maintain my research into his way of thinking. But when it comes to threatening my child, let me make this clear: that's it, the show's *over...*

STARKE STORIES
by G. J. Schaefer

NEWCOCK

Newcock... That's what we call them. Brand spanking new and fresh off the prison bus. The first timers entering the prison system. They come alone into our world, as terrified and vulnerable as a babe spewed from the safety and comfort of his mama's womb. Young boys graduated from the juvenile justice system into the Bigtime. They've heard all the stories about the gang rapes, the cell burnings, the stabbings, beatings and mindless brutality of the guards. Every motherfucking swinging dick on that bus is shitassed scared and trembling in his chains that he's gonna be on the receiving end of one of those horror tales - and many of them will be. The name of the game, Baby, is Survival. The boys are about to be given a special education in the finer points of "Corrections", compliments of the State of Florida. It's a sink or swim program, and they won't be writing home to Mommy about it-or to anyone else. I'm an Oldcock. A survivor. I know.

When the County Sheriff's van rolls through the cold stainless steel garage doors at the Lake Butler Receiving & Medical Facility and the trembling load of human meat in back hears the gates slam down like a clarion of doom, they know they've entered the proverbial Belly of the Beast. They've entered a separate reality and are at the mercy of a System that knows no mercy.

The introduction to that System is a crude, degrading experience that brutally strips a man of any vestiges of human dignity that the Criminal Justice System may have inadvertently left intact. The new environment is entirely hostile, devoid of love, concern and compassion. There is no friend to turn to for support. Each man walks the path alone in these social rites of passage the politicians refer to as "Corrections".

The Newcock comes out of the back of that van in a cloud of uncertainty, dragging his chains, stumbling in his shackles. Shining steel belly chain, ankle shackles that cut the flesh if he makes a wrong step. Take it low, Newcock.

First hour. Listen to the comments: Pretty boys! Nice ass on that one! Hey Blondie, you like black cock? You need a Daddy? Coming to you tonight, Sunshine. Grease that doughnut and have it ready for me!

The brown uniformed guards, or shiteaters, as we call them, line the boys up. The transport deputies begin to unlock the chains. The line of felons grim, like wraiths in a scenario from *Dante's Inferno*, or a sketch right out of Breughel's *Hell*. These slabs of meat are now Inmates but in the twisted world of prison parlance they are yet to gain the status of Convicts. You don't become a Convict until you've paid your dues in blood and guts. Plenty of this new bunch won't make it, and nary a one of them will ever be the same again.

The first thing we do is watch them get naked. The calloused uniformed shiteater tells them "Strip!" There is no alternative. Off come the rags. The street clothes are tossed into a box. Wanna send them home? Pay the postage, otherwise the duds are trucked out to the Goodwill, the Salvation Army, or even a Chain Gang Guard's closet.

Pay's low. Union County is the poorest in Florida. Newcock won't be needing those fancy threads, that warm coat. No more. Naked men stand in line, rows or them, ten to a row, ten rows deep. They shiver in the stinging chill of a North Florida morning. They wait their turn, dulled by humiliation, as nervous as beasts in an abattoir slaughter chute.

The room is an institutional yellow: puke yellow, babyshit yellow. The area reeks from years of the accumulated dripping sweat and body odor of tens of thousands of prisoners, ineffectively masked with the pine scent of institutional cleansers. The place smells like a public toilet, from the waste of society flowing down the stinking corridors into the septic tank of the prison system.

Here in the prison sewer, the Newcock sheds his past, his identity as a free citizen of value; he becomes shit on the heel of the taxpaying public and is treated in accordance with his new status. The Newcock is a chattel of the State. At best he might keep his shoes, his watch, a wedding ring. Little else. The power of the State is absolute. The name of God is   and the shiteaters do his bidding, lick his bureaucratic boots and suck his ass. Truth is written in Policy and Procedure Memorandums and enforced with mace and clubs.

"Bend over and spread that ass! Show me that doughnut boy! Now cough!" That's what the Sergeant with the beer belly says. He has a blue coated medical orderly at his side and they walk down the row of nude men extending their invitation to show your asshole. What sort of human being takes a paycheck for peering at 500 assholes a day? Is it any wonder they are called Pigs? They suck up the monetary slop from the State trough, too lazy or uneducated to do honest labor. The System hires the dregs of the community to work in the sewers. At some prison the yearly turnover is 90%. Not every man or woman in brown is a human maggot, but too many are. They wallow in the opportunity to wield limitless power to degrade, beat and even kill the people in their care.

The fat shiteating worm and his partner are looking for some indication that the Newcock has secreted something up his anus. Looking for that little ring of grease around the hole. "Ring around the collar" they call it. Could be cash up there, more likely drugs. It's a common practice, the only effective way to beat the strip search and the pig knows it.

He's seen countless assholes. It's his duty as an agent of the State of Florida. He wears a uniform and calls himself a *Correctional Officer* to assuage his own self-contempt, knowing what he is and loathing himself for it: shiteater. An asshole examining assholes. He ain't fooling nobody, not even himself and the hate comes off him in waves like heat from a warm stove. Give him a reason, any little comment or sign of your true feelings will do, and he'll order his "medical orderly" partner to perform a "finger wave".

With a hundred pairs of eyes watching, the victim of this "Official's" bilious nature will have his anus violated by the medical representative of the State. Not a single scrap of dignity is awarded; more likely a sly remark about how he's being greased up for his first night in the cell block. Sick, foul, disgusting maggots in brown dragging men down into the slime of the System. The victim has no choice. The brown maggot is there because he loves his work, poking his snout up the unceasing array of assholes sent to him every day for scrutiny and correction.

"Show me that shithole, boy."

"Yes sir, Boss."

And the oldcocks enjoy the daily entertainment. We look forward to it, like TV wrestling. Only live, on the bare cement floor. Someone almost always blows. There's a joker in every deck and the pigs use the joker to set the example for the day. Talk back. Show any sign of resistance and the goon squad will come and "kick you to sleep." Happens every day. Ass stamping. Rub the Newcock's face in the cement, take him off to the "infirmary". He fell in the shower, tripped on the stairs, fainted and hit his head. Poor kid...*NEWCOCK!*

DEATH HOUSE SCREAMS

From 1972 until executions started up again in 1979, the Death House was like a little museum. Wardens would invite the budding social scientists out from the University for this little tour. The climax was the trek down into the bowels of the death house, to the electric chair. The coeds plunked their cute butts into the chair while their pals snapped pictures and made *ZZZZ* noises. It was a regular hoot, the most popular social science field trip. Best of all was when the little ladies got to meet the real live criminal fiends: Murf-the-Surf, the Catch-me Killer, myself and others. More feral types like Ted Bundy were not allowed to mingle with the dollies.

In May 1979 all that changed forever, and it was the fault of one man - John Spinkelink. "Spink" as we called him, was a prison punk, a faggot and a product of the correctional system who couldn't quite get his sexual identity straight. He'd swish, but though he didn't mince or go about with a limp wrist, there was no doubt in your mind that he was a sissy.

Spink had shot a man in a Tallahassee motel room - an ex-con known to be a "jocker" - a bull faggot. To hear Spink tell it, the jocker had "ripped off his ass" (raped him), so Spink shot him. Mind you, Spink was not criticized for this amongst his peers. Had Spink done his murder in prison, he'd have just told the prison inspector that the jocker ripped off his ass so he killed him. He'd do 90 days in the Hole and that'd be the end of it. After all, prison investigators know what a young punk has to deal with. Jocker comes into the cell with a hard-on and says: "Put blood on my face or shit on my dick." The punk fights or he drops his pants and bends over. Spink had lived like that many a year in prison, and since he was a bit of a femme, his asshole was about like the entrance to the Holland tunnel. Maybe it still wasn't big enough.

Spink believed he had done the right thing shooting the rapist, so when the D.A. offered him a plea to Murder II he turned it down. Big mistake. He went to trial, and the good citizens of Leon County found him guilty of premeditated murder, which it was, and sent the no-good mad-dog murdering queer to Death Row, which was where he was on May 25, 1979, the day he loused things up for the rest of us with the tour chicks.

Day dawned, and there across the road from the prison were the usual fields full of protesters and execution groupies. One field for anti-CP, another for those who enjoy the vicarious thrill of a good electrocution. Vendors abound: fried meat, drinks, souvenir T-shirts, miniature electric chairs that light up when you flip a switch.

We were looking out the windows at the show across the street. Signs on sticks, posters going up and down, everybody chanting and howling. Big party rolling along. That's when we heard the scream. It came rolling up the stairwell and under the door, and you just knew something godawful was happening.

In prison you hear a lot of screams. The one we heard was a scream of outrage, not a death scream. Not the kind you hear when someone gets a shank in his guts and the killer rips open his victim's belly and his soul goes screaming off to Hell. It wasn't like that at all.

We all looked at each other. Nobody had to say What's *THAT?*" The question was in everybody's eyes. Even the old cons who'd been death house orderlies back in the sixties couldn't get a handle on that scream. We'd all heard the yarns the old timers would spin over a cigarette and cup of joe. Good stories. You had to listen because the tales would sort of reach over and take you by the throat, or hit you like a guard's slap upside your head.

We heard of the men who spit in Death's eye. And the craven baby rapers who'd piss their pants and faint at the sight of Old Sparky on the upraised dais, all festooned with leather straps and buckles to hold them steady while they "ride the lightning."

They call it the three-minute electric enema; 2800 volts of blazing hellfire smack through your brain down your spine and out your leg. The executioner gives you that first pop of 2800 volts: it raises you right off the chair to strain against the straps: shit be slithering out your asshole like a big brown eel, eyeballs be hanging out on your cheeks, brain be boiling in your skull. Then the executioner draws back a touch and takes the current down to 1600 volts. Sets you smack down in your own slop. Then he runs it up the scale to 2800 again till your flesh smokes, slobber and droll be oozing, blood be running out your nose, your trousers be soaked in piss and semen. Cuts the current and you slump in the straps. Dead meat. Fried in your own shit.

We soon found out the story of Spink's death house scream. What infuriated Spink was the unexpected way the State violated his body.

Ladies of the media had been invited to the execution of Brother Spink. ERA time. Can't be prejudiced against women at executions: so here they come. All dolled up in their fancy go-to-execution ensembles, their sober skirts and blouses. Fancy hairdos, cheeks rouged, lips glossed, eyes shadowed, black stockings - nice touch there. We can all imagine the black silk panties riding tight against the perfumed cunt. Oh yes. Spectacles and notebooks and gold pens. Lordy, Lordy, Lordy! One old timer comments that the fancy ladies will soon be heaving up their home fries in the discreetly provided vomit bags.

The gallant gentlemen of the FSP administration, gracious fellows that they be, had decided that pretty media ladies ought not to be subjected to the baser elements of criminal execution. No unpleasant manure odors should offend those patrician nostrils, and urine on electrodes turns to noxious steam.

So to keep the execution tidy, the Death Strap Squad held Spink down while a medical orderly stuffed cotton batting up his backside. Not just a few little cotton balls either. And when the orderly finished that unsavory task, he looped a surgical ligature around the base of Spink's penis and tied it nice and tight. Naturally the sissy screamed. Wouldn't you?

His scream when they crammed his asshole was so terrible that he went to the chair gagged. Prison Admin. caught hell in the papers about the "brutality".

But at least Spink didn't scream in front of the ladies.

The medical orderlies have got it down to a science now. Nobody screams when they get packed; they gag them first. After the business is concluded the gag comes off and he's hustled into the electric chair. People couldn't understand why Ted Bundy seemed a little unsteady on his feet there at the end. Maybe they shorted him on the Vaseline, who knows?

From midnight until they pulled the switch on Ted, the prison grapevine was buzzing with his every word, his every movement and attitude. All considered, Ted got good marks.

The all-time high for brass goes to Art Goode, who told the press his only regret was that he couldn't have a naked little boy sitting in his lap there in the Chair. Truly fiendish. I knew little Art well. One of the nastiest psychopathic child killers imaginable. He was radiant with evil. Even on the Row, people shunned him like the plague. Bundy was a bore compared to Goode, so far as sheer evil is concerned.

Miss Andrea Jackson, the Queen of Florida's Death Row, is scheduled to burn soon. They have a nice roomy cell right behind the Central Control Station all ready for her. I've been in the women's death cell, swept it out. I've sat on the press bench where the women are held down for "preparation". Up behind Control is the infamous Seatless Toilet where they make the condemned woman squat before they take her down that polished, spotless runway for her date with Old Sparky. As she nears the door to the Death Cell, all eyes will be on her - but it will be the eyes of her peers, not the public. She'll be making Chain Gang History and every convict in the System will hear her legacy: the tale of how she went down the Mainline.

The guards are talking about Southern Fried Cunt. Last night they told me they're bringing in three Death Strap Matrons to handle Andrea. The medical tech is laying on an extra box of cotton for Miss Double Barrel. The cons are gonna watch her make her last mile, and she won't be brutally gagged. We'll all get to listen to her screams.

JESSE IN FLAMES

State killings are a spectator sport in Florida. Tickets to these events are always much in demand, and the atmosphere is surprisingly festive. There is a sense of expectation as if fascinating secrets are about to be revealed.

The electrocution of cop-killer Jesse Tafero at Florida State Prison on May 4, 1990, promised to be no exception.

Political dignitaries from the Capitol were on hand; representatives from police agencies pushed and shoved as they angled for the most favorable viewing positions behind the thick glass windows that allowed an unimpeded view of the death drama.

Jesse Tafero was a vicious criminal in his day. He topped off his career in burglary, robbery and rape with the murder of two fine police officers. There were some doubts about who actually pulled the trigger on the lawmen. Jesse claimed it was his rat partner Walter Rhodes and his hooker companion, Sonia Jacobs. After all, Rhodes pleaded guilty to the murders and became a witness for the State. Rhodes' testimony guaranteed both Sonia and Jesse one-way trips to the Death House.

I remember the day Jesse Tafero came to Florida State Prison. The first thing he did was scream for someone from the law library: I was a law clerk. Officer Campbell, the librarian, sauntered over to my desk and said, "The cop-killer Tafero wants to see a law clerk. I'm assigning you to handle it." Campbell laughed and turned away, amused by his own sense of irony. There was no way I could refuse the order. Life had thrown me another curve, so I picked up my legal pad and left the library.

I walked down the polished corridor that led to the death cells... the infamous "last mile" walked by men and women fated to die sizzling on the death chair. I've walked it year after year, never failing to thank God that at the conclusion of my visits to the condemned that I could turn my back on the grim portals of the death house and walk back to my job in the law library. But on the day I was scheduled to meet Tafero, my feelings were in turmoil. He had a reputation for violence.

A tobacco-chewing guard escorted me into R-wing and opened the security gate that gave me access to the death house cell blocks. As he opened the iron gates he laughed and said, "If you have any trouble, give me a call and I'll have the goon squad come pick up the pieces."

The man had good reason to be amused. He was putting me into an area with seventeen condemned killers, men facing certain death at the hands of prison cops. Me, an ex-police officer, now an inmate; facing the collective wrath of men adjudicated savage beyond redemption. I sucked in my breath and entered the cellblock and walked to Tafero's private cell. I stood in front of his bars and said, "I'm Jerry Schaefer, the law clerk assigned to help you."

Tafero took one look at me, picked up his television set and slammed it into the concrete wall. I stood there as the TV exploded into a thousand bits and made no comment. "I know you!" He screamed, "You're that ex-cop who killed 34 women! Aren't you!?"

"That's what the prosecutor says," I deadpanned.

Tafero cocked his head at me and howled, "But I'm in here for killing cops!"

"You killed two lousy cops. I've got 34 kills. You've got a little catching up to do, don't you?"

Jesse began beating his fists against the walls and yelling, "I don't fucking believe this!"

Three hours later were on a first-name basis and he was showing me photographs of his bimbo, Sonia. She was fine, and I told him so. I didn't mention that the guards were already talking about what fun it would be to watch them both fry. It was their fondest fantasy: the double execution of a pair of cop-killing lovebirds. John Spinkelink had yet to make his historical debut on the Chair, but for the prison guards at FSP the frying of Tafero and his whore was something to live for, to speculate upon, day after empty day.

The death house guard who let me off the row said with a sense of awe, "I don't know why you ain't dead, boy."

"Jesus loves me," I told him, and it wasn't a joke.

One of the most powerful inmates in any prison is the skilled legal clerk, and before the public funding of lawyers for Death Row inmates, "jailhouse lawyers" literally held the power of life and death over men whose death warrants had been signed by the Governor. Thousands of executions have been blocked by a timely filing of a petition for the writ of habeas corpus to a United States judge. The key to saving the lives of the condemned is legal knowledge and articulate representation of constitutional issues.

I learned this skill as though my very life depended upon it, which in fact it did. Within one week of entering FSP, I was under the tutelage of an imprisoned union boss and labor racketeer who needed my literary skills to draft his motions to the U.S. District Court in Jacksonville. During the next four years of my imprisonment, I studied law during every spare moment and by 1977, I was regarded as one of the foremost legal minds at Florida State Prison. I was sought out by some of the most virulent criminals in the State, and learned prison lawyering from ex-judge Joe Peel, who was serving a life sentence for his part in the double murder of Palm Beach County Judge C.H. Chillingsworth and his wife.

Jesse Tafero was damned lucky to have me assigned to help him research his legal issues, but as I told him after reading his trial transcripts, it would only be a matter of time before he'd ride the lightning.

Jesse Tafero was a professional criminal with almost limitless unsavory connections in the prison system. He spoke well of me to his associates, telling them of my research efforts on his behalf and my unquestionable integrity concerning confidential matters. His esteem for me as an adherent to the Convict Code of Silence was so strong that I was the person he chose to deliver the death message to his former partner, Walter Rhodes, late in 1979. I will not reveal what that precise message was, but it was the driving force behind Rhodes rescinding his trial testimony and swearing he'd earlier committed perjury, a tactic that delayed Tafero's execution for almost six years.

I sat down with Walter Rhodes and coached him about what to say. I opened law books and showed him that the rescinding of his testimony would not change the outcome of the case, only delay it a few years. Rhodes was slated for a prison rat's death. His execution contract was given to one of the most feared prison gangs of the eighties. Rhodes was reduced to quaking jelly, knowing full well of Tafero's ability to reach out from Death Row and be the instrument of his doom.

Rhodes called the Broward County State's Attorney's office pleading for protection. I was standing beside him when he made the call. The police establishment had everything they wanted from Walter Rhodes in the way of testimony. They told him that they could give him no special protection; they implied that he was being thrown to the prison wolves, and Walter Rhodes lived in deadly fear for his life. I watched that fear eat away at him. Such is the power of prison crime syndicates, and the indifference of the police to informants, once the snitch has been milked for everything of use to them.

I met with Tafero again in late 1989. He looked good, healthy and handsome, bedecked in gold jewelry and chains. He saw me and smiled like a Mafia Don bestowing a favor on an underling. We spoke of serious matters, of life and death. I suggested he turn to Jesus, but he told me he was relying on Bruce Rogow, a respected constitutional lawyer from Ft. Lauderdale.

Tafero ran down the issues that were being considered before the Eleventh U.S. Circuit Court of Appeals in Atlanta. I told him he was riding a loser, that the decision would go against him, and that he'd be dead meat in 1990.

"I'll never quit filing petitions," he smiled.

Tafero was good to his word. On Monday, April 30, 1990 the law clerks spent an entire day helping Jesse file his last-ditch appeals. He'd fired his lawyers and returned to the inmate law clerks. But for Tafero it was too late... two lawmen had been riddled with gunfire and left in a lake of blood on the roadside. Somebody was going to have to pay for *that.*

On Friday morning, May 4, 1990, the Warden ordered a full prison lockdown in anticipation of general rioting as a prelude to the Tafero execution. No chance would be taken that a revolt might disrupt the course of Justice.

From my cell window, I looked across the fields of spring wildflowers toward the State highway. Beyond the road I saw the media vans, and fleets of police car bubble lights blinking festively in the early morning. The crowds of morbid curiosity-seekers and anti-death penalty demonstrators milled in adjacent pastures. I stood at my window and took it all in, measuring the emotional tone of the event.

Bundy drew a larger crowd, but the pulsing emanations of hate flowing from the mob were no less intense. There was no attitude of even-handedness to be applied, only an amorphous surge of unrestrained violence and projected enmity that flowed from the crowd toward the prison and those within its walls.

Less than 50 yards away from my cell Jesse Tafero, devoid of smiles and gold chains, was showered, shaved and diapered, and led to Old Sparky. It was 7.00 a.m.

Within five minutes Tafero was strapped to the oaken seat and at a nod from the Warden, the Executioner threw the switch, and fire leapt up from Jesse's head as if Satan himself had come to claim him. The Warden let Jesse burn alive for thirty seconds before ordering the electrician to cut the flow of current. Officials tinkered with the mechanism of death while Tafero writhed in agony on the Chair, and smoke from his charred flesh drifted toward the ceiling. A few minutes later the Warden gave it another try. Once again, flames burst forth as Tafero's flesh ignited and was consumed. The Warden stopped the execution once more, leaving Jesse to squirm in desperate pain. The electrician continued to fiddle with the wires and electrodes. At ten minutes past seven the Warden, seeing that Tafero was obviously still very much alive, ordered the switch thrown for the third time. Five minutes later Tafero was pronounced dead by the prison doctor. It had taken the State of Florida almost ten minutes to kill the man.

I observed the laughter, the self-satisfied smirks of the prison guards who regarded the burning alive of a fellow human being as great sport, an entertainment akin to hog butchering. They clearly relished the idea of the cop-killer stripped of his gold and his dignity, writhing against the death straps with flames curling up around the metal skullcap.

I returned to my cell early that day, reflecting on the Jesse Tafero I had known: a man of many passions, not all bad - and not as evil as many who would live a long life. I was there when he walked through the front door, and I was there when his roasted corpse went through the back gate in a hearse. For Jesse it was over, but for others it was just beginning.

I sat down on my bunk, opened the bound trial transcript of another condemned man, and began to read - searching for the legal challenge that could save his life.

EARLY RELEASE
by G. J. Schaefer

The bus crawled through the darkening Florida countryside, the soft hum of rubber on macadam floating up from under the wheels.

I was sitting in the back of the thing feeling edgy and impatient, smoking my RIP and contemplating the coming evening. I'd done sixteen years in the slam, straight up. One day the fucking warden says, "Pack your shit, Boy, you're being turned out. Early release, Prisons are full. Gotta push some of you old-timers out, got too many newcocks coming in."

I packed my shit. It fit in the front pocket of my jeans. They gave me a hundred bucks and offered me a bus ticket to any city in Florida. I picked Tampa. What the fuck? One place is the same as another, ain't it?

I reached down and stroked the hilt of my shank. It was jammed in my boot convict style. I'd feel naked without it. In prison a man learns to rely on himself and the comforting presence of cold steel next to his leg on a hot summer night. My shank had saved my ass more than once from the wolf packs of asshole bandits that prey on the weak after lights out. Only the fittest survive the brutality of prison with their manhood intact.

The only other person I knew on the Trailways was a baby-faced punk from Florida State Prison at Starke, known among the criminal brotherhood as the East Unit, or just the Unit. There is no tougher prison in the U.S. of A. - only Folsom Prison in California comes close in terms of murderous reputation. The only question in my mind was whether the slender boy with the shaved legs was a fuck-boy or a killer queen. The kid had himself a copy of *Hustler*, and was sipping liquor from a bottle concealed in a paper bag. I was feeling high with freedom and I needed to bat the breeze a bit.

I leaned over toward the punk and gave him a wolfish grin.

"Hey, Boy. Whatcha got there inside the tote sack? Think I can't smell free-world hooch when it's uncorked?"

The punk had thick light-brown hair; he glanced up and over, blinking his watery no-color eyes. They were white trash convict eyes: guarded, fearful, ancient. Eyes that had known pain, and expected to know it again. The eyes of a prison fuck-boy. His answer was an apology.

"Sorry. I didn't catch what you said."

"I *said*, I want to know what's in that fucking sack you're sucking on, Kid."

The punk shifted in his seat, quickly looked around, then offered me a sly, shit-eating smile. "This here is Jim Beam Whisky. Scored it right at Big Bad Daddy's Lounge in Starke. Five finger discount."

"Stole it?"

"I gave that lonely little feller a new home, is all," he drawled in his cracker, grit-sucking voice. "He was just sitting there with nobody paying him a lick of attention, so I boosted him up under my arm and here he is. Besides, tastes better when you steal it."

"Think so?"

"Sure. Wanna try a little snort?"

"Fucking-A on that, Kid."

The wheels squeaked and hummed along the cement pavement, the tropical countryside oozed past. It was so green - a wondrous world of a million different shades of *green* after sixteen years of solid grey. I took up the bag, wiped the neck of the bottle with my hand and belted down a healthy slug.

"That's damn fine shit there. Beats plum wine all to hell and gone. Fiery. Sets the sparks to jumping, don't it?"

"You betcha," the punk said.

"Got me some Bar-B-Cue corn chips here. Got 'em at the Kash-N-Karry store. Walked right into the little joint. Ten thousand kinds of shit to choose from. I didn't know what to do. It made me nervous seeing all that stuff, so I grabbed the first sack on the rack and hauled ass. Paid my kash; and karried the shit away, just like it said up there on the sign. Little girl at the money taking place up front had tits out front like Jane Fonda in *Barbarella*. I stared right at 'em. She smelt like a whore. I liked to skeeted in my drawers." I passed the bottle back to him, my eyes automatically scanning for a guard as I made the pass.

"I'll slide on the munchies, Oldcock. I'd probably just puke those corn chips up. I'm aiming to get *drunk*." He took another pull on his bottle and gave me a grin. His eyes were already slightly tinged with crimson from the powerful 90 proof hooch. Niggers had been at him. It was in his eyes: it came off him like a bad case of B.O. He'd be a walking death factory full of AIDS. I knew that for a fact. Mess with a pussy-boy in the joint and it's like Russian Roulette. Hell, play Russian Roulette with a pistol, your odds are safer. I was looking at a walking dead man. I motioned to the magazine open on his lap.

"You read that pervo shit or just look at the pictures? That Larry Flynt is the sickest fucker that ever put out a skin rag; I never have understood his brand of humor."

The punk picked up the magazine and set it on his knee, leaving me to see his dick stuck up like a flagpole. He opened the rag to the centerfold where a bare-assed lady was showing her Vaseline-slickened tunnel of love. The punk bent over and ran his tongue over the page, leaving a wet trail between the model's legs. He made a growl like a hound dog and said, "I like it when the girlies show the pink. *Hustler* gets my blood moving around, heats me up, ya know: I don't read it - I don't look at the cartoons. I just stare at those titties and those gorgeous hairy cunts and jack my dick. Doesn't everyone? Ain't that the reason they show them in the fucking thing?"

I grinned back at him, wondering what an asshole bandit would see in a naked whore. Maybe the same as anyone else; who can tell what goes on in a faggot's twisted mind? I'd been around them for sixteen years straight now, and never could figure them out. "So it heats you up and now you're hot stuff."

The punk nodded agreeably and took another pull on the bottle.

I snapped my finger at him and he quickly handed the jug back my way. "Here you go," he said. Nice polite kid.

I drank his whisky, felt it burn down inside me. It brightened me up, made me more aware of myself. Shit. Maybe stolen booze was better. I closed my eyes for a minute. Felt the sonorous hum of the bus all around me. Heard the snick-snack of the tyres snapping across the expansion cracks in the rural highway. It was a pleasant sound. I was tense. I needed to ease up, relax a little. Too many changes too fast. I wasn't used to it. Riding this fucking bus with no mesh welded over the windows was making me nervous. I realized I could simply throw open the window and leap out. I had a crazy fleeting urge to do just that. I saw the big headlines: *Man Dies Jumping From Window of Moving Bus.* Nobody would ever know why. It would be another unsolved mystery. I smiled at the thought.

I opened my eyes again, glanced at the kid. His eyes stared at nothing. He was leaning back against the bus seat, his hand playing with his dick. He smiled in a self-contained, distant manner at visions only he could see. He scratched at his balls like a whipped cur. I wondered if he was insane. I decided to chat him up and see what sort of worms came to the surface.

"Hey, Boy."

He turned to me. "Yeah?"

"They give you that early release thing?"

He perked up. "Yeah, I got one of those. I earned day for day gain time working in the broom factory. Maxed my nickel with a deuce, two months and six days. I kept close watch on it."

"Listen. You a street queen?"

"Naw. Bi."

"Niggers turn you out?"

"That's it. Turned my cracker ass out all right. First night too," the kid sighed.

"Bad shit there."

The kid giggled, a high screechy sound, his slim girlish body wriggling with grim recollection as I passed back his little jug. He needed a hit. Drank. Wiped his mouth with the back of his hand.

"Mama Herk comes up to me. The biggest fucking nigger I ever saw in my entire life. I figure I'm gonna die, right?" I nodded his way. "Mama Herk says, 'White Boy, I want to suck your dick.' I figured I'd heard the fucker wrong, like he wanted me to suck *his* dick, but no. He wanted to suck mine. And then I had to fuck him in the ass. You believe that shit?"

"Sure. Mama Herk is famous for it."

"He's a 280 pound queen."

"I know. I've *seen* Herk. I've been in sixteen fucking *years* and you want to tell *me* about Mama Herk? I've done more time in the box that you've done in the joint."

The kid gave me a worried look.

"Herk turned me out, but I got protection too."

"You sucked nigger cock. Herk pimped you."

"OK, sure. That's it."

"What'd you get for two and a half years of swallowing black cock? AIDS? Clap?"

"I got half of everything."

"Niggers let you keep it?"

"Yeah - Herk made them let me keep it."

"Herk would be the only one who could help a little stringbean like you hold green money at The Unit."

"Oh, I made plenty. I made fucking plenty." He patted a fat roll in the front pocket of his jeans. "It all adds up, Oldcock."

I leaned back, enjoying the heat of the booze. What it added up to was AIDS. But for him, not for me. "So now you are one loaded white boy."

The punk giggled again. His face was flushed and almost trusting. "I got me a big roll of green, and I'm on my way to spend it. I tell myself I earned it. That's how I see it."

He obviously hadn't learnt his lessons at Starke. The first one is to keep your mouth shut - tight. The boy was no convict, not yet he wasn't. I mulled over the news about the fat bankroll while I squinted out the dirty window as the clapboard nigger shacks of drab, impoverished West Tampa slid past. Pest holes of crime. Nigger comes out a place like that and prison life looks damned good by comparison. Steady meals, basketball, TV in the evening, some piss-ass job in a grungy prison factory, and all the white ass a coon can pump at night. Correctional officer asleep in a locked office and a dorm full of sex-crazed criminal perverts running wild all night. Rehabilitation. I felt the wheels swish along the pavement; the bus swayed from side to side, rocking along at a steady clip. I looked back at the Kid and said, "Yeah. You might as well enjoy it while you still got it. You get the AIDS and you're through dealing." I waited for him to argue around that one.

"I know. I figure I've got those AIDS things swimming around up in me somewheres. But it takes a while for them to breed enough to where they kill you. So I'm gonna hit that fucking Tampa on the run and I'm gonna get drunk and suck me some pussy, and then maybe I'll jump off the Sunshine Skyway Bridge right into Tampa Bay. Hey, I just don't give a fuck. OK?"

The punk gave me his best killer-convict junkyard-dog stare. He lookd like Garfield. I was trying not to laugh, so I said, "You ever sucked a pussy before in your whole damn life, Boy?"

He shrugged. "Never did, I admit it. Gonna start learning how to do it today. Heard me a lot of talk in The Unit about it, told myself I ought to give it a try. Hey, I sucked plenty of cock. Why not try a pussy?"

At least the kid had a sense of reality about life - or so it seemed. "How you figure to get ahold of this pussy? You gonna walk up to some lady and say, 'Excuse me, Ma'am, I'm fresh out of prison. Heard talk of pussy-sucking while I was in the joint, and figured I'd like to have me a try at it; would you be agreeable to lower your drawers and let me have a lick or three?' Or maybe you just knock her down, put a knife to her throat and tell her to fuck or die. About like that? Out where we're heading, Kid, is a thing called polite society."

"Just can't ask 'em flat out?"

"Well I reckon you can ask, but it's probably against the law to ask someone to commit a sex crime. Solicitation for criminal acts or something. I ain't no fucking lawyer."

"What's the criminal part?"

"Sucking pussy is a goddamned crime, Kid! It's called oral sodomy. You'd be right back there with Mama Herk in two shakes."

"You shittin' me? It's a *crime* to suck pussy?"

"No lie, Boy. It's a crime in the State of Florida."

I put the bag to my lips and sucked some liquid fire, let it trickle down my throat. I belched. Tasted corn chips at the back of my throat. I wondered if I could get AIDS from the neck of a whisky bottle. Damn depressing thought. I dismissed it. Quickly handed the Kid back his bottle.

I watched him take a pull, then closed my eyes and suddenly I was back in the darkness of the Hole. I saw the big brown sewer rats come out of the toilet hole in the floor, heard the dry rustle of thousands of cockroaches, the screams of insane and desperate men. Seven years in the Hole. Then the bus began to slow down. I looked out the grimy window, saw the terminal, a big sign reading *Trailways*. End of the fucking line.

"I'm getting excited," the Kid said.

I knew what he meant. The feeling was as contagious as his AIDS. The kid closed one eye and peered into the empty bottle. "Dead soldier," he remarked as he dropped the empty. It hit the floor with a dull clunk. An old lady gave him a dirty look. Started to speak, but held her tongue.

I got to my feet. Ran my hand down the side of the Kid's face and gave it a meaningful pat. He looked at me with new eyes, asking the unspoken question. He was borderline drunk.

"Got your heart set on sucking pussy, Kid?"

He nodded, "I did. Now I'm not so sure what I want to do."

"Yeah, but I know what to do."

"You do?" the Kid brightened.

"Damn right. Stick with me. I know Tampa pretty good. Worked armed robberies along Dale Mabry during the early seventies."

"You did?"

"Sure. And I've got phone numbers for a pair of cunts who done time down to Lowell. And you know what they fell on?"

"No. What?"

"Organized prostitution. I've got me a pair of whores on the line here. A pair is two, Kid. What do you say we call them up and I ask them to teach my homeboy from the Unit to suck honest-to-god pussy. I figure any girl come out of Lowell, she's got to be an expert at that happy pastime. Way I heard it, they don't do nothing else but lay around and lick each other's titties and suck those cunts. Now do you wanna tag along, or go to a motel and jack your dick?"

The punk gave me a look of gratitude. "Hey. That's OK! You really don't mind?"

"Hey, I done 16 years Kid. I dig young boys, I just don't advertize it."

"What about the AIDS?"

"What about it?"

"...if you tell those girls I've been ...you know."

"I ain't telling them double-barreled bags of shit nothing. Are you?"

The punk smiled from ear to ear. "Fuck 'em!" he said.

"So what do you say?"

"I say *DO* it!"

So we hit the streets of Tampa running.

It cost me a quarter to get one of the whores on the phone. She said they were French teachers and could we meet them at the Blind Pig for our lessons? She said to look for her in a red dress with a big black flower at the waist. She'd bring her friend.

The next quarter went to call a cab. I didn't want to waste a minute getting to our first class.

The air in the Blind Pig was thick with the smoke of a thousand cigarettes. The people inside were loose and uninhibited. We stood just inside the door and watched everyone shouting and laughing. The lighting was subdued. Smoke swirled around the room, turning the air into a layered blue haze. The punk was agog.

"Outta sight!" he breathed.

We inched our way into the lounge and walked up to the bar like free men. Nobody tried to stop us. We weren't arrested or searched for contraband. Buying a drink without being searched for loose canteen coupons was a novelty. So was the selection. The faggot bought the first round. Dickel on the rocks. First ice cubes I'd seen in sixteen years. They were little tiny things, curved on one side and flat on the other. Sparkling and tinkling as I swirled them in the glass.

I checked out the Kid's fat wad of cash. He's sucked him a lot of black cock to get that stash. I hoisted my glass.

"To survival, Kid."

He nodded. We clicked glasses and drank, glancing around the place and checking out the action. It was a honky-tonk kind of joint. Country music going wide open on the juke box. Cheap wooden tables with low benches. The room was three-quarters full and the conversation was roaring along. The tables were piled high with empty beer bottles and ashtrays overflowing with butts. The crap was falling onto the floor and being trampled underfoot. It was a real dump. It reminded me of the open dorms at the Unit. Sloppy as hell but as alive as an anthill. I decided I liked it. The punk loved the shit out of it. We'd been there 15 minutes already and nobody had cracked on him for some ass. For him, that was a whole new way of life.

But there was one thing at the Blind Pig that the Unit never had: real whores. Not chain gang pussy boys, but genuine double-barreled, ass-swinging cunts. There were whores wandering around the joint smiling at everyone. Big wide smiles to pull in them big stiff dicks. Same smiles you see on the queens at the Unit. A lot of them in red dresses, but I was looking for that black flower.

A bitch with a mop of tangled hair dyed three separate shades sauntered past with a bottle of Pabst Blue Ribbon in one hand and a pickled pigfoot in the other. She smelled real fucking sweet.

"Check out that real live snatch," I said to the queer.

"What about her?"

"She's trolling for dick. Down here at the Blind Pig twitching her fanny at us. That's your basic working girl. Needs to pay her rent same as us. Look at her move. You like whores, Kid?"

"I like 'em. I like how they move in those tight little skirts...Whoooeee! If she'd bend over a little, I could see clear up to where the sun don't shine. Maybe see the wet spot!"

"What wet spot?"

"There was this old con down on M-Wing. For some money or some canteen, didn't matter which, he'd tell about a gal he saw get 'lectrocuted up in Alabama. Told me all about it. He looked up her dress and there was a big roll of pussy up there and the crack part was wet. He said it was the girlie's wet spot and they all got one. Reckon she's got one up under there?" The punk seemed genuinely curious.

"That sounds like old Curly Bill's yarn."

"That was the guy: Curly Bill. A nasty old fucker with long yellow teeth, and not too many of them. I had to give him a whole jar of Maxwell House to hear his story."

"Was it worth it?"

"Hell yeah! Best story I ever heard."

"You heard some others?"

"Sure, plenty. I saw Ted Bundy, Murf-the-Surf, the Catch-Me-Killer, and the Ghoul.

"The Ghoul?"

"Sure. You know, that cop that killed the 34 women down around Oakland Park. Cut 'em up. Drank their blood. Fucked 'em when they were dead."

"Go on! You saw this guy?"

"Walking around on two feet."

"Wha'd he look like?"

"Big ole scary looking fucker. Looks like Hoss Cartwright."

"You say he killed 34 women?"

"Men, women, kids. Nobody knows for sure. I read the whole true story in *Inside Detective*. It had pictures of two girls he ate, plus one he hung by the neck. That one was drawing flies."

"Showed a picture of that!?"

"God's truth."

"You talk to this Ghoul?"

"Are you crazy? I seen that fucker coming and I got the hell out of the way. I wasn't gonna piss him off and become Number 35. Know what I mean?"

I laughed. The Ghoul. I wondered who had come up with that one. Some media asshole no doubt. Last I heard it was the Sex Beast. Now it's the Ghoul. Christ on a stick.

I finished my whisky; went up by the barmaid and ordered two more. We knocked them back. The night was young. The cigarette smoke and music swirled around us. The voices banged away at our ears. We took it all in, feeling right at home with the ear-splitting din.

I felt like talking. The booze was loosening me up, and the night was starting to glitter in my brain. I checked my watch, then felt foolish for wanting to see how long we had before cunt.

No count to stand at 8.00 p.m. Stand to attention, rattle off your number like a robot. No name, just your number. No nigger jive blasting from those black boom boxes. No prancing homos swishing off to the shithouse to suck black cock. The Unit - a place of rehabilitation. If the taxpayers only knew the truth.

I leaned closer to the pussy boy, put my elbow on the bar, and took a knock of bourbon. Damn good stuff.

"I done more than fifteen years, hard time. They bum-rapped me. I ain't no altar boy but you know a bum rap, it don't sit too well in a man. Festers in there like a cancer. A convict does his time. You get caught and you take the fall and you pull the time and you come out and you go back to work. You don't cry, you don't snitch for a plea. You've heard it said, if you can't do the time, don't pull the crime."

The punk nodded sagely into his drink. "What you fall on, Oldcock?"

"Murder! Bloody...fucking...murder."

"Jesus."

"Yeah. Chopped them up with a machete, they said. So when I get to Butler I go straight into Solitary. You know the drill."

The punk nodded.

"And for nothing, on the house. I get four years in the Box. Can you believe such shit?"

The punk's eyes widened as he shook his head in sympathetic understanding. "I know a guy. He raped the Warden's secretary. He got two years in the Box. This other guy, he got caught with a .38 caliber pistol inside the prison. He did maybe five years in the Box. So if you get four years in the Box from jump street, I figure the Warden plain don't like you, or a buddy of the Warden don't like you. That's it, couldn't be nothing else."

"Good, you understand. So you can see how I might be tempted to get me a machete and settle a few old scores."

"I can understand the temptation."

"I ain't saying I'm gonna do it. But after that first four years in the Box, you could say my attitude turned a tad radical."

"But you did manage to get out of the Box, right?"

"Right. And here's what happened. Along comes this new warden, Braselton. Big fucking gorilla runs about 280. Lifts weights. Came down from Cook County. You know, Chicago. Me, I'm from the Windy City, grew up on the Northside. That was back when Old Man Daley was Mayor and the cops were real mean. Capone, he came out of Chicago. Word I got was that Capone had Cermak bumped off down on Miami Beach..."

"What? You lost me. Who's Cermak?"

"Mayor Anton Cermak. He got killed in Miami. They said it was an attempt to kill that Jew Roosevelt."

"Roosevelt? Hey, that was before I was born, Home. Tell me how you got out of the Box," the punk groused.

"Well I done a few short stretches at Statesville, one longer at Menard.

Braselton knew me there. He comes down here to Florida and finds me in the Box. He takes a look at my jacket, sees I ain't got a single write-up, so he decides to give the homeboy a break. Gets me a transfer out of the Box right over to Union County, Raiford Prison. I go straight to the Rock. F-Floor. Nasty grungy place. Then I get assigned a job. Put me in the packing plant. Ever been in the packing plant, Kid?"

"Never was." He took a knock at his drink.

"Well it's a place you wouldn't forget. You know that bacon they serve in the chow hall with the hog bristles still in it?"

"Yeah. Not that you'd see me eating it. I do admit the niggers scarf it right up. They'll snatch it right off your tray if you so much as blink an eye."

"OK. That's the bacon I'm talking about. The packing plant is where that crap is made and the noise alone is enough to drive you fucking insane. Machinery crashing and slamming all day long. The squealing pigs."

"Is that four-legged or two-legged pigs?"

"Very funny. This is serious. Now pay attention."

"OK, run it."

"So Benny drives down to Avon Park for a truckload of pigs. Great big fucking sows maybe three hundred, four hundred pounds. He comes back and we run them out of the truck and into a pen."

"A pigpen."

"Right. Then someone gives 'em a jab on the ass with an electric prod and they go running up a narrow chute. They're lined up in there snout to asshole; squealing like mad, crapping all over each other, just like the poor slobs on their way to Sparky. Same exact thing. Joe fastens some iron shackles around the rear hocks and this other fella gives the porker a pop on the noggin with a sledgehammer."

"Jesus."

"Yeah. Wham! Then they press a button and the hoist jerks the pig up into the air. The fuckers ain't even dead, just stunned, and they come to while they're hanging upside down. You never heard such screaming. The hog comes swinging down from the slaughter chute toward the killing floor and the thing is spewing shit and piss out its ass like a volcano."

"Gross."

"You ain't heard it all yet. Bobby Batson is there with this huge fucking knife and he slits their throats. The blood comes splashing out all over the place. They spray blood from the front and crap from the rear, and there's four hundred pounds of bucking meat writhing in the chains, gurgling and squealing and screaming like hell."

"So what was your job?"

"I gutted them. Slashed their fucking bellies open and got a snoot full of stench for my trouble. Let me tell you, Kid, there ain't no rehabilitation in the packing plant. Raw meat. Yellow tallow. Greasy coils of spilling guts. And the stench. I come out of four years in the Hole and walk into that. They told me it was supposed to be job training. Educational. Yeah, teach me the Work Ethic. The parole man would like it, they said. I'd have a skill to take with me to the streets. Make me a good parole risk. You've heard that story?"

The punk nodded. Caught the bartender for two more Dickels with ice. Good sipping whisky. We sloshed them down. A whore rubbed her tits against the pussyboy as she pressed through to the bar. He gave me a look. Big eyes, big wet smile. Thinking about a little cooze, he was. It was around. All around.

"Where are those French whores, Oldcock?"

"Don't cum in your drawers, Kid. They'll be around. You think you're the only stiff they got lined up to bury tonight? We got 'call girls' coming. They ain't like some snaggletooth rummy you find in a tonk. Call girls - you call 'em on the phone, make you an appointment. They get top dollar. But you've got a wad of green to spend."

"Damn right. Top-notch pussy, that's what we want!"

"Yeah, that packing plant was a real trip. Every time I see a cop I think of it. Never could get the blood washed off me. It'd be under my fingernails, my toenails, between my toes. Slice one of those sows and she squirts blood and crap right in your face. It's in your hair, dripping down your arms, soaked into your clothes. August, September - it was hotter than hell in there. Sixty million flies buzzing around eating that liquid pigshit mixed with blood. We were drowned in that slime, Kid. We died. Our souls flew out and went away."

"Sounds bad, Home."

"You don't know the half of it, Kid. The old Rock was nothing but fucking madness. The noise and the stench alone was enough to drive any man insane. They built the place about 1920, so there's 60 to 70 years of sweat and piss soaked into the cement. August comes around and you can't hardly breathe for the stink of the place. We'd put in a day in the packing plant and then the screws would herd us back to the cellblocks. F-Floor, H-Floor, G-Floor, all that was the packing plant crew."

"Big gang down there, huh?"

"Oh, hell yes. There was goddamned niggers in the cells, too. Nasty fucking dirty black-assed niggers that never had a bath in their whole sorry lives. Filthy animals."

"Mama Herk was OK."

"Some are OK, some ain't. And that's a fact."

"Where are our whores? You think they'll be here soon?"

"Forget the whores for a minute. I'm getting to the part about when they cut off newcock Benson's head."

"Cut the guy's head off? What was it, an accident?"

"Not exactly. Those niggers, you know they were bad, but at least they speak English and they understand when you tell them to hit the showers. Then we started getting them Cuban assholes. Marielito scum. Castro opens the door to his insane asylums and lets all the nuts go to Florida. Guess where they end up?"

"The Rock?"

"Fucking-A. And these are crazy insane fuckers, not convicts. No habla ingles. No comprendo. Let me tell you what they comprendo, is a big fucking knife. And even normal guys were driven mad by the stench and the filth and the blood-sodden clothes stinking up the whole cellblock. Guys were bugging up every day - regular white guys. You never knew when it would happen. It was a 24 hour red alert just to stay alive. Bad on the nerves, Kid, I can tell you that."

"What about cutting off the head?"

"Shit. Some guy would pull out a knife - a hog slasher, pig sticker, even a meat cleaver. And he'd start swinging. Slaughter guys in the cell just like they were pigs coming off the chute, hanging from a chain. Get the picture?"

"I'm seeing it. Living color."

"OK. One day we are in this 20 man cell and a shiteater name of Dennison comes along with this newcock to put him in our cell. Swede Perkins, who was the boss coon of the cell, tells Dennison we ain't got no more room, the cell is full. Twenty bucks, twenty guys: White, Nigger, Cuban. Dennison tells Swede the newcock is coming in as number 21, and we ain't got jack-shit to say about it. So Swede tells Dennison if he puts the newcock in the cell, we're cutting off his damn head. Dennison just laughs and open the door. He pushes the newcock into the cellblock and walks away. An hour later he comes back for a security count and the head is laying out on the tier."

"No shit?"

"No shit."

"So what happened?"

"We didn't get more guys than bunks, that's what happened. Every other cell was stacked up with guys like they're sardines in a damn can. Cell H-4 has twenty guys, just what it's supposed to have."

"What'd the cops do?"

"Nothing. Every guy in the cell said he killed the newcock. Twenty guys. Twenty confessions. So the State said fuck it and put it under the rug. Called it a suicide or some such shit. Suicide my ass. Dennison was told. He murdered that newcock. That was the old chain gang, Sonny. Pussyboys don't have that kind of solidarity. No snitches stayed alive in them days. Ain't like now."

"What about the screw, Dennison. Did he get fired?"

"Dennison got fucking killed, Kid."

Whaaat?"

"Time goes by. The cons seen the cop who was responsible for the murder is still around. One day they caught him in the hallway and gutted him like a porker."

"But... why?"

"Because Swede told him, *IF* you put the newcock in the cell he's dead meat. Dennison put him in. The newcock had to die. Real convicts don't run off at the mouth, Kid. Dennison killed him. The State should have fried Dennison same as they fried Aubrey Adams, that baby-raping pig from Marion CI. Since nothing was gonna be done officially, it got done unofficially. A lot more of them shiteating DOC motherfuckers are gonna die before it's all over. You watch and see."

"Home, it sounds even worse than the Unit."

"It was." I took a drink and leaned closer to the Kid.

"Check this out: I lasted one week. Then I walked down to Classification, asked that old shithook Parks for a job change. Kitchen, laundry, farm squad, anything. Parks pulls out my jacket. He scans through it. Looks me dead in the eye and tells me his paperwork says I'm a butcher. I tell the fucker, 'I never done no butcher job on the street. Armed robbery, button work. That was my trade. Never done an honest day's work in my life, at least not in no straight john detail. What the fuck is this butcher trade crap?'

"Parks, that miserable shit, he says: 'Right here on your sheet, Boy, says *The Butcher of Blind Creek*. Got you some experience, says here.

Hung 'em by their ankles and opened up their bellies. Figured you'd like it in the packing plant since that's your style. Heard it said them sows scream like real women. Hang 'em, gut 'em, listen to 'em scream. Talk about hog heaven, says right here you get off on that shit. Now get the hell out of my office.'"

The kid groaned. "Fucking Parks! I know him. What an asshole. Kept a bottle right in his desk. I went to a Progress Review with him once, and he was drunk on his ass. Parks. Sweet Jesus. Everybody hates that fucker."

"I seen it my own self, Kid. I seen a lot. Parks and plenty more just like him. I don't know where the State dredges up the human shit they have running these prisons... Someone must tack job opportunity notices up in gay bars. Half the staff of the Unit is faggot. The citizens say they want rehabilitation. I've seen their program. What it is, see, this rehabilitation program, it's a flip-flop deal. You flip into the system one way and flop out another way. You know? Go in straight, come out queer. Go in healthy, come out diseased. Go in normal, come out perverted. Flip-flop rehabilitation theory. An education man could write a book about it."

The faggot nodded his agreement. How could he argue? His program might have been a little different, but he knew what I meant. The dickeater never had to ask a silly question about rehabilitation. He understood.

I watched his pretty-boy long-lashed eyes surveying the action. A covert oblique swing of the eyeballs, always on the alert for the sudden move, the danger of the knife in the back. He slid up to the bar, copped two more bourbons, and paid for them. We slurped them down, the heat of the alcohol exciting our senses.

"Where's those fucking whores?" the Kid moaned.

"Home douching out their cunts getting ready for two hardheads out on early release. They squirt perfume on their tits, powder their assholes, use cherry-flavored juice up in their pussies to make them taste nice when you suck on 'em."

"Cherry flavored pussy?" The punk was in awe.

"As I live and breathe."

"Real call girls."

"The McCoy. Call 'em and they come."

"Like a couple of bitches. Here, Girl! Here, Girl!" He was getting giddy.

"You got the picture, now hold it."

"I've been holding it. Now I want to stick it in one of them pussy rolls."

"Don't worry, you will. Tonight. Now listen to my philosophy."

"You make up a philosophy in the Box?"

"I did. Now listen."

"Tell me."

"Blood." I said, "that's where it all starts. I was up to the Unit during the riot back in 79. There was plenty of blood to see there. The shiteaters came in on us with clubs and mace and spilled our blood. They broke our bones, bruised our meat. All you are to them, Kid, is an animated bag of meat and blood. I seen it go down. I had a vision. Teeth were all over the quarterdeck. Smashed teeth. Step on them, they crunch like gravel. They'd run you down to Q-Wing and work on you with those clubs and cattle prods. Obedience training. Attitude adjustment. Rehabilitation. The beginning and the end of it is blood. The blood fills your mama's insides. She squats and squeezes you out her cunt like a lump of crap. You come sliding down her chute right between her piss and her shit. There's a cosmic message there, if you study on it. We eat shit and die. Just like it says on the back of the Scooter Tramps jackets."

"That's your philosophy?"

"That's it...blood. That's where it starts and that's where it ends."

"Makes sense."

"You gotta let it all out, Kid. You can't keep it locked up in the Box in your brain any more. To the public you ain't no more than a carcass on a hook. They don't know nothin'. They don't want to know nothing'. They think we live at some kind of summer camp. Tell Joe Sixpack what goes on inside a prison and he'll just call you a liar. But now we're out. First we're gonna have us some fun and then I don't know about you, but I've got some people to look up. A few folks who owe me."

I lifted my glass and realized it was empty. I started to order another round when I saw a hooker in a red dress come swinging through the door with a jaunty black silk flower pinned to her waist. She had her blond hair up in a French twist. The other French teacher was right behind her, a brunette with fluffed-out hair in a shiny royal blue number. I gave them the high sign and nudged the punk, "Here comes our French lesson."

The two bimbos bounced over to a table and sat down. I took the cocksucker by the arm and steered him through the crowd. We walked up to the women and sat down, just like free men.

The women were both obviously professionals, with painted crimson lips slick and wet. Their cheeks were rouged, their noses powdered. They were ready. I gave them a sharp, knowing grin. The women smiled back with avaricious eyes. They studied me and the punk, looking us up and down. I stared directly at their tits. They both had nice big ones. The punk snickered and sucked up some booze. His eyes were as red as a vampire's. His baby face was pink and greasy. He gave me a callow grin. A full boner curved up toward his navel. He was a randy boy.

"I'm Jerry, and this is my road dog, Danny." The whores looked at him and smiled to each other. They knew easy money when they saw it, and they were both licking their lips.

Danny gave up a self-conscious giggle. "You ladies the schoolteachers we called about private tutoring in French?"

"Oui,oui, I'm Candy," said the blonde.

"And I'm Tiffany," chimed in the brunette.

"You guys afford lessons?" asked Candy.

The kid flashed his roll and asked, "Can I buy you ladies a drink?"

"French champagne," Candy gushed. "The French lessons are two hundred an hour. Each."

The punk blanched.

Tiffany arched an eyebrow. "Can you handle it, Big Daddy?"

"Sure - no problem." The Kid put on a lopsided grin and shoved off toward the bar for a round of drinks.

"A couple of twenty-dollar hookers fleecing a lamb. Shame on you!" I grinned.

"Lambs were born to be shorn," Tiffany snapped.

Candy nudged me. "How'd you get our number?"

"Willy the Weasel."

"What'd Willy fall on last time - he tell you?"

"Murder Two. Willy has him a wart right here." I touched my finger to the side of my nose.

"So you know Willy."

"Sure. You think I'm Vice Squad?"

"Just being careful."

"Yeah? Willy told me you two pulled time at Lowell."

Candy groaned. "I did ten months on a bar-tack machine in the garment factory. Job training for the street, you know?"

"I know."

"Tiffany pulled a deuce at Broward. Armed robbery. She ain't as genteel as she looks. Where'd you pull yours?"

"Raiford - the Rock."

"Did you see Andrea when they took her up there?" Tiffany asked.

"Didn't see her but I damn sure heard her. Bitch screamed her lungs out. Took four matrons to get her down the mainline. It was a real show. I got the story from the Deathwatch Commander, Mr. Crowe."

The two hookers exchanged a glance and laughed.

"What's the joke?"

The Kid came back just then with a fifth of Dicket and a big green bottle of champagne. He popped the cork. While he was pouring a round, I asked the kid if he was around the Unit when the Jackson bitch came up for a ride on the lightning. He said he was.

"Did she scream?" Tiffany asked.

"Screamed like she was being murdered. Everyone in the Unit heard her. The Captain told me there would have been a shit trail from the back ramp to the death cell, except they had her in sanitary briefs."

The two whores laughed some more.

"What's the joke?" Danny asked.

"My exact same question," I added.

"Tiffany saw when they put her on the transport van to ride her up to the Chair," Candy said.

"She was shrieking like a maniac," Tiffany giggled.

"Old Lady Venziano, she's the Warden down there, goes trooping down to Andrea's cell and reads her the Death Warrant and Transport Order. The goon squad is there with chains and locks. The nurse is standing by with the old-fashioned Kotex on a belt, and a green diaper."

"What's that about?" Danny asked.

Tiffany arched an eyebrow his way. "The electric chair is at Starke. The Women's Death Row is west of Lauderdale, out in a swamp next to the County Dump. It's a 6 to 8 hour ride to Starke. Maybe you think they'll stop and let her pee at a gas station?"

The kid shrugged, blushed a bit. "What they do is strap a piss sop to your cunt, Honey, so you can piddle in it if you take a notion to go. The diaper is just in case you get real scared and start to shit. A girl on the way to the Chair might get the urge, don't you think?"

The kid obviously didn't know what to say.

"Any more dumb questions?" Tiffany huffed.

"Lighten up, Babe," Candy quipped, then turned to the Kid and said, "She's only been on the street three weeks. Takes a while to shrug off the stresses and tensions of that lousy joint. Women screaming and hollering, sex-crazy for a man, everybody angling for the cutest dykes and trying for early release. It's insane."

Tiffany's ire subsided. She said "Andrea came back to Broward on a Federal stay. She told us she took the mainline by storm. Went down with a tail-swinging strut and at least five hundred men calling out for her to fuck them."

"Her fantasy," I said.

Tiffany continued, "Then they gave her a cell next to that Adams guy and they talked."

"That part could be true," the punk said.

I nodded.

"Then they took Adams and burned him up in the Chair, and that was the end of him."

Candy said, "Then when she came back to Broward she was full of shit about how she had charmed the whole Unit. True or false?"

"A little of both," I allowed. "The guards had the Unit on lockdown when she made her walk on the mainline. Cruise said she was crying and screaming. We heard that in the cellblocks."

"Lying damn bitch", hissed Tiffany.

We all drank up. The girls were originally from Atlanta and both were kicked out on early release. They were working the senior citizen trade at the condos. Lonely old men paid a mighty sweet dollar for juicy young snatch. Business was booming. I told them about the Rock. The rehabilitation. The packing plant. The early release.

The pussy was telling them about Ted Bundy, the Catch-Me Killer, and the Ghoul. The drone of conversation hummed around us and the caustic smoke stung our eyes. We discussed the mindless violence, the bloody murder, the sexual slavery of men and women in prison. How their bodies were bought and sold to the highest bidders, unleashing the perverted lusts that gave hopeless men and women a reason to live from day to day.

The blonde put her hand on my crotch. Sighed with anticipation as she rubbed her hand along my ready shaft. Tiffany snuggled with the punk, her professional hands busy under the table. The sluts were already beginning to stink of rut. They gurgled and moaned, their minds clouded by the sexual business they needed to conclude. I looked at them with both contempt and lust. I slapped my empty tumbler onto the table and announced to the steamy group, "So let's get laid!" Everyone understood that. We got right up and off we went.

The fuck-boy was giddy. He couldn't believe his luck. We left the Blind Pig with the early release whores on our arms and lurched out into the humid warmth of the summer night. Nebraska Avenue was blazing with light. Cars with glaring headlights cruised up and down the Strip, their makes, models and styles all foreign and unrecognizable to me. Neon signs flashed and blinked, advertising places and products I'd never heard of. Music throbbed and boomed from the doorways of bars and clubs. The whole city of Tampa was a gaudy whorehouse catering to the pleasures of tourist flesh.

A stinking coal-black nigger in a dirty T-shirt rattled a paper bag in the shadows of a doorway. "White Lady, White Lady," he sang out, "Crack."

"Get fucked, Nigger!" I snarled.

Candy giggled. The dope dealer retreated into his lair.

We turned off Nebraska. The side street was in darkness. The whores had them an old two-storey flophouse trick pad. Danny was anxious to get it on. He was almost dragging Tiffany up the stairs. The stairwell stank of dry rot and stale piss. Familiar smells - prison smells. The stairs led up a landing. There were rooms on the right and left. Whores and transients.

Candy fished a key out of her clutch purse. She unlocked a door and flipped on a light. Hundreds of cockroaches fled, scuttling for the cracks. Thee were a pair of unmade ratty beds along the far wall, an aluminium chair, a Formica table strewn with Big Mac wrappers, cigarette butts and black ants.

"Home sweet home," Tiffany announced blithely.

"Fucking pig pen," I said.

"You don't like it, hit the road, Jack," Candy spat.

Danny toppled onto a bed. There was a half bottle of Dicket in his hand. He unscrewed the cap. Tiffany grabbed the bottle, drank up, handed it to me and began pulling off Danny's clothes. His trousers were hung up on his boner. We all laughed. I took a hit on the bottle, and passed it on to Candy. She drained it, tossed it in a corner and unzipped her dress. The cheap red fabric fell in a puddle at her feet. She caught it with her foot and kicked it into the same corner with the Dicket bottle. The bedraggled black silk flower was twisted and broken off its stem. It lay on the floor by the naked feet of the blonde whore. I watched her strip, burning with a puritanical rage as she shook her creamy udders free of her lacy black brassiere.

The punk and his dark-haired whore were wrestling on the bed. The blond pulled off her black silk panty, put it to her nose and sniffed it, make a wry face and tossed it. She cleared her throat. "Straight French, half-and-half or around-the-world?"

"French for me," I said.

"Pay up!" the blond said, holding out her mitt.

"You don't trust me?"

"Fuck no!"

I laughed. Fished out Danny's roll from his pants and paid the freight. The whore nodded. Put the four hundred in her shoulder bag.

Danny gasped and giggled on the bed. The dark-haired slut on top of him was naked. She had tapered fingers with the color of fresh blood glistening on the long enamelled nails. Her hands fluttered around the boy's dick with professional skill. They knew what to do and were busily going about it.

The nude blonde stood there like a cow in a slaughter chute. Her eyes were bovine and dumb. She scratched absently at her pubic hair as we watched Tiffany work her magic on the fuck-boy's dick. What a pro. The queer was gasping. The slut was straddling his cock, her white legs spread wide. A lavish mop of dark pubic hair hung down between her legs. She took the punk's boner in her right hand and carefully angled it into her hole. She lowered herself with a grunt of pleasure. Danny's hands clenched the pillowy white buttocks, his fingers kneading the soft flesh. The impaled woman levered herself up and down on his pole growling deep in her throat. Her eyes were closed. A ropy tendril of saliva hung from her chin. We listened to the building tempo of passion, the wet smack of sweaty flesh meeting. The brunette kept sliding up and down Danny's cock until he arched his back and emptied his load, leaving her infected with the AIDS plague.

I unzipped my jeans, took out my own stiff boner, turned to the naked blond and commanded her, "On your knees, Bitch!"

The whore did as she was told. She took my root in her mouth and sucked on it. She'd done it before and was just fine. I let her work. I stood there and looked down at the dandruff on her head. It looked like she might have lice as well.

I listened to the slurping, sucking sounds she made as they mingled with the whimpers coming from Danny. I felt the head of my dick rub the back of her throat. I relished the slippery warmth of her spit, heard the gurgle and mewl of her efforts. I caressed Candy's blonde, dandruffed hair. It had a greasy feel. She hummed as she sucked. It was a nice touch. I tried to pick up the tune, but couldn't recognize it. Must be a new one.

Outside there was the distant whoop of a police siren. Trouble for somebody, but not for me. The thought of being free was exciting. I speeded up my thrusts. Finally I held the blonde whore's head steady, shuddered and came in her mouth. She struggled to break free. I wrapped her hair around my hand and held her head tight on my cock. Danny was amused. He caught my eye as he giggled: probably remembering his own head locked on a man's spurting dick.

Tiffany wiped her cunt with a big wad of Kleenex and dropped it on the floor. "Ride 'em, Cowgirl!" she yelped at Candy.

I felt the blonde's teeth close around my dick, and I shoved her away from me. It was the only thing to do. She fell back on the floor landing on her backside, gagging and heaving. She spat a gobbet of semen on the grimy floor.

"You motherfucker!" she shrieked.

I kicked her hard in the stomach and she doubled up. "Teach you to bite my dick, Bitch!" Bloody vomit spewed up from her gut and splashed from her mouth onto the black flower on the floor. She retched and gasped. Her eyes were swimming with fear and disgust. Two tendrils of slick puke ran from her nose. "Like to bite my dick? I'll teach you to bite!" I kicked her in the face. Teeth flew from her mouth. The force slammed her back into the wall. She bounced off and collapsed onto her side. Her head thumped the floor.

Tiffany screamed. Danny sucked in his breath and jerked upright, suddenly alert, his prison instincts overriding the alcoholic haze. The naked brunette made a lunge for her skirt. As she made her reach I drop-kicked her in the jaw. She spun around and crashed into the bedpost and flopped down to the floor into Candy's champagne-laced vomit. I leaped in the air and came down full force on Tiffany's chest with my knees. Her rib cage collapsed under my weight.

She coughed, her chin slick with glistening blood. Gurgling rasps were her only sound. Her body stiffened slightly, and a thin bubbling sound came up from deep in her throat. The breath snagged and then stopped. Her legs began to jerk in spasms and a pool of yellow urine widened around her hips. The breath came back with a start. A few rapid gasps rattled in the back of her throat. Pink frothy lung blood gushed from her mouth, and she was dead.

"Jerry! Jerry!" Danny yelled.

"Fucking sluts," I growled.

The punk's face was fishbelly white. The grey eyes widened with sudden terror. I smiled. Pulled my knife from my boot. I strode toward him. Danny cringed back against the wall, his delicate fag hands waving before him. Cowardly little AIDS-ridden queer.

"Jerry! No! Please!" he blubbered.

I swung the blade in with a sharp upward motion. It glanced off a rib and sliced up into the faggot's yellow heart . I pulled the shank out and chopped it across his face. A fountain of blood erupted. He started sliding down the wall. I held him up with my left hand and drove the shank into him again. And again. And again. His body slumped sideways, toppled over and hit the deck. I sank a kick into his balls. "Cocksucker!" I hissed. He never heard me. He was dead.

The blonde whore had rolled onto her back. Her face was bloody and broken, her eyes rolled in their sockets with the pain. Vomit and blood streamed from the corners of her mouth. Bloody bubbles formed and burst at her nostrils as she attempted to breathe.

I felt the pounding of my heart as the excitement fanned my rage. The coppery smell of whoreblood had me sweating and my nerves on fire. The blonde bitch groaned. The brunette was splayed across the floor in a ghastly pool of blood and urine and vomit.

I walked over to her to get a closer look. Her open eyes were dilated. The blood oozing rom her nose and ears was beginning to thicken. She looked dead. I leaned over and punched the blade into her heart, just to be sure.

I picked up Danny's discarded trousers and removed the still-fat wad of cash from his front pocket. I searched the pocketbooks of the two hookers and came up with a couple of C-notes, in addition to my own four hundred. Chump change.

I heard the blonde whore groan. She was still on her back, lips swollen, eyes puffy and blackened. I walked over to her. I could see the cheesy crack between her legs, with the cooties crawling in her bush. She wasn't a natural blonde. I examined her ruined face and noticed that somehow her narrow, aristocratic nose had remained unbroken. I lifted the heel of my heavy boot and brought it down smartly on her snot locker, driving it up into her brain.

The whore didn't move and made no further sound. I set the point of the blade into the hollow of her white throat and shoved it in until I felt it grate bone. Then I twisted it. I picked up the sodden black flower and placed it in her evil mouth. It looked just right.

I opened the door to the flophouse flat. The hallway was dusty and empty. I walked down the rotting stairs to the street, with Danny's roll to keep me company. I thought of Canada, the Bahamas, the coast of North Africa. Then I thought of the cop who had framed me for murder sixteen years ago. Within an hour I was on a bus to Miami.

The author steps out to meet his public. **195**

NIGGER JACK
by G. J. Schaefer

The Warden of the Florida State Prison at Starke strapped John Spinkelink into the electric chair and fried his ass on May 25, 1979 and right away convicts began scheming for the job of Death Chamber Orderly; that was because of a hooker named Sonia.

Sonia was the whore who'd murdered two cops down in Broward County: Trooper Black of the Highway Patrol and Constable Irwin from Canada. She'd shot them dead at a rest area off I-95 hard by Pompano Beach. A stinking scum-sucking rat by the name of Walter Rhodes had turned State's Evidence and put Sonia's pretty young tail in line to fry on Old Sparky. She'd burn with her convict boyfriend, Jesse Tafero. It would be an event to see.

It all added up that Sonia would be riding the lightning. Spinkelink had murdered an ex-con rapo-faggot and the State had burned him, so there was no doubt that Sonia would be coming along to pay us a visit by and by. Everybody in the joint believed it would happen and almost everybody wanted to be on hand to watch - not because Sonia was disliked, but because she was prime pussy. She'd been a high-priced hooker on the streets, she'd blown away a pair of law dogs, she had great teats, and was the reigning Queen of Death Row.

The State would burn Sonia and some lucky convict would be assigned the job of mopping up her pee and emptying her knickers after the execution. The prison guards always have someone handy to dump the executed person's drawers before turning the smoking corpse over to the free-world undertaker, so we all knew someone would luck into the job of dumping Sonia's. It was a job to covet, and there was more to it than the chance to see real pussy. The job carried a guarantee of an endless income of coffee and cigarettes tendered by anyone wanting to hear the true story of Queen Sonia on her electric throne. Look at it as a form of chain gang Social Security.

We knew this to be a fact because of Curly Bill. Curly had personally watched a cunt sizzle in the Alabama electric chair in 1957. This unusual event occurred while Curly was pulling a stretch at the Holman Penitentiary, and for a small gratuity he'd sit down and tell anyone the whole story. I'd heard he told it well, so being of a curious nature I went down to the prison canteen, picked up a jar of Maxwell House Coffee and a bag of Oreos, and moseyed on down to Curly Bill's cell. I found him sitting on his bunk rolling a smoke.

I poked my mug in his door and said, "Curly Bill, if you're in a yarning mood I'd like to hear the story of the fried cunt." I took the jar of coffee out of the paper sack and tossed it on his bed. "Talking can dry a man out. I brought you a little something to wet your whistle while you talk." A flagrant bribe.

Curly Bill eyed the coffee. His tongue ran out and dampened the rolling paper for his cigarette. "Whole damn jar, all for me?" he enquired.

I shrugged. "Sure, why not? I heard you tell quite a story."

He lit his cig and took a drag. ""What sort of story are you wanting to hear?"

"What kinds you got, Curly?"

He pursed his lips in thought. "Well, there's the kind I tell the Man when he comes snooping around. And there's the kind I tell the social science girlies from the university day trip every month. And there there'nthe true fact of what really happened the night the Captain strapped a Tutweiler cunt to Old Sparky and she rode the lightning down to the flaming pit of Hell." He cocked an eyebrow at me and said, "That pussy was so hot steam rose from between her legs. Now... what sort of yarn did you fancy, Jerry?"

"The one with the smoking hole."

Curly Bill grinned. "That's the one the free people don't want to hear."

"I ain't free for awhile, Old Man."

He nodded the truth of that statement. He'd been seeing me on the yard for over ten years. He told me to come on into his cell and set my tail on a Number Ten can. I hunkered down while Curly cracked the seal on the jar of fresh mud and put a stinger in his cup to heat water. Steaming coal-black coffee, roll-you-own smokes, and all the time in the world. No place to go, nothing to do. Pulling a life hitch. May as well listen to an Oldcock tell a tale of the way things were in the Alabama chain gang, not so long ago, not so far away.

Curly Bill was one of the slimiest human slugs ever to crawl out from between a whore's legs, but he was a good storyteller. He perched himself on the edge of his rack, took a sip of the smoking joe and began his story.

"Her name was Rhonda Martin and they'd drove her up from the Julia Tutweiler Penitentiary for Women earlier that day. She rode the prison death train north, a chained bitch in an unmarked van with a one-way ticket to the State Electric Chair. She was condemned meat, the kind the prison screws burn at Holman Penitentiary. They kept her in a cell right by the electric chair for a few hours, then Warden Hobbs got him a call from the Governor's Office at the State Capitol. The message was plain and simple: 'Fry the Bitch.'"

"Were they burning women regular back then, Curly?"

"More than these days, but not a passel. Now, a bitch figures she can get away with murder, but back then it wasn't such a sure thing."

"So they brought her up from Tutweiler, and then what?"

"It was a little bit secret actually. The first sign we men on the cellblocks had that she'd burn was when a death house screw come up into our living area to fetch Billy Mumford out'a his cell. Billy had the job to shave the condemned. Head and leg."

"What kind of job is that?" I wondered.

"That's Special Barber assignment. Before they take you and set you in the chair you got to have a body shave so the electricity runs all around you nice and smooth. Billy does the leg where the electrode fits on, and he does the head. They let a man shave around his own peter..."

I gave Curly Bill a snort of disbelief. "I have my doubts anyone has to shave the hair around his peter for a ride on Sparky. What's the sense in it?"

"It's a rule, Boy. And if you don't care to believe my true tale you can march your dumb ass down to L-Wing and ask that Nigger Jim Richardson about the body shave he got when they was making a practice run on him back in 1970. Body shave means they take every single hair off, even the ones on your nuts, Boy."

"And a woman?"

"They skin her beaver."

"Hard to believe."

"I ain't asking you to believe. I'm telling you how it was and what I saw up at Holman when Rhonda Belle sat on Sparky." Curly Bill slurped some coffee and continued.

"So Billy went off to the Death House with the screw and later Billy comes back and tells us we won't believe it but there's a cunt from Tutweiler down in the Death Cell and they are fixing to fry her bottom real soon. He damn sure had our undivided attention when we heard it was a real female. Then we wanted to hear about the body shave. You know, did he shave her or what?"

"Well? Did he?"

"Billy told us he did shave her. He gave us the entire story. And it was his claim that when he was shaving her leg, her skirt was raised and he could see all the way up to where some brown pussy hair was sticking out from underneath the elastic around the leg hole. We were all asking him, 'Did she just set there and let you look?' and Billy swore that she didn't seem to mind his admiration of her charms at all. Now ain't that a treat?"

I bobbed my head acknowledging that it was indeed extraordinary and Curly Bill continued, "Billy told us she wore a white panty. Nothing fancy, just the plain kind the State issues to the gals at Tutweiler, but he could see a pelt of dark brown hair under the crotch part. And he truly believed that he could make out her crack right there in the centre part, there was like a little furrow where the panty indented and running along this groove was a wet spot dead in the centre, right where her hole would be underneath the cloth."

"I'd have been looking my own self. Bet on it!"

Curly Bill hooted and slapped his knee. "And remember how in those days a gal didn't show her leg all the way up to her asshole like they do now. It was a real unusual sight for Billy to behold, especially her being alive and setting in a chair right smack dab in front of his face. We all wanted to hear more and Billy told us everything two and three times, and each telling got better as he recollected little details and related them to us."

"What sort of details do you mean?"

"Her name for one: it was Rhonda Belle Martin. Ain't that a lovely name - Rhonda Belle? Her eyes: she had these big brown sad eyes with long eyelashes. Her voice: it was a lady's voice. Southern and polite, and sexy when she answered a question. He told us about her bosom: a real nice big one, and when she breathed it moved. Billy was taken with her hair... long, clean, pretty brown hair halfway down her back, almost to her waist. And then to prove it to us, Billy reached into his jacket and pulled out a swatch of thick brown hair held together by a rubber band around one end. It reminded me of one of those Red Indian movies where they scalp a pioneer lady then run off with her hair and hook it onto a pole."

"They let this guy Billy walk off with her hair?"

"He's the Special Barber, ain't he? He cuts the hair and hauls it off to the trash bin. Only this time he took him a little souvenir to show us in the cellblocks." Curly smiled a little, remembering her hair.

"We all smelled that long hank of hair. Put it right up to our noses and inhaled: it smelt real nice. Billy couldn't get enough of it. For a long time he would lay on his bunk, spread that spill of curly locks over his face, and jack his dick. For Billy, it was love at first sight between him and the cunt. He told us how he walked into her cell and right away saw she was no sweat hog. She was a sweet, pretty little woman. He had to tell her what to do. Take off your shoes. Peel down the nylon stocking. Put your foot in the bucket. She was shaking like a virgin and he had to calm her. Be gentle with her.

"There he is, soaping her leg and it's trembling in his hands. Billy knows where she's going, so he tries to go slow to give her a few extra minutes. She's about to die, but he's making love to her with his eyes. Maybe she loved him back. He said she did. She cried when he cut her hair."

"Sounds like Billy was gone."

"Billy was speculating about that wet spot in the centre of her crotch. He claimed it was love dew seeping, due to the way he was rubbing his hands up and down her leg. I reckoned it was plain old pee. I told Billy not even the horniest nympho at Tutweiler would be oozing love dew while sitting in the Holman Penitentiary Death House, even if Frank Sinatra was rubbing her leg."

"He took it pretty serious."

"Billy went all moony. We respected that. Didn't mention a word about the meat wagon from Bates Funeral Parlor that rolled in the back gate while he was down in the Death Cell sparking Rhonda Belle. Freddy, down by the gate, he saw it roll in and put it on the grapevine. I reckoned that gal from Tutweiler was thinking about something other'n Billy Mumford's passionate love while she was shaving the hair offen her own snatch. But I didn't tell Billy that."

"What did you tell Special Barber Billy?"

"We told him she'd get a stay from the courts. They'd send her back to Tutweiler and she'd write him fuck letters about what she'd do to him when he got out. What else?"

"Wishful thinking."

"Sure. And we were joshing Billy about it when Captain Scotty Crowe came walking up to the cellblock door. Captain Crowe ran the Death House. Enjoyed his work too. Got his name in the papers the time they burned that preacher's daughter from Anniston. Cute little blond with big tits, ekilled her mamma and her daddy. Told everyone the Devil made her do it. Maybe so. Then she come up to Holman and starts up that the Captain made an indecent proposal to her, so Warden Hobbs let him strap her cunt to the Chair. He did such a fine job they let him supervise every time a bitch burned. For all

I know he's still up there frying those girlies."

"So you think he made an indecent proposal to that preacher's daughter?"

"Bet your hairy ass he did. Told me so hisself. Said that little blonde was so fine it would give a man a hard on just to look at her. One night he goes down by her cell and suggests he could fit it so's she'd die with a smile on her lips. She wanted to know how. He told her. She went off like a firecracker. Preacher's daughter. What the hell?" Curly Bill took a long drag on his butt. Exhaled. Sighed. "So Captain Crowe calls me over to the door and told me a white woman would be executed within the hour and would I go down to the death chamber and keep my eye on Nigger Jack."

"Who was this Nigger Jack character?"

"An asshole, a real asshole."

"I gathered as much, but why the need to eyeball the man?"

"OK, Nigger Jack was the colored boy they had to clean up the mess after each execution. 'Lectrocutions are a dirty sort of business; when it's done Nigger Jack unbuckles the corpse from the Chair and takes it back to a little room where it gets hosed off. He'd strip the cadaver down, turn the hose on 'em, and stuff 'em in a rubber bag for delivery to the folks from Bates Funeral Parlor. It was nigger work and they had 'em a real Nigger to do it. Sorry excuse for a human being. Yeah. Nigger Jack was about as sorry as they come."

This story was getting good. I broke out the Oreos, took a handful and tossed the bag to Curly Bill. "Well tell me, Curly, just how sorry was this Nigger?"

Curly Bill dunked an Oreo in his coffee and crammed the whole wet cookie in his mouth. "When he first came on the yard he told us how he ran dope and whores. Had him a string of ten white ladies, *he said.*" Curly Bill sighed.

"Every nigger's fantasy," I smiled.

"Right. We should have seen through that right away, but we didn't. What happened was that Sandy, the guy who cleans up in the Classification Office over by the Administration Building, found his Commitment Order from the Circuit Court. It was under a desk. Dropped by accident, I guess. Fact was that this Nigger Jack had worked in an undertaking establishment catering to the colored trade in Mobile. One day the owner of the joint comes walking in unexpected and there was Jack with his radiator hose up the behind of a six-year-old nigger baby that died in a car wreck. Jack wasn't just raping a baby, he was raping a dead baby."

"Pure fucking slime."

"You got the idea. So Sandy ran off some Xerox copies of this unusual rap sheet and passed them around the cellblocks and Carl Jones from Mobile happened to know the dead kid's family. So Carl walked on down to the machine shop and made himself a big fucking shank and set off to hunt down Nigger Jack. Carl was telling everyone how he planned to get ahold of Jack, cut off his johnson and feed it to him like a chow-hall donkey dick. Jack went screaming off to Captain Crowe's office begging the Captain to save him from Carl Jones and his sword of retribution.

"Now the Captain is a merciful man, and he has a sense of humor. So the Captain gives Jack a little private room right down next to the Death House. Gave him a job mopping up the shit and the piss, let him clean the crap off the Chair after each execution. Best of all, Crowe figures the Nigger can pump him some hot ass fresh out of the Chair; after that, word on the yard was Nigger Jack takes a fancy to hot ass. *Smoking* hot."

Curly and I both laughed at that. He finished off his cup and plugged in the stinger for another round. He stacked three cookies neatly next to his cup and continued the story.

"So Captain Crowe had strong feelings about leaving Nigger Jack alone with a naked white woman, even if she was dead meat. He was sure the Nigger would climb on her in a heartbeat. Figured a well-known cornhole artist like Jack wouldn't hesitate at real white pussy like Rhonda Belle. Fresh dead and still warm. Captain figured I wouldn't let a nasty thing like that go on, knowing how I feel about niggers. So I told him sure, I'd help him out. Stand around to watch the show. I had nothing better to do, and that's a fact. So the Captain opened the cell door and he took me with him on down to the Death Chamber. I'll tell you the truth. I wanted to have a look at this Rhonda girl that had Billy Mumford running around with cow eyes and a stiff dick."

"Did you see her?"

"Of course I saw her. Another cup?"

I passed him my empty cup. He tossed me the Oreos and I hooked out a fistful. Munched one down and said, "I've been thinking about trying for that Orderly job for when they fry Sonia. What do you think?"

"Good looking bitch. Nice tail."

"Better than Rhonda Belle?"

"I'd say so. They say Sonia sold her ass on the street. Jesse says it's true. She'd play Hide the Banana with Old Scotty, I'd bet that. Maybe scratch his eyes out for him too." Curly smiled at the thought of it. "Rhonda Belle weren't much actually."

"What did you think when you first saw her?"

Curly poured us our fresh cups and told me how it went down. "Me and the Nigger was standing off to one side when they brought her in for the Chair. I was figuring I might see me a cat fight. The sight of the Chair can fire a gal up, get her to scratching and biting and howling. I'd heard some women go out that way. Screaming. But luck wasn't riding with me on that pass. She was no screamer. It makes for a better story if I tell it with Rhonda Belle screaming and begging but you said you wanted the *true* story." He blew on his coffee. "What actually happened was that Warden Hobbs marched off into that room where the condemned wait for the call to the Chair and told her pure and simple it was her time. He gave her the usual choice; she could come strolling in like a lady or he could have her drug in by a couple of big screws on the execution detail. It didn't matter a lick to him one way or the other. Miss Rhonda chose to go peaceful."

"So much for the cat fight."

"Maybe. Maybe not. With a woman you never know. Captain Crowe used to say it was because a gal is a high-strung, emotional type of creature. Women can get hysterical fast. He told me he'd seen it happen."

"So she said she'd go peaceful. Then what'd she do?"

"Nothing much. The door from the holding cell opened and there she was. Two big bulldagger matrons from the Tutweiler Women's Penitentiary were with her. Big mean looking bitches in black uniforms. Rhonda Belle weren't no young gal, thirty years old if she was a day. Her big brown eyes were roaming around the room, flickering here and there taking everything in. She seemed a little shaky but not too much. I'd seen men worse."

"What was she wearing?"

Curly Bill thought on that one for a few beats. "She had a flowered scarf over her head. Covered up her being bald. She was dressed nice. Ladylike. A black dress. Sunday-go-to-meetin' clothes. Maybe like she'd wear to a funeral come to think of it. Nylon stockings. Black patent leather high-heeled pumps that make a clickety-clack sound on the cement when she walked. There was make-up on her face: shiny red lipstick, rouged cheeks, powdered nose. She was wearing nice perfume. Back then a woman wore what she pleased to her own execution. Rhonda Belle fancied heels and hose, plenty of Chanel perfume. You could see how Billy had fallen for her.

She was pretty. She smelt real sweet." Curly Bill licked his lips at the memory.

"The two matrons had her by the elbows and steered her straight to the Chair. Warden Hobbs asked her to take a seat, so she turned herself around and sat down. She did it quick and smooth. She made a little squeak of alarm, like maybe she figured she'd get a shock from the Chair. But when nothing happened she scooched herself around and settled her nerves. She looked at Warden Hobbs and grinned sheepishly. He asked her if she was comfortable, and she bobbed her head.

"Then Warden Hobbs turned to Captain Crowe and ordered him to strap her in for the ride. She was looking a bit dazed, like maybe she really had been thinking she'd be going back on down to Tutweiler where she'd sit in her cell and write steamy letters to Billy Mumford at Holman and all of a sudden it dawned on her that a stay wasn't coming after all. She was in for a big shock, compliments of the State of Alabama. I asked the Nigger, 'Who'd she kill?'

"'Captain say her husband ate poison. Rat poison.'

"'Cold bitch to do that to a man.'

"'Fixing to warm her right up, Curly Bill.'

"That was a fact. The pretty flowered scarf was gone and the Captain was taping a strip of metal to the egg-smooth skin of her head. The Nigger explained that was the primary electrode; he told me that at the pull of a switch, 4500 volts of electricity would boil her brain. Rhonda Belle sat in the Chair and quivered. The fat matron with the dishwater blonde hair unceremoniously pulled up Rhonda Belle's skirt and unfastened her nylon stocking and peeled it down her left leg, impatient as a lover. The skirt was so high we could see the rubber strap holding up her other stocking, and the white fabric of her panty rucked up in her crotch. Me and the Nigger looked hard but didn't see the pussy hair curling out. I reckoned maybe that body shave rule applied to Tutweiler gals after all.

"'Oh my God!' the Nigger sighed.

"'Amen, Brother!' I added.

"We could see everything between the top of her stocking and the white panty. Meat the color of chicken breast at Sunday dinner. The tender, sweet kind. *Rhonda Belle* was tender, and she was sweet. I couldn't believe they were about to kill her. I had an impulse to step forward and tell them to leave her alone."

"Bullshit," I said. I just couldn't see old Curly Bill going sentimental on a condemned piece of ass. Curly cocked his eyebrow at me. It wiggled like a caterpillar crawling across his brow.

"God's truth. I'd never seen a woman put to death. It stirred me, way down inside somewhere." His eyes clouded and he looked away. The bastard seemed to have feelings of some kind and I waited for them to subside.

"Anyway. They fastened another metal electrode on her leg just below her knee. Clamped it on real tight with a butterfly nut. Her stocking was in a little heap around her ankle. Then they took her ankles and set them in the wooden stocks and locked them in."

"Stocks? Why'd they do that, Curly? I mean she ain't going nowhere."

"Holds 'em steady so they get an even burn."

"Oh." That shut me up.

"Yeah, and when they fix the ankles that way it spreads the woman's legs. Opens them right wide, and when that happened we could see all the way up." Curly Bill clearly relished this part.

"What did you see, the famous wet spot?"

"Nope. Looked like a nice fat jellyroll wrapped in white cotton cloth. The Nigger gave me a little elbow and we were both straining our eyes looking up her skirt, but we couldn't see no wet spot at all."

"So you really didn't see that much, did you?"

A smug look spread over Curly Bill's wide face.

"We saw plenty, Sonny. *Plenty.* You ever seen a woman sit on Sparky?"

"Sure."

"You have! Where?"

"Right here on Q-Wing. Girls from the college tours sit on Sparky every month... used to anyway. They'd sit up there and some of 'em would show their panties. It ain't that much to see, unless you see one that ain't wearing no panty. Then it's worth a real hard look."

Curly Bill rubbed his crotch and eyed me like he wasn't too sure he was going to give up any more story. I'd have to prompt him.

"Well? What was Rhonda Belle doing in the Chair, Curly?"

"She weren't doing a damn thing but sitting there warming the seat - legs spread like some honky-tonk tramp looking for a boner. Her forearms and wrists were strapped down to the armrests on the Chair. There was a black rubber belt drawn across her belly and another one that run under her arms just beneath her big ole bazooms; made it so they were pouched up like a movie star's titties. She was sticking them out like she was Jayne Fucking Mansfield on a casting couch. Bet you never seen no college girl wearing a set of death straps!"

"Well..." I shrugged.

"Damn right you ain't seen no woman's ass *strapped* to no goddamned 'lectric chair. When they lay that belly strap across her gut and snap it tight, the gal lets out a grunt like some stud just ran a ten-inch hardhead up her box."

"No shit! Why so tight?"

"Because, Idgit, when she rides the lightning she arches her back just like she does when she comes. They got to hold that stuff down in the Chair, Boy, or it would be an *obscenity.* Decent folk don't want to see no whore with her cunt raised." He caught my look and quickly amended, "Not at an official proceeding at any rate."

"What were you and the Nigger doing all this time?"

"Sheeeit. We was standing right there looking at her snatch with our tongues hanging out!" Curly stuck his tongue out and panted to give me the idea. I punched his arm.

"Go on, Man!"

"OK, once they got her body restrained, then they ran another rubber strap across her forehead. So she was pretty well immobilized. Warden Hobbs stepped up right in front of Rhonda so she could see him and read off the Execution Order from the Governor's Office. He read it slow and clear, so she wouldn't miss a word. When he was done Chaplain Curtis came in and read a few words from the Good Book over her."

"I wonder what she was thinking."

"I never found out. She had a chance to tell us but she was a quiet one. Warden Hobbs approached her and asked her real nice if there was something she'd like to say because if so she was welcome to speak up. She seemed to be contemplating an answer. I was thinking she might crack wise and ask Hobbs to hold her hand, or sit on her lap or something. But she just said she didn't have nothing to say about nothing. Very polite. Nice soft Southern voice. The Nigger was real disappointed. He'd been expected a speech, he said. Captain Crowe had told him some ladies get downright chatty at the last moment. Captain said the Preacher's daughter ran on for more than twenty minutes about how hard liquor and sex was the cause of her trouble. She'd finished up her story by giving everyone a charming smile and going '... and here I am.'"

"Wow. What happened to the Preacher's daughter?"

"Same as what happened to Rhonda Belle Martin. Warden Hobbs gave a nod to one of those big bulldaggers that rode up from the Women's Pen and she walked right up to the Chair and commenced to pushing wads of cotton up Rhonda Belle's pretty nose.

"The fat matron went right to work at it. She'd take a wad of cotton out of a blue box and work it into Rhonda Belle's nostril, then jam it on up there as far as she could with her finger. Didn't wear no rubber glove or nothing. Stuffed that cotton way to hell up there too. Me and the Nigger couldn't hardly believe it when we saw it happened."

"What the hell was the reason for the cotton?"

Curly Bill gave me a look of disgust. "So her fucking brains wouldn't leak out of her nose, Bozo. When they throw that switch and four or five thousand volts zap her in the head, the *brain boils*. And then it plain runs out your nose and down the front of your shirt. Or in this case, you'd see her sweetmeats dribbling down between her tits onto her lap." He leered at me. His eyes had the evil glint of a jackal.

"That's disgusting!"

"Happens all the time. You want to hear the story? Or maybe we'd better quit while we're ahead." He stood and hitched up his pants. "I don't want you puking up your Oreos, Kid. Think you're up to it? It ain't no pretty tale."

"Naw, naw, Curly, I ain't no pussy. I came here to hear a yarn and I'm a-gonna set this one out. That is, if you're still pouring coffee."

"You finished already? Well I guess you been drinking while I been yapping..." he was teasing me. "I reckon I could fix another cup, if you're gonna stick around."

"Yeah, Curly, come on and run the story. I want to hear it."

Curly settled the stinger for another round and continued. "The other fat dyke had an ass on her like a John Deere tractor. She was cramming cotton into Rhonda Belle's ears with the eraser end of a Number Two lead pencil. Sometimes the brains squirt out the ears too, you know?"

My mouth twisted with disgust. "How'd the girl react to all that poking into her head?"

"Howled like a fucking maniac is what she did. She was having a regular damn fit and shrieking 'What are you doing? What are you *doing*?' over and over again like a busted Victrola record. The two matrons didn't pay her no mind. They were as busy as a son-of-a-bitch pulling cotton from the blue boxes and making it disappear into Rhonda Belle.

"While they were packing her, the two matrons were clucking and crooning, 'Be still now! Act like a lady! This don't hurt! This is for your own good! Behave yourself!' and happy horseshit like that. And I'll tell you something else what happened just then."

"What?"

"The Nigger leaned forward and lowered his voice. Muttered, 'Curly Bill' toward the floor. I leaned toward him to catch it. 'You reckon they'll pack her hole?' he whispered."

"The Nigger said that right there in the execution chamber?"

"Sure, he was a sex freak, remember?"

"Yeah, I see what you mean."

"I said I'd never heard of no such thing, but I kinda hoped they would, now that I got to thinking about it." Curly slurped his java. "What the Nigger said next was even more interesting."

"I'm on the edge of my can."

"Nigger said, 'If they put something in her hole, I'll be obliged to take it out later.' And I looked over at him and saw that he was serious. I could see it in his bugged-out eyes. His mouth was wet with spit because he kept licking his lips."

"Pure freak for that hot pussy, huh?"

"Hell, yeah. By then Rhonda Belle was screaming and trying to wriggle out of the Chair. She wasn't getting nowhere, just howling like a bitch. Her nose was swole up with the cotton. She was crying. Tears running down her cheeks making wet trails through her make-up. She was a pitiful sight. We were watching it close, taking it all in. The Nigger whispered to me, 'That there be a *real* cunt, Man.' I gave him a look, trying to make out where he was coming from, and he came back real quick. 'Curly Bill, in here you can get a boy to suck your dick; you can bend him over and get you some shithole, but where you gonna get you some real pussy at Holman Penitentiary? Where else but right here?'"

Curly Bill paused and looked straight at me, waiting for me to say something.

"He had a point, I suppose."

"Bet your cracker ass he had a point. I told him I wasn't too sure about what he was getting at. I said Rhonda was wired for the electric enema, and that put me off my feed, so to speak."

"Did I miss something? They give her an enema?"

"That's what they call it when you hit you with 4000 volts and it blows the shit right out your ass and down your leg. I had heard of it. There was a good chance I was about to see it. That is, unless the bulldaggers put cotton up Rhonda's asshole. Now don't get me wrong. I like a boy to suck me off same as anyone in the joint. But I told the Nigger that dipping my wick in some whore's shit wasn't my idea of an afternoon delight. But the Nigger had an answer for that." Curly smirked and sat back.

"What was the Nigger's remedy?" I prodded, intrigued.

"The black son-of-a-bitch said the electric enema weren't nothing at all. He said, 'I've got me a water hose back there and Ill just stray some over her hole, wash it off real nice, and she'll be ready to ride. That juicy thing is gonna be as hot as a two-dollar pistol on a Saturday night.'"

"That makes sense," I commented judiciously.

"Damn right it makes sense. So I told that slimy fucker that maybe I'd go back there and give it a closer look after he'd rinsed her off. Maybe hit a stroke or two. You should have seen those rubber lips smile. That boy was grinning like a weasel in a hen house."

"He knew he was gonna get him some white pussy now."

"Yup, sure as hell did," Curly Bill snorted.

"Did the prison matrons put cotton up her butt?"

"Nope, those bulldaggers didn't fool around with that. I figured they'd dive right into her panties and straight up her hole. But they never messed with her."

"Too bad, that would've been a sight to see."

"Yeah. There was nothing to look at but the panties, so I looked up at her eyes and they were like Billy had said: large and brown and wet with tears. And miserable. She *knew* she was on her way to wherever fried cunt goes, and she wasn't too anxious to take that ride. Those eyes. They were desolate. Then Captain Crowe covered her face with the rubber death mask and she started going, 'Oh. Oh. Oh.' behind the mask. The strangest sound you ever heard a woman make."

"Sounds like it took a long time to get her ready."

"Well, not really. The event moved right along. Everyone seemed to know just what to do. They'd had plenty of practice. They burned men regular at Holman. Women only came in once in a while but it went down smooth enough. When the fat matrons were done, Warden Hobbs walked around the Chair giving Rhonda Belle a close inspection. He checked the straps and apparently he liked what he saw. He thanked the two dykes from the Women's Penitentiary for their assistance and asked Captain Crowe to show them to the door.

"Back then the only woman allowed to see an execution was the guest of honor, and she didn't really see it. The two matrons took one last fond look at Rhonda Belle sitting there on the Chair making her funny little noises. It was so weird. She kept going, 'Oh. Oh. Oh.' over and over, and making a noise like a hiccup. She'd twitch, and she was sort of trying to wriggle around. She had the Warden's attention. He watched her for a minute like he was memorizing her reactions.

"He pursed his lips and scratched behind his ear. Then he turned and gave a nod toward the black drape hanging off to one side."

"What's that for?" I asked.

"The executioner stands behind it, and when he gets the nod he pulls the switch."

"And he got the nod..."

"He damn sure did. One moment Rhonda Belle was wriggling around making squeaky noises, and a second later she was slammed forward into the straps so hard it make the leather creak. She came up off that Chair like a gymnastical gal trying to arch her body toward the roof."

Curly Bill was checking me out, to see if I got the picture.

"She came right up off the Chair?"

"Damn right! They gave her a straight shot of 4500 volts and when the power took her, it lifted her up and tried to fling her right out of the Chair."

I could just see it. Curly Bill was smacking his lips, warming to his topic. "When those straps bit into her, she gave a grunt like someone hit her a punch in the belly, and at the same time she let go a fart. A real ripper, lewd and unladylike. And listen to this: a jet of pee squirted right through the white crotch of her panty like it was coming from a pressure hose."

"You mean it shot out in front of her? How far would you say?"

"A coupla feet at least. Came jetting right out. Made a little pool in front of the Chair and between her legs. Her butt was maybe six inches off the Chair. The pee wet her pants and dribbled. There was only that first jet that came through, when they put the juice to her. She didn't pee a whole lot, just that puddle for her behind to sit in when it came down. Course, when the panty got wet we saw the crack. The McCoy. I recollect it perfect to this very day." Curly Bill was licking his lips, and I imagined that the bright look in his eyes was not too different from the one he had seen in Nigger Jack's.

"Is it true what you heard about the electric enema?"

Curly Bill sucked in his breath. "Oh, it's true all right. All the shit up inside Rhonda leaped right out her asshole and slithered around inside her drawers like a damn snake. The turd came out and coiled up in her pants. Made 'em sag with the load until they drooped down and touched the seat under her. The stink was vile. It rose up from under her and radiated around the room. There is no smell like it on this earth. Smoke was coming off her head. Her flesh was sizzling like bacon at the electrodes and her drawers were full of shit. The stench would gag a maggot.

"The Nigger's eyes were popped wide. He said 'Curly Bill, that's what they call the electric enema.' I didn't know what to say. The he said, 'Don't let it put you off none. All that washes off. I'll take care of that.' You see, he was coming on strong. He wanted that white pussy, and he'd do just about anything to get her. He knew I was standing between him and her, and he was working on me the only way he knew how."

"He was trying to work you up so you'd want a little piece yourself."

"Right. And he could see I was about to go a little green around the gills from smelling her frying flesh, so right away he started in on that."

"The smell?"

"Yeah. He said, 'Curly Bill, did you smell her perfume when they brought her in?' I gave him a nod while drilling my eyes on her body. It was changing color from white to deep pink. She was turning colors like one of them lizards that can go from brown to green when they take a notion. Only she was going from white to red. Her leg where the electrode was around it was as red as a lobster in a pot above the electrode and white as a catfish belly beneath."

"She was changing colors while you were watching her?"

He nodded. "She was cooking between the electrodes is why. A big ole burn blister rose up on her leg just above the electrode cuff. It swole up with liquid and then it popped and smoke rose up from it. The watery stuff soaked down into the cuff and hissed like a snake. Steam came up in a white cloud. Smelled so awful I could feel my dinner coming up on me."

I stared at him. He was really into the story. His lips were curled up in a grimace as if recoiling from the stench of frying flesh.

"Curly Bill. Didn't the Nigger say something about her perfume?"

"Oh yeah," he sniffed unconsciously. Maybe that cleared out the memory of the deathstench, because his face relaxed. "Nigger Jack told me she put perfume on her tits and in the crack of her behind."

"How'd he know?"

"He watched her through the security mirror."

"What's that?"

"It's where the prison officials watch a woman when she's naked. They watch her when she takes off her prison uniform and puts on her execution clothes."

The *men* watch her?"

"Sure they do. That's security. Suppose she jumps on those matrons? Anything could happen in that room. She could kill them two matrons in there and who'd know? They *got* to watch.

"Makes sense. But it must really embarrass the woman."

"Well, they do it in a polite way, so she don't feel embarrassed."

"Who watches?"

"Oh, the Captain and whoever else he lets come in to see the strip show," Curly Bill chuckled. "He would have killed the Nigger if he knew he was watching the white woman, but Nigger Jack slipped his sneaky black ass into the room while Captain Crowe was off checking on the death straps and had himself a nice long look. That Nigger, he got him an eyeful, and he was giving me an earful."

"Wanted to get your cock up for Rhonda."

"That's it. He said he'd watched the white lady shave the hair off her cunt. She squatted on the toilet and soaped it, then she shaved it, washed it by pouring water from a plastic cup over it, and patted it dry with a paper towel. Then when she was done she stood up and the fat matron handed her a little bottle of perfume and Rhonda Belle put some on her finger and went up behind her ears with it. She dabbed a bit on her neck, then ran her finger down smack between her teats. Lifted up each titty and put a dab under each one. Finally she rubbed some between her legs and reached around and drew her finger up the crack of her ass. The Nigger told me he took out his cock and jacked off into his bandanna just from the sight of her."

"Think he was lying?"

"Nope. I saw the look on his face." Curly Bill took out a cigarette paper and sprinkled some Kite tobacco onto it. He rolled it, licked it and fired it up. He puffed away at it, recollecting Rhonda's perfume.

"Nigger tell you anything else he saw?"

"They took away her brassiere. Made her go to the Chair without it."

"That's weird," I remarked. "Why?"

"No metal is supposed to be between the electrodes. None at all. The brassiere she had been wearing had metal fasteners and stuff on it, so they confiscated it from her. They made her wear special underpants too."

That got my interest. "Special in what way?"

"The Nigger knew all about it. He told me the panties the State issues convict women have elastic at the waist and leg. The elastic melts when they cook the gal, so before she comes up here, they sew up a special panty for her, one with no elastic. It 's got drawstrings like one of them bikini suits Brigitte Bardot wears.

"So after Rhonda Belle was shaved and perfumed, the matron tied the bikini on her ass. They knotted that sucker up tight too. We had to slice it with a razor to get it off."

"So you *did* get to see her pussy!"

"Damn right I did. I saw it snuggled up in her panty when she was alive. I saw it squirt pee when they ran the lightning through her. I saw her raise that pussy up off the Chair like a woman ready to fuck. And I saw it bleed - "

"What do you mean, *bleed*?"

"What I mean is...she was arched up in the straps and turned red as a cooked beet. Her hands were curled into grotesque claws with her fingers angling out in every whichway. She was shaking so hard her shoes fell off and her toes were curled up like she was coming hard. She was sizzling like a pan of fried meat. Up inside her belly some female part of her must have burst, because the blood rushed out from her. It gushed from her hole, it soaked her panties dark red. Made a pool on the Chair and dripped onto the floor."

I took a deep breath. I was trying to think of some reasonable explanation. "It must have been her time of the month, Curly Bill."

"Nope. For that they put the woman on the rag. She wasn't on her period. She just busted up inside and the blood ran out her cunt, that's all."

"That is totally fucking *gross*." Curly Bill's story was starting to get to me. I started to tell him to stop, but I figured it couldn't get any worse. Curly Bill looked like he was in another world, like he was actually seeing the whole disgusting spectacle and couldn't tear his eyes away.

"Now you know why they don't let ladies come in and see the executions. Even a girl reporter might be upset by a sight like that."

"You can bet the women will be here to watch Sonia Jacobs when she cooks."

"Yeah, and you can bet Sonia will have more cotton stuffed in her than a teddy bear. This ain't like the old days. Sonia won't get no 4500 volts neither."

"What will she get?"

"Not more than 2800 volts, about enough to just knock out her eyeballs. Damnedest thing you ever saw, eyeballs popping out of the head and hanging on the cheeks by the optic nerve. Happens every time. Why do you think they make them wear a mask?"

"I guess I never thought about it, Curly Bill. Or at least, not enough."

"Sonia will have it easy compared to girls in the old days. They'll stick cotton up her cunt, up her butt, let her wear a ministration rag to pee on, and give her plastic pants to boot. Then they'll tickle her to death with a measly couple thousand volts." Curly Bill spat out a shred of tobacco on the floor.

"1800 volts will kill you."

"Sure. After awhile, so will these RIP's." He blew smoke at me. "But Rhonda Belle, they ran the power through her for three minutes, then quit. Rhonda Belle went limp in the straps, sat down in her own fucking pile of slop as dead as anyone you ever did see. Doctor Garcia, the prison sawbones, was called in to examine her. He told everyone she was dead. Captain Crowe said, 'No shit, Sherlock?' and the sawbones scuttled on out of there. The stench was so thick you could almost see it; and it wasn't Rhonda Belle's Chanel we were smelling. That smell is really something. They ought to bottle it and make juvenile delinquents take a whiff every time they get to feeling ambitious." Curly chuckled at his own little joke, and I urged him on.

"So the fried lady was sitting there..."

"Oh yeah. Well, Warden Hobbs yelled to Nigger Jack, 'Git this damned mess out of my 'Lectric Chair!' and the Nigger comes back, 'Yes Sir, Mister Warden, Sir!' He unfastened all the straps and buckles, then loaded her onto a metal gurney and wheeled her away to the back room."

"Where were the screws."

"The screws were fucking gone - *long* gone. The show was over and the audience cleared out fast. Like I said, the place was stinking so bad, people were ready to puke. It's a *real bad* smell."

"So nobody was around but you and Nigger Jack?"

"Me and Nigger Jack - and Rhonda Belle." Curly Bill grinned like the very Devil himself. "We took that cutie into the back room and the Nigger got to work cleaning her up. He pulled down those nasty panties, cut the knots with his razor, and slide them off her ass. It was like he promised, exactly. He had his hose and he played it all around her hindparts. Steam rising off that hot ass, swear to God. Got after her with the lye soap. The mess came off her and went down the drain. He stuffed her soiled clothes into a bag. He poked her eyeballs back into their sockets and stuck a piece of adhesive tape over them to hold them in."

"Why was he going to all that bother?"

"That part was his *job*. He has to fix her up for the free-world undertaker. But soon as he was done with his job, he took her and draped her over a nail keg. He put the garter belt back on her and attached the stockings. Her head was down and her bottom was up. There was a big smile on those nether lips. Smooth as a baby's behind, and bright pink. The Nigger ran his hand over the full round ass end of her. He took his fingers and dropped them down to the centre of her pussy and spread the petals. It was a gentle gesture. Nigger Jack was very tender with Rhonda. He asked me, 'When do you figure she last had a man, Curly Bill?'"

"You stood there and let that Nigger handle her that way?"

He shrugged. "Hell, I had my eyes on that pussy. You would too. That stuff looked real good - pink and soft. And there was no more nasty smell at all. She was nice and clean from the soap job the Nigger gave her. I got up a little closer to her, and I caught a whiff of her perfume too."

"She was dead."

"Fresh off the Chair, Sonny. And still hot - about 106 degrees and cooling fast."

"But she was dead, Curly Bill, *dead*!"

He paused a beat. "More like dead drunk, actually. She weren't stiff, and she didn't smell bad at all. That Chanel on her neck..."

I licked my lips. Puffed out my cheeks. Held my peace while I waited for him to come back.

"It was the Nigger that did it. Had him a hard-on from sticking his hands in Rhonda's privates to clean her. He started to rub on it, then opened his pants and took it out. He spit in his hand and rubbed it on his dick. Then he just turned around and stick his johnson right up her poop chute."

"Cornholed her?"

"As I live and breathe. I watched him."

"What did you say to the black bastard?"

"I told him I had first dibs on her cunt," he answered with a straight face.

"First dibs," I repeated. "Then you fucked a woman who just got off the Electric Chair?"

"I never said that," Curly Bill disclaimed.

"Was it good?"

A look at Curly Bill's long yellow teeth was my only answer.

I got up off the buttcan and stretched. "I think I'll get moving, Curly Bill."

"Oh? What's the big rush, Sonny?"

I looked him in the eye and said, "I'm going down to see the Death House Captain about an Orderly job."

"Figuring you might get that job?"

I nodded. "Sonia. I've seen her picture. I'm in love. Hearing what you say, I'm ready to give it a try my own self. I know I'll never get me no more live pussy. So what the fuck."

"You can forget Sonia," Curly Bill said, a little smile curling one side of his mouth.

"Oh? Why is that?"

His curious smile became an outright leer. "Because the job's been took already. They gave it to the only convict in this joint with experience handling a burnt woman."

"*You!*" I whispered.

"Yup. Me. And when it's done, come on down and I'll tell you how she was." Curly Bill gave me a big wolfish smile as I turned on my heel and went back to my own cell.

3
OTTIS TOOLE
by Sondra London

My Friend the Cannibal

With over a hundred murder cases to his name, confessed serial killer Ottis Toole summed up his life for me, "It was living a nightmare. It won't never be over with. It don't make no difference what I do or say, it won't never be over with."

Psychiatrists have labeled Toole schizophrenic, psychopathic and retarded. Said one, "To him, life itself is so unmeaning, and the distinction between living and dead people so blurred, that killing is no more than swatting an annoying fly... He trivialized the distinction between living and dead, believing himself to be dead. Retarded and illiterate, he has been out of control since early childhood. A severely drug-dependent individual, he is unsafe under any conditions outside of a secure prison, and perhaps unsafe there."

Interviewing any maximum security inmate is always intimidating. It's not so much the inmate as the prison environment itself. Every prison is diferent, but there's always that distinct and unforgettable institutional ambience grating on my every nerve: the musty disinfectant smells; the loud, harsh sounds; the hot eyes of sex-starved criminals frankly appraising my femaleness; the coldness of the big, burly guards; the invasiveness of the no nonsense matrons as they conduct the mandatory body search; the irrational fear of being thrown out or worse - confined... and the sick feeling of finality as those big steel gates slam behind me with an ominous crash-*BANG*!

After a seven-month correspondence with Ottis Toole, I finally met him in July of 1991 under the highest security conditions afforded by the State of Florida. The East Unit of Appalachee Correctional Institution was completely locked down: all prisoners were confined to their cells the entire day of our interview. While I was undergoing security processing, six double-armed guards brought Ottis from his solitary cell to the tiny interrogation room, cuffed and chained hand and foot. When I commented on the extent of the security precautions, one guard chuckled, "If I let *this* 'un get away, I could forget I ever even *wanted* a job in the state of Florida!"

As I was escorted through the prison to the interrogation room by a cadre of various uniforms, I was so tense I could barely speak. I had heard so much about Toole's sudden fits of irrational violence, and as eager as I was to finally meet my new friend face-to-face, I had the feeling anything might happen, anything at all. I maintained my composure, but frankly... I was scared.

So they opened the double-locked door, and suddenly there he was, looking at me - this savage killer drag queen that was said to eat the flesh and drink the blood of his victims in ghoulish devil-worshipping rituals. As I approached him, he rose to greet me with a tight, anxious smile. Ottis Toole is not some kind of brilliant, clever Hannibal the Cannibal. To say he lacks charm is an understatement, but while his manners are most often crude and offensive, rising to greet a lady is one of those few little social graces he did manage to acquire at his mother's knee.

As I squeezed through the door into the cramped little room while he was rising to his feet, I found myself standing less than six inches away from a human being as unpredictable as any wild animal - I was right in his face. I stopped there to greet him, intending to shake his hand. But his hands were both cuffed to his waist, and as he started to reach toward my extended hand, the gesture was caught up in his restraints.

In that first moment, I stood there looking deep into his eyes - braced for wildness, cruelty, hatred. But what I saw cringing way back there, far behind the flat coldness of his hooded eyes, was a tormented child, crazed with pain... and fear of more pain. He wore a tentative smile, yet it was fear that filled his eyes... I was stunned to realize that deep inside, this brutal killer was even more scared than I was.

OTTIS TOOLE

In that moment, when I touched his fear with my own, my maternal instincts stirred toward the child huddled up inside the man, and I placed both hands lightly on his shoulders and touched my cheek to his, in an impulsive - if unprofessional - gesture of reassurance. "It's OK," I was telling him without words. "I'm your friend." I wished there were some way this wounded child could be healed, and the damage to his soul undone. If I could have kissed it and made it better, I would. But of course, therein lies the tragedy of the whole situation... there will be no rehabilitation, no return to a normal healthy state, for since birth Ottis Toole has been the Devil's own child. By now, he told me, his head is so full of devils that if a priest were to run all those devils out, there would be nothing left of him at all; he'd go "stark, raving insane." I believe him.

The Devil's Child

Born in the shadow of the Gator Bowl, Ottis is a real live gator - a bottom-feeder almost more reptilian than human, scuttling through the swamps of society, ceaselessly scanning for helpless prey. But how did he get that way? This is what I had come to find out.

By the age of four, Ottis had been run over by a car, and by the age of eight, he had fallen through a hole in his front porch, impaling his forehead on a nail that went three inches into his brain, resulting in *grand mal* epileptic seizures for the rest of his life.

His mother, whom he idolized, was a hardsell Baptist who chanted Bible verses to cure his ills, and dosed him with barbiturates to calm his nerves. He remembers his alcoholic father sexually abusing him from the age of six, and when the man left to go live with his own mother as man and wife, a stepfather came along who picked up where he left off - but this time, the child was passed around to his stepdad's friends as well... all along, his mother turned a blind eye to the abuse, denying to herself and her child that her husbands would ever do a thing like that.

Ottis was the youngest of a brood of eight, and his roughneck brothers beat up on their sissy kid brother regularly. Howell, the eldest - who is said to be the *real* homicidal maniac of the family - has shot at him numerous times over the years, once wounding him in the head.

His older sisters, Drusilla and Vonetta, dressed him as a girl and made him wait on them like a little Cinderella. "I started to think I was a girl after a while. Sometimes I feel like I'm about half and half, I do." He said he enjoyed dressing like a girl so much, that "when someone would take my wig off, I'd snatch it back and put it right back on." Drusilla, who later killed herself, compelled him to service her sexually. When asked, he denied any sexual contact with his sisters, but upon being reminded that juvenile authorities had sent Drusilla away for it, he changed his story without batting an eye: "Oh yeah, Mama did catch us once."

Taunted in school for being dirty and slow-learning, and for playing with fire, stuttering and wetting his pants, Ottis often played truant to visit his father's mother Cornelia. He loved this tall, striking woman in her long, dark skirts and high-heeled boots, and yet... he feared her, for she was a spell-casting, grave-robbing witch from the Okefenokee Swamp, a member of a hereditary death cult whose blood-drinking rituals had been passed down through the family for generations.

Ottis told me his earliest memories were of midnight trips to graveyards, where Cornelia urged him to rob graves for her, while the voices of the dead cried out to him, and the menacing "devil-trees" waved their black branches and leered down at the frightened child "like they were looking for something to eat."

He trembled as he told of falling through one rotten casket right into the flesh of a decomposing corpse. Screaming hysterically as he clambered out, he was shoved back down into the grave and forced to pull the bones from the rotting flesh. Cornelia needed those bones for her witchcraft, she told him, and he was the one the Devil had chosen to help her do her sinister work. He was born, she told him, to be the Devil's child.

Ottis described a typical scene from his home life... his grandma would go to bed with the chickens, but get up again late at night and take the old black dresser drawer that had served as his cradle, turn it upside-down, and arrange her makeshift black altar with the magical implements: the glass filled with blood, the black candle, the knife, the bones, and the wooden hands Cornelia called the Hands of Death. He would wake up to hear the chants she mumbled and smell the herbs she burned. "What you saying, Grandma?" he would ask her. "Hush!" she would tell the curious little boy, "You don't need to know! You know too much already!" And as she made up her bags of herbs, feathers, roots and bones, the drowsy child drifted back to sleep with the Devil's chants weaving through his dreams.

Already Dead

So, what's he like? Not a pretty sight, I'm afraid. Tall and gaunt, with rough, pallid skin, he looks like he might have AIDS. Though he doesn't appear very robust any more, when he was arrested, he was a strapping 6'2" with large hands and a powerful 200 lb physique. His mannerisms veer from tough macho to delicate femme. He must have been a real sight in his makeup, his long blonde wig, and the flashy, full-length ballgowns he used to wear when he put on his shows for his neighbors, lip-synching *Sugar Shack* and *It's Raining Men.*

Though he has a wicked laugh, and every other word is an obscenity, he is usually passive and soft-spoken, and guards call him their model prisoner. Inmates call him Grandma, because in prison society, he plays the femme, and the jockers highly prize the feel of his toothless mouth. He rarely wears his dentures except for the rare court appearance or interview.

He is unaccustomed to talking around his dentures, and on top of that, he has a speech impediment. Quite often, he is unable to articulate a word, and if asked more than once to repeat it, he becomes frustrated and irritated. His accent and idioms are pure gator, to the extent that his speech is often unintelligible to those outside the swamps. Apparently, I was able to interpret him better than most, as he told me gratefully, "Ain't nobody understands me the way you do."

His concerns are two - coffee and cigarettes - and any interview must begin by satisfying those basic needs before the conversation may proceed. Once he has his fuel in him, I found him relatively cooperative, but inaccessible. His literacy is at about third-grade level; he cannot understand abstract concepts; and while he may not actively resist questioning, his ability to respond is severely limited. While he does write simple letters, he is virtually unable to put his thoughts in writing, and all of the statements I have obtained from him have been through interviews - either with me personally or with reporters doing interviews I produced behind the scenes.

When asked how many he has killed - or when, or where, or how - most often he just says he doesn't know. When asked why, he will just shrug or respond vaguely. "I don't know why I did do it, to tell the truth. I'd have a pistol in my hand, and that's just what I done at the time." The best clue to *WHY* it happened was his image of the years he spent roaming the country with his lover and crime partner Henry Lee Lucas. "It was like playing Bonnie and Clyde. It was a murder rampage." Once, after a particularly barren interchange, he leaned forward. "Listen," he said with a pained squint, "Some people keep track of stuff. I don't keep track of *nothin'*. Most times, I don't even know if it's *day or night.*"

His memories are fragmentary, remote and recovered only with a marked effort. When asked a question about his past, he often lapses into a far-off, dreamlike state which may be quite extended before he responds. Law enforcement finds this behavior particularly unnerving when all they want is the facts; yet it's fascinating to watch, as you can practically *see* his brain malfunctioning. As Ottis explained to me, "Whatever I talk about I always go back and try to remember and sympathize. And it's just like I'm, living it, you know, like I'm doing it when I'm talking about it. Like it's really happening to me all over again." It's as if he leaves his inert body there with you in the interrogation room and time-travels back to the remote event, goes through it again, and then finds his way back to the room. Only then can be respond to your question. His eyes come into focus and then he speaks.

To some extent, his memory loss can be attributed to brain damage, but years of abuse of drugs and alcohol also contribute to his confusion. "With my mind fouled up so much, how was I going to know where I was at, my own self? I didn't pay that much attention to where we were going, because if we had some pot to smoke, I was smoking pot, and if we had some pills to pop, I was popping pills, and if we had beer to drink, we was drinking beer." During the years he spent roaming the country with Lucas, he claimed that between the two of them, they regularly downed a case of beer a day, often topping it off with a fifth of liquor, and they had unlimited access to drugs, including acid, coke, heroin and his drug of choice, speed. "Anything I could get my hands on, I'd take it."

Besides his memory impairment, he also has difficulty with telling the truth. "If I tell the truth, I'll get in trouble," he explained, sensibly. "If I don't tell the truth, I won't get in no trouble. So I'll just keep on telling lies." Like Lucas, he has given numerous false confessions. "I figured what's the difference between one murder and another, if you killed one or if you killed a thousand. I was playing a dangerous game."

It's hard to imagine living like that. Indeed, his existence is so remote from *LIFE* as we know it, that it barely justifies use of the word. "I'm already dead," he says plaintively. "I'm already down in my grave. The sides just ain't caved in on me yet." He has tried to kill himself by hanging, cutting, and overdosing many times. "I lost count. I'd say about a dozen times." He told me of a psychiatrist who had asked him if he thought he was crazy. "I told him yeah, and the doctor said, I believe you are too." He has been declared competent to stand trial, and the McNaughton guidelines for legal insanity seem to apply, in that he does appear to know the difference between right and wrong and to understand the nature of his acts, still... it's hard to avoid the use of an old-fashioned unscientific term like "crazy" when you behold the evil joy radiating from his face as he relates his vicious crimes and depraved pleasures.

False Confessions

The most shocking confession he has given to date was in 1988, when he told reporter Bruce Ritchie how he had raped, killed and cannibalized little Adam Walsh, whose father John Walsh subsequently went on to carry out landmark work on behalf of missing and murdered children, and now hosts the television show *America's Most Wanted*.

"The way it happened to Adam Walsh reminds me of my childhood too. It's really a filthy killing. It ain't no killing is clean. His head was chopped off and throwed in a canal. Otherwise he was molested and chopped up, and I left some parts all through the canal, and I took some of the parts back to Jacksonville, and I barbecued it just like ribs and ate it, ate his ribs, you know. I deal in cannibalism too, I do. I mostly chopped him all up in little pieces. I can't really deal with people too much, 'cause I don't know how to approach being around people. So I have to stay locked down. I can't approach the population or anybody else, because I might go haywire again, and just start chopping up somebody... I have different people say if they take me out, they wouldn't get no bad time, and they wouldn't get put in the electric chair for taking me out. I reckon they want to make me go off and take one of them out, the way they keep acting. I been doing all this since I was a child, I didn't just start doing it yesterday or the day before. I'm charged on a case I did way back in 1968. I choked a woman when I was fourteen years old... How this one happened was... (Adam) started whining a little bit, wanting to get out, you know. I hit him real hard on the chest and knocked the breath out of him. Then I got further down the road and I chopped his head off. Soon's I hit him in the chest, I put a blade up to his throat and cut him inside his neck, so I reckon that went on and drownded him inside his lungs, you know, that blood got inside of him. And then I put him face down and I took out my machete and chopped his head off. And I used a butcher knife on him too. Otherwise Adam Walsh was fucked too, and I made him suck my dick, otherwise I put my dick in his mouth afterwards, but I went on and fucked him after he was dead, you know. After I cut his head off, I drunk some of that blood. And after I cut his hands off, I scattered some of his parts about ten miles up and down that freeway. And

I kept the rest of his body in the trunk of the car. It was bleeding all over. When I chopped his head off, I throwed his head in the back of the car and I got blood all over the back seat of the car. That's when I throwed his head in the canal."

Even though Toole is still considered the prime suspect in the Walsh murder, police have not charged him, and most believe his lurid confessions to be a product of his vivid imagination, fueled by the desire to compete for headlines with Lucas. Even so, many of the details of other crimes he has confessed to have been corroborated by witness statements and forensic evidence, and there is no doubt that, regardless of the actual count, he and Lucas are both every bit the dangerous homicidal maniacs they claim to be. Even though some of the stories they tell might be fantasies, it takes a certain type of person to find pleasure in relating such tales...it takes a *serial killer*.

Like every serial killer I have known, Toole shows extreme mood swings, inexplicable changes in demeanor, and angry disavowal of his previous statements and actions. "I'm happy one minute, and sad one minute, then I forget all about it the next minute." Sometimes he might realize that he has changed and dismiss it casually; other times he doesn't even realize that he is contradicting himself, and when confronted with the discrepancy, he might just calmly admit that he's been lying again, or he might angrily deny it.

I have come to suspect that this combination of denial and instability is an essential component of the personality of any serial killer, inasmuch as the violence is sealed off from the more acceptable behavior, providing a mask of sanity that allows him to interact at some level of society in daily life, while conducting his criminal career unapprehended for long enough to rack up the numbers that earn him the *serial* rank. If he were overtly disturbed, he would most likely come to the attention of law enforcement rather quickly, and be apprehended right after the first offense. A serial killer might be articulate and attractive, like Ted Bundy, or he might just be your average gator like Toole and Lucas, but whatever level of society he occupies, it appears to me that he must be able to split off that part of his personality that commits crimes, in order to pass for normal.

Whether or not this trait is actually a symptom of a clinical multiple personality disorder, or merely an artifact of legalistic denial combined with typical psychopathic blame-shifting, it is disconcerting at the very least, and can become a real problem if you expect to form an understanding or agreement with one of these individuals that will endure over a period of time, as I have.

I remember a confrontation with another serial killer, when I told him I didn't believe he was telling me the truth about his crimes, because his stories were inconsistent. He leaned forward and gazed steadily into my eyes as he slowly explained, "You don't understand... because you're not a killer. My statements are inconsistent... because the experience itself is inconsistent. It's like I'm throwing rocks at your window... and you're trying to figure out where the rocks are coming from... and you can't... because they're all different colors. But you see... they're different colors... because they're all coming... from different places."

His imagery conveyed a fragmented mind where every truth conceals its equal and opposite, just as a smile masked his simmering anger... except when the mask slipped, and the fire of madness flared in his eyes. Everyone has their latent aggressions, but with serial killers, in time the anger that is so carefully concealed always emerges, if not in overt violence, then in fantasies, threats, or other evidence of the never-ending struggle with the murderous demons within.

In my interview with Ottis at Appalachee, I asked whether he ever got confused over whether he had done something or not, and he volunteered, "That's just like that case in Colorado, I still say that's my case." He repeatedly insisted that the case, a double murder at a massage parlor, was his. I asked him if he wanted to tell me about it. He nodded. I asked him three times, on tape, if he was *sure* he wanted to talk about it, and after repeating that he was sure, he added, "After *he* gets done here," referring to the psychologist in attendance. I told him I would try to arrange it.

It took phone calls, letters, affidavits and time, and meanwhile, Ottis was going through quite a few changes. For a while he was furious at me for "turning state's evidence" against him and trying to get him electrocuted, and raved that he wanted to stuff my head in a toilet. In considering his action, I was reminded of a statement he had made about the love of his life, Henry Lee Lucas: "My love turned to hate. That's what kind of love I got."

I continued to write to him, explaining over and over that I was just following through on what he told me he wanted to do, that he wasn't being charged with murder, that I would not testify against him, and that if he didn't want to talk about it any more, he could *JUST SAY NO*. I'll never know what he understood from my letters, or what might have changed his mind, but eventually he recovered his sunny demeanor, and seemed to understand that I was not about to betray him. At any rate, he went back to writing that he loved me, and old queen that he is, even asking me to marry him. At least for a while...

Nine months later, in April of 1992, we found ourselves in a Colorado court, where Ottis had been transported by Lear jet at a cost of a half-million dollars. Another man, Park Estep, had been convicted of the crime, had served his sentence, and had recently been released. Toole had taped a series of extended confessions to the two slayings in 1988, and the video tape was played back for him as he sat there in court watching how he had described every detail of the crimes, even drawing an accurate layout of the massage parlor and diagram of its location on the street. As he told the story in 1988, he had stabbed one woman and shot the other, raping one and setting the other one on fire.

The tape was periodically paused while Richard Tegtmeier, Estep's lawyer, walked Toole through the details step-by-step. Toole had stated in 1988 that before he left, he had taken some petty cash from a jar in the kitchen. "So you took some money from a jar on the kitchen counter..." recited Tegtmeier. "I did *NOT*, stupid!" snapped Ottis, "The jar was on top of the *refrigerator!*" He smirked at how he was humiliating the attorney, but lacked the insight to realize he was just once again graphically demonstrating that he was the only living witness to the murders.

The State of Colorado promised him that he would not be prosecuted for this crime; they just wanted to know whether there was sufficient reason to give Park Estep a new trial. But Ottis adamantly refused to admit that he had committed the crime and behaved like a bratty kid. He called the attorneys, the investigators, and the judge obscene names, and told them all to go fuck themselves in a variety of colorful ways. "Y'all can take that confession and shove it up your ass whichever way it fits!"

Every time he acted up, he would mug and grin at me like he was so cute. Like I would get the joke. He claimed the 1988 confession was just a game he was playing to embarrass the police, and said the details he had furnished were just lucky guesses. "I ain't killed *nobody* in the State of Colorado!"

For three days, Ottis sat on the witness stand in waist-chains, shackled hand and foot, watching himself chain-smoke his way through his explicit confession. By the third day, he was more fractious than ever. He leapt to his feet and shook his fists, rattling his chains and hurling obscenities. The court had no way of knowing how meekly this raver would have responded if they'd let me handle him: "*Ottis, behave yourself! You sit down there and hush your nasty mouth! This is a court of law, and don't you be acting up like that! You got to show some respect!"* But the judge, a somber-faced young woman, sat perfectly still and made no response at all.

Perhaps because no attempt was made to correct his naughty behavior, he continued to outdo himself at showing off. After one outburst, the attorney asked him how he felt, and he responded: "I feel like I'm about to go off," he leered, panning the courtroom to gauge the reaction of his audience. "Y'all won't let me smoke a *damn* thing, that's why I'm not going to cooperate." He had not been allowed to have a cigarette since he left Florida, and no exceptions were to be made.

And even though the court had subpoenaed me and brought me out there directly pursuant to his statement that he wanted to tell me about the case, they would not allow Ottis to talk to me. So the crimes he had insisted he wanted to tell me about were stubbornly denied, as a mischievous Ottis Toole once again had his fun with law enforcement, gloating and gaping, basking in his moment of glory.

OTTIS & HENRY

This conversation was taped by police in 1988:

O I want to ask you something, Henry.

H What is it?

O How many niggers did me and you kill?

H Ah, niggers. Ah, let's see. That'd be, ah, approximately twelve altogether.

O About twelve?

H Yeah, somewhere around that area.

O Some of 'em was ah...

H Well, what they call niggers, or half-niggers and half-white.

O Some of 'em was gay and what have you too, wasn't they?

H Yeah. They's been a mixed breed of people, as far as the killings themselves go.

O Remember the way I liked to burn 'em up and all that mess too.

H (Laughs) Well, I've been accused of that too. I have done it, you know. I'm not gone deny that.

O Are you counting just the ones you killed by yourself, or me and you killed together?

H I've only told 'em about the ones that I've done.

O You told 'em 150, didn't you?

H Yeah, I gave 'em 150 positively, identifications on the ones
   that I've done.
O I told 'em with me and you together it was maybe about 50 or
   60.
H (Laughs) They's a lot more'n 'at, boy.
O I've killed over a hundred and something by myself.
H Well, I know that's a whole lot.

I couldn't stop...so I just kept going....
by Ottis Toole

I used to hear voices...

Right now I could go to my mother's grave and lay down on the dirt and hear and feel the dirt vibrating... and I can hear her moving around down there... and I know she was hearing me when I was talking to her... laying down and talking to her... and I could feel the dirt vibrating... I used to go out there all the time...

And I used to go with my grandmother into graveyards... we used to dig up all kinds of bones... get all kinds of herbs... and she used to take the bones and do devil worship... she would put spells on you with the bones... she would make voodoo dolls... take a chicken and wring the chicken's neck... I had to do what she said... she told me I belonged to the devil... she'd say you do what I tell you to do... you can't quit... you ain't never going to quit...you do what I say... I said, well maybe she's akin to the Hands of Death, you know... but she was a real witch... she wore long dresses... long hair... she covered her face... she went through graveyards... and barns... putting spells... burning altars... she had skulls in her house... she showed me how to take a drawer and turn it upside down and build an altar out of it... and take hands and a knife and a cup, and put it all up there... it was real interesting... there was no slowing up...

When I was real little, my dad put me under the clothesline and he tied these two cats' tails together... I was under the clothesline and these cats just scratched each other's guts out...blood was running over the top of me... I was yelling... I was real young... and he was akin to the devil... and they used to make meat with a dog...

I was real little... he made me have sex with him... my real dad and my step father too... I just kept going...

couldn't stop... I used to dress up like a little girl when I was real little... so it got wilder and wilder over the years... couldn't stop... worse and worse... it just kept coming... wide open... I didn't know what to do... stop or quit or what, so I kept going... doing what my grandma told me to do...

I just kept going... sometimes she'd get a fresh body... and cut the head off and all... and then she'd take the head in her hands and hold it until the skin dried and sometimes she'd take the skin and put it up against her skin... I don't know why she was doing that... she cut the skin open and put it over her skin... I don't know why... she said it made her skin stay young... I don't know why she did it... I just did what she said...

Sometimes she would pee in a big jar and pour it all over me and tell me it was a way to keep the devil in me... so that's what I did when I was a little kid... right or wrong... I couldn't figure it out...

Since this chapter was written,
Ottis Toole has begun to
participate in a series
of exclusive interviews
with Nemesis,
giving highly personalized
reminiscences of his past life,
recountings of his life in prison,
and nightmare descriptions of those
crimes he is known to have committed.
DEVIL'S CHILD - the Story of Ottis Toole
is coming soon...

4

THE ROLLING PAPERS
by Sondra London

"To sing about someone you love is one thing but oh, the blood's hidden guilty river-god is something else."
- Rainer Maria Rilke

Danny Rolling, as sketched by Sondra London

The Accused

Danny Harold Rolling is the mysterious singing drifter who is facing the death penalty for the gruesome 1990 mutilation murders of five Gainesville college students.

After a massive two-year manhunt and investigation costing the State of Florida a record five million dollars, 39-year-old Rolling, who had been jailed shortly after the murders, was finally connected to the crime scenes by the DNA fingerprint left by the killer, and charged with five counts of murder and three of rape. He has pleaded not guilty to all charges, and is scheduled for trial in January 1994.

Rolling is currently serving five consecutive life terms plus 170 years. As an habitual offender, he received maximum sentences for a string of robberies and burglaries committed immediately after the Gainesville slayings. He has also been named as the prime suspect, but not charged, in three similar slayings in his home town of Shreveport, Louisiana.

He has done time in Louisiana, Georgia, Alabama, Mississippi and now Florida. His record was consistent, and it was not that of a killer. His crime of choice was pulling a handgun in a grocery store and running off with the cash. When caught, he would confess, plead guilty, and go directly to jail, almost as if he thought that was where he belonged.

The Gainesville Slasher

On August 26, 1990, the day before fall classes at the University of Florida began, the bodies of Sonja Larson, 18, and Christina Owell, 17, were discovered when Christina's parents called the police after they had been unable to contact their daughter. The anxious parents waited downstairs while Officer Ray Barber and a maintenance man opened the door with a passkey. The maintenance man opened the door, took one look, and ran downstairs to throw up.

One victim was nude, the other partially clothed, and both of their faces were slashed. The nipples of one victim had apparently been cut or bitten off, and Christina Powell had been raped anally.

"I think he's somebody who likes to do it," speculated Barber. "It's one thing if you're so mad you lose control and shoot somebody or stab somebody. He's sick...the guy's just a very, very sick person. I don't mean sick in a mental way. I mean sick in a disgusting, shocking type way."

"I was ill," said police spokesperson Sadie Darnell. "There was some decomposition and the apartment was warm, musty. And there was the 3-D of it... not just a picture kind of thing. A lot of sensory things were occurring at once. It was an unusual death situation. Evil."

At about 1.00 a.m. the next morning, 18-year-old Christa Hoyt, a student at Santa Fe Community College who worked full time as a records clerk for the Alachua County Sheriff's office, was found murdered in her duplex apartment.

Ms. Hoyt's body was discovered by Alachua County deputies after she failed to show up for work. She had been decapitated, raped vaginally, slit from public bone to breastbone, and her nipples removed. Her nude body was found in bed, and her head had been placed on a shelf which had been positioned, along with several mirrors, to project the grisly image out the front window.

"That image... incredible," recalled Lt. Spencer Mann of the Alachua County Sheriff's office. "I mean far different from and exceeding anything I've been exposed to in my life."

Later that same day, a bare-chested Danny Rolling robbed the First Union Bank, in the same part of Gainesville. He vaulted over the counter, using a gun to smash the video camera, and, talking constantly, ordered everyone around, snarling sarcastically as he left, "Have a nice fucking day."

On the next day, August 28, Tracy Paules and Manuel Taboada, both 23, were found murdered at the Gatorwood apartments, a popular complex midway between the two last crime scenes, with a smiling gator at the entrance announcing that the Gatorwood is "The Place to Be".

The other victims were all pretty, petite, dark-haired young women, but Paules' roommate Manuel Taboada was not just a man, he was an athletic 200-pound ex-bouncer. He appeared to have been attacked while in bed asleep, and he, like the others, was stabbed to death. Both Manny and Tracy had apparent defensive wounds on their arms, and Tracy had been raped anally. But this crime scene was not quite as carefully staged as the first two, possibly because the killer had been caught in the act.

The Gatorwood maintenance man who discovered the bodies believes the killer might have still been lurking about. When he unlocked the door to the apartment, he says he saw Tracy's body on the floor, along with her purse. He immediately closed the door, re-locked it, and went to call police. But when he returned to the apartment, he found the door standing wide open, and the purse gone.

In each of these five related cases, the crime scenes were elaborately staged, with blood being apparently collected and removed, and fingerprints meticulously wiped. In each case, the killer entered the apartment by prying open a glass door which opened onto a dark wooded area; used duct tape to bind the victims (later removing the tape), raped, assaulted, and/or mutilated them with a knife; then washed their lifeless bodies with a household cleanser and posed then for maximum shock value.

Dr. Michael West, a crime scene analyst who was brought in from Mississippi especially for this case, spent one and a half days combing the scenes with a light intensifying device. "I thought I'd seen everything," he said. "This is the most difficult crime scene I've ever seen. All the areas the killer touched or manipulated were free of prints. Nothing. I've never seen so many incidents of violence at a crime scene without leaving any evidence."

But the staging went beyond the mere obliteration of evidence. Common household objects were placed around the bodies in seemingly-significant patterns. What these arrangements were, or what they might signify, will remain unknown until the case comes to trial. "It was strange, very quiet and very different," said Sadie Darnell. "And it meant something."

"In the scene, the setup, there was a message - to authorities, to law enforcement, to whoever," observed Gainesville Police Captain R.B. Ward. "The primary purpose was not the deaths. It was organized violence. This whole thing was packaged in such a way as to make some sort of statement... The person doesn't necessarily want you to say Why? as much as he wants you to be shocked by the way he committed the crime. Although we didn't realize it at first, this person is leaving us messages or signals. He's saying, 'You're not stopping me. Catch me if you think you can.' He enjoys the control he is exercising and the confrontation with authority."

DNA testing later identified semen found at two of the crime scenes as Rolling's and a single pubic hair from a victim was found at his campsite. It is on this evidence that the state has built it's case.

A Flash of Brilliance

Rolling was arrested ten days after the murders for a string of robberies, but the attention of the task force did not focus on him until early 1991. One of the first leads that pointed to him was a VICAP printout from the FBI. Nine murders that had been committed nationally were listed as similar to the Gainesville cases, and among them was a triple murder in Rolling's home town, Shreveport.

Julie Grissom, 24, a petite brunette who modelled clothes at a mall, her father Tom Grissom, and her 8-year-old nephew Sean Grissom, were found in their Shreveport, Louisiana home in November 1989, slain in a fashion similar to the Gainesville victims. The killer used duct tape to bind Julie, raped her and assaulted her with a knife, left bite marks and saliva on her breast, then carefully cleansed her vaginal area with vinegar and posed her body, removed the duct tape, cleansed the crime scene of prints and blood, and left her just-washed blouse in the washing machine.

While the initial evidence showed that the killer was blood type B and a secretor - like Danny Rolling - later DNA testing failed to conclusively link him to this crime, and to date, although he is still considered the prime suspect, he has not been charged.

Indeed, many who have considered his past record, in contrast to the profile generated from the crime scenes, believe that Rolling doesn't fit the profile of the Gainesville Slasher. "I have doubts about this guy," says psychiatrist, John Philpin. "I would want to see some flash of organization, deliberation, calculation, something well thought-out. I would want a little flash of brilliance." However, Philpin was intrigued by Rolling's relationship with his father, James Harold Rolling, a retired police lieutenant. "What clicked for me was the taunting that was done in the arrangement of those murder scenes. The people who have to come in and deal with that are police officers. If you wanted to express the rage that you feel toward police officers or people in authority, that would be the ideal way."

It's standard operating procedure for the friends and family of a serial killer to express disbelief that the person they had known so well could be capable of such crimes. It's always disconcerting for those who knew someone in a non-violent, law-abiding context to be told that this person they thought was a regular guy was actually some kind of monstrous human atrocity. Cops realize how ordinary law-breakers can be, but they too like to think they can size a guy up. What disoriented law enforcement about Danny Rolling is that he was known to them as an habitual offender, with a set MO as a gun-toting stick-up man.

"He may have committed other crimes that we just don't know about yet, but he's obviously not a real good thief. He's been caught a bunch of times," Philpin reflects. "These robberies almost seem like an invitation to be caught. He makes an effort to get away, but it's a fairly inept effort, and then when he's caught he sort of rolls over and gives it all up. Whereas the Gainesville killer has obviously gone to great lengths to plan not only the crimes, but his escapes. These are very well-thought-out killings."

He is My Dad

If Danny Rolling is indeed guilty of the Gainesville student murders, it makes mincemeat of the FBI's neat distinctions between "organized" and "disorganized", as well as "spree" and "serial" killers. And the art or science of profiling provides absolutely nothing to connect this apparently inept robber to the hyper-organized killer that staged those eight murders. Either Danny Rolling is "a puzzle inside a mystery wrapped in an enigma," or he didn't commit those murders after all.

Because of his pre-trial status, it is impossible to explore his actual involvement in the Gainesville student slayings at this time. However, he has confessed to shooting his father, and has shared some insights into this crime.

It happened at home in Shreveport three months before the Gainesville murders, when a family argument erupted over Danny's drinking. As he described it to me, "After our argument, Dad chased me out of the house with his gun in hand. Once in the front yard, he fired his weapon three times, stormed into the house, slammed the door, and locked me out. I was worried about Mom's safety. I went and got my .38 caliber revolver, and kicked the door in. Dad fired three more times, missing me by inches. I answered his volley with three of my own. One went high to the right, missing him entirely. One struck him in the abdomen. The last hit him between the eyes. I did kick him. Lord God forgive me... how I regret it all... Sure, Pop has made his share of mistakes. He is a man... like I... and I have sure made my share of mistakes. The one big scare that etches across my heart is that I shot my Dad and blinded him in one eye and caused him to be deaf in one of his ears. It was only because of the good Lord God above and his mercy that the bullet that hit my Dad between his eyes didn't take his life. It doesn't matter that I fired in self-defense. He is my Dad."

Danny's mother Claudia Rolling said in a letter to the court, "I know this man... I'm not going to say he's perfect; he isn't... I'm just a mother who loves her son very, very much... Danny was an abused child from the day he was born. My husband was jealous of him. He never wanted me to hold him or show love in him. He was told from the time he could understand that he would be dead or in jail before he reached the age of 15. I would have to write a book to tell you all we as a family have suffered because of my husband's jealousy. You see, both my husband and my son have a mental problem. My husband by birth and my son because of physical abuse."

His aunt Agnes Mitchell told the court, "Danny was rejected by his Dad when he was born, and he said the baby was not wanted. He grew up knowing he was not loved or wanted by his father. He was not allowed to eat at the table when his dad was in the house or watch TV with the family. He was told all his life he was stupid and no good." She also stated that Danny's mother was not allowed to wash Danny's clothes or cook his meals.

Neighbor Bernadine Holder also observed, "He has a father who hates him! Danny's father wants him dead and has stated this to me." She also stated that as a boy, he often played alone in the yard. "When he was older, he didn't go to movies or football games like other kids."

Danny's friend Bunnie Milles told the judge that Danny was not allowed to wear shoes in the Rolling house except in the kitchen, and she once saw him put his shoes on and off seven times in a 45-minute visit. She described Danny as "a worthy, idealist person at heart," who actually had his father on a pedestal. "He told me the more he tried, the more he was condemned and criticized by his father... Danny would get on his knees like a little child and say, 'I love my Dad, I try so hard to please him... How can I ever be somebody? I want to so bad. I've always wanted to make my Dad proud of me... I want to make it in this world, but how can I? How can I?' and then he would cry; his heart was breaking... The only way I can described Danny is that he has... multiple personalities. In one he is so humble, a wonderful human being trying his best to do the right thing. Sometimes I'm not so sure he is aware he has done anything wrong, because it's like something clicks, and when he comes to the realization... he says, 'Oh, my God, what has happened? Why did I do that? I would not have done that for the world.'"

Danny's recently departed grandmother, Mrs. Cavis Rolling, made this last statement about him: "Danny is just like the clouds in the sky. Some days it's shining and some days it's stormy and raining. Danny changes just like the clouds, and nobody knows why. But he's a good boy."

His father has made only one statement about charges leveled against his firstborn son. "He ain't killed. He may be disturbed, but he ain't guilty of that."

The Rolling Papers

While I had been keeping a file on the sensational Gainesville co-ed murders, I had given little thought to Danny Rolling's personality until May 22, 1992, when he was convicted of bank robbery and given five life sentences. What caught my attention was that, at sentencing, he *sang* his statement to the judge, in what reporters called "a melodious tenor voice that never wavered off-key." That was my first clue that Danny Rolling was *different*. My second clue was the letter I got from him a month later.

He was held in isolation, on suicide watch, and under constant observation, when he wrote to me on June 23, 1992: "Madame Sondra, Media Queen, let me introduce myself... I am Danny Rolling. I'm sure by now you've heard of me." He started right in, telling me about a tape of his songs. "This tape has brought about quite a stir in the media. CBS News has tried all they can do to get their hands on it. How would you like to be the first?" So *dramatic*! Continuing, he said, "Sondra... many people in the media have tried desperately to get an interview with me. I have refused all. Until now... I extend my hand...to you." And he included a hauntingly beautiful song lyric illustrated with fine hand-completed color artwork.

His grandmother observed that he changes like the clouds, and I for one would tend to agree.

For the first six weeks we exchanged letters, getting to know each other gradually - at least I thought we were. Then I innocently mentioned something about his notoriety, and also said in passing that I was not a criminal. His response troubled me:

"Sondra... you have really pissed me off! Do you think I ask for all the publicity I've received over the past two and a half years? My name and face plastered on the front page of newspapers all over the world... my face bounced off satellites around the globe. Do you actually think I get a kick out of all this? *YOU ARE WRONG!*

"You said you're not a '*CRIMINAL*'... Well! I don't like being called a '*CRIMINAL*'. I don't feel like one and I don't want to be one. The very mention of that word turns my stomach. Yeah! I've made my share of mistakes. But... I do not consider myself as a *CRIMINAL*! You don't hear me calling you an 'ambulance chaser' or 'gumshoe' do ya? Of course you don't. Because I give you more respect than that. I expect the same."

And then his rough angular printing went back to his usual jaunty script:

"OK. Enough ass-chewin'! Back to home base."

I honestly didn't realize *CRIMINAL* was such a loaded word, for him or any other prisoner. It seemed logical to me that since he had confessed so readily to all these robberies, that he'd recognize that this was *CRIME* he was committing. I tried to soothe his injured pride by apologizing, and suggesting that maybe I should have said *OUTLAW*.

That was a dicey moment, but it was nothing compared to what came next. Two days later. Even though he signed off with his usual "See ya later alligator, after awhile crocodile" and "Your friend, Danny," still he was telling me goodbye:

"Sondra, our roads have crossed one another. I for one am glad to have made your acquaintance but now... we must go our separate ways... at least... for the time being. You have... like you say... other interests... and you really don't need Danny. Hey! That's OK... I understand... Don't blame you a bit... Maybe... Down the road one day... our paths will cross again? Who knows?"

I had no idea what he was talking about, as I had already put all other interests aside to give him first priority, and I had never said or implied that I didn't need him. All I could do was wonder what in the world went wrong... and wait four days.

"Sondra, my last letter was written in haste. I've since regretted I ever wrote it. I don't want to throw away what we have already built together. So... I'm eating crow... can't seem to get you off my mind... I still want us to work together... if you will still have me? I won't ever say goodbye again... Promise, and I'm good to my word."

How curious! I was glad he got over it, whatever it was! That was August 24. For a couple of weeks, he again sent me beautiful songs, poems and drawings, and warm, friendly letters. Until September 6:

"I'm sorry... I must say goodbye now. There is no need to try and contact me. I will not respond."

I couldn't believe it - here we go again! More doubts, more wondering what happened... until ten days later:

"Don't go! I have erred in saying goodbye... so here I am again... standing in the rain... with egg on my face... asking to be part of your life. I've really made up my mind! I want your friendship and expertise. You do excite the artist in me. I don't want to lose that part of me I share with you."

I was delighted to have him back. Our work continued. Gradually, in *The Rolling Papers*, a complex and revelatory self-portrait has emerged, in narrative and verse, artwork and song, and in the process of our bringing it forth, has transformed both of us in what Danny calls a "shocking and magical way."

The first volume was completed while Danny was at the Corrections Mental Health Institution undergoing observation 24 hours a day, and he could only use a pen three hours a day. After a five-month stay, he was transferred to Florida State Prison at Christmas. Nearby cellmates were Bobby Lewis and Ottis Toole. It was there that the second volume was completed in early 1993.

The Beast Within

As we continued to exchange letters, our relationship slowly changed. I was asked to define that relationship on the first visit application for the mental health institution. In Florida you can't visit someone both as media and as a friend. The Department of Corrections had already informed me that I was not "legitimate media" under their terms. I asked Danny if he'd like me to visit him as a friend. In reply, he sent me a drawing of a stallion in flames and a heartfelt poem: "You asked me if I wanted you as my friend? My answer is in this poem I send. From the ashes springs this fiery steed, that our friendship will grow and you may know, I am your friend until the end."

My application to visit Danny during his stay at the mental health institution was ultimately rejected, because our relationship was not leading to marriage.

I had always felt a certain fascination with him, but I resisted it. Somehow I managed for months to keep things on an intellectual plane, and maintain a degree of emotional neutrality. We started our collaboration in July, and by October we had become personal friends. By Christmas I was embroiled in a real moment of crisis over the way my own emotions were responding to his. After all, this was supposed to be "just a story" and the Book says you must never get involved with your subject... much more so when that subject is a convict. Taboos are broken when a writer falls in love with an accused serial killer.

Once Danny and I professed our love for each other, we had to decide what to do about that part of our relationship. I told Danny that while I loved him, I could not risk admitting it to the public. I feared it would hurt his feelings if I concealed the truth about us, but he was very understanding, and readily agreed that it would be best to keep our romance private.

Then... a stunning development. In mid-January of 1993, without consulting with his attorney, Danny made an extensive series of incriminating statements about the Gainesville murders to Bobby Lewis. He authorized Lewis to relay his statements to the state's investigators. Danny understood that his co-operation would be reciprocated by the State granting my long-delayed application to visit him at Florida State Prison. The talks proceeded to a certain point, and then Danny balked. The prison wasn't sending me the application for visitation, and the State wasn't getting what they wanted.

On February 5, even though I still hadn't received the application, I was contacted by a State's investigator and summoned to the prison on a special pass.

Danny and I were given two hours together behind an inch of bullet-proof glass. And on the day I met him face to face, the powerful emotions I felt were undeniable. All at once, what had been warmth became an apparent heat.

I approached my meeting with Danny thinking I was prepared for anything. But there was one thing I was not prepared for. I had no idea what a fine-looking man he is today. Instead of the broken and dejected loser I'd seen on TV... standing before my hungry eyes was one gorgeous hunk of man. I'm sorry, folks, but it's the truth. My Maximum Man stands an imposing 6'2" with muscles out to here. His color is bright, his youthful skin is glowing, his hazel eyes are clear... and so is his head. The news footage publicized the courtroom image of him stumbling about awkwardly, stupefied by Thorazine and seeming lost in his own body. But now my "dangerous pussycat" strides across the floor with a languid power and instinctive grace that makes me highly aware that I am a *woman*, and this is a *man*. It's easy to see how he recently snapped the chain on the heavy boxing bag, kicking it a dozen feet across the prison gym. "I'd fight a sabre-toothed tiger for you," he swears, and I believe it. While he shows me his gentle side, it is obvious he can be ferocious.

I had wondered for so long how his smile would look. The face in the mugshots and courtroom footage was always a tragic mask, and even the family photos he sent me were unsmiling. When his unwavering gaze met mine, I could see within his luminous eyes the trusting and open soul that I had learned to love from the phone calls, letters, songs and drawings, he had shared with me.

My heart literally melted as I heard his soft voice saying, "You are so beautiful, Sondra...so much prettier than your pictures."

I was speechless. My hand touched the cold glass pane, and his reached out to meet mine. But even though most of our time was spent wordlessly gazing into each other's eyes or laughing and talking as friends and lovers, he did find time to ask me to put out a press release about his recent talks with the State. This was the only thing he had ever asked me to do for him, and I readily agreed.

All too soon, our visit was coming to an end. One last time I leaned toward the glass, and heard his husky whisper. "I love you, Sondra... I want to cover your lips with kisses."

"Some day you will," I promised with a bittersweet smile, though I still don't know when that day will come.

A Current Affair

I took me a few days to compose an appropriately discreet press release, and to get the wording approved by the State's investigators. Finally on February 8, 1993, I faxed out to major media outlets my cautiously-worded statement that in a recent exclusive interview with Danny Rolling, he announced that he was co-operating with the State "in exchange for the pleasure of my company."

On February 9, my revelation about Danny's co-operation with the State hit the front pages... and right next to it was a story reporting an interview with an FSP inmate, claiming that Danny Rolling had confessed to the Gainesville murders, that Bobby Lewis would become a State's witness against Danny, and that I was exploiting Danny by feigning a love I did not feel, in order to get his story.

In the resulting media feeding frenzy, the State's investigators seemingly washed their hands of the matter and denied everything. The Department of Corrections announced that I would no longer be allowed to visit Danny because I had "misrepresented the purpose of my visit." Of course, no statement had ever been made or requested regarding the purpose of my visit. It was the State that summoned me to the prison, and if they had not done so, the gates of the prison would not have opened for me in the first place.

I was hit by a barrage of requests for interviews. I denied them all, as I was planning to give Danny exclusive national exposure on *A Current Affair*. My relations with the Florida press are not the friendliest. Since I announced that I had the inside story on Danny Rolling, they expected me to give it up to them. I have been, and continue to be, characterized by some of them in the most unflattering terms possibly because I am keeping my story, and Danny Rolling, closely-held and under wraps.

Danny was stunned by the unkind slurs being made against my character by the daily press. With characteristic dark aplomb, he took it upon himself to make a grand gesture that dismayed me when I first heard about it, but endeared him to me all the more when I found out the whole story.

He had asked me to announce that I was his exclusive media contact. No statements were be released or interviews granted except by me personally. When I told Kathy Belich of Channel 9 in Orlando there would be no interviews, she wouldn't take no for an answer. She made a request to Danny directly. I was flabbergasted to hear he had granted their request. They began airing promos for their big *EXCLUSIVE* interview with the mysterious Danny Rolling. News reports commented snidely that this was being done "without the approval of writer Sondra London, who claims to have exclusive access to Rolling."

I was humiliated, not knowing what to think of Danny. He continued showering me with passionately loyal and supportive letters, like his hand-made Valentine inscribed, "You can run, but you can't hide...Hold on tight, cause you're in for a hell of a ride!" I couldn't believe he was intentionally betraying our exclusive commitment - and yet it was true, Danny was talking to the media.

Kathy Belich was only able to air 30 seconds of her Valentine's Day "interview". Danny calmly read a prepared statement singing the praises of his one and only Sondra London, refuting the nasty rumors about us, and scolding those who had been so unkind to me.

"Ms London and myself have been corresponding for almost a year now...she is of the highest caliber, sincere and honest, a woman with extraordinary talents," he stated with a composed and sophisticated delivery, glancing from time to time into the camera. "She did not deserve the things being said about her or what the newspapers have printed about her. It's just not so. Sondra London is a colorful and bright woman, and it's a shame the way the media has bashed her of late. She hasn't done anything to deserve that."

Danny carried on this way for about five minutes concluding, "Ms. London represents me as editor, agent, and media go-between. From this point on, I shall make no further statements to the press unless Sondra London arranges it. You want to talk to me, you speak to Ms London."

He politely thanked Ms. Belich, declined her pleas to comment on the Gainesville murders, and excused himself. She was so hard-pressed to find a scrap of footage that didn't contain the words "Sondra London". She used only his statement that "the wheels of justice turn slow, but they do turn." She called his statement "enigmatic". It wasn't to me.

It was a month before I obtained a copy of the raw interview footage, Only then did I realize that his quixotic gesture, which I originally took as a betrayal, was meant only to authenticate our relationship. I had sent him a Valentine through the newspapers, and he sent me one over the TV.

The Department of Corrections spent a month nervously shuffling before approving the request of A Current Affair, to interview Danny. Danny wrote on February 20, "I love you, Sondra, and I want you for myself completely. I bend my knees, kiss your beautiful hand, look into your warm eyes, and ask your hand in marriage. Yes, I want you for my wife... I love you that much."

And he proudly told viewers of A Current Affair, "I'm madly in love with her." Genuinely touched by Danny's heartfelt pledges of love but with considerable trepidation, I responded. I revealed on A Current Affair that I loved Danny Rolling, and then on Geraldo that I intended to marry him. I wanted the world to know.

I am always confronted with the same question: "How can you love this monster?" My answer is that there's much more to Danny than just the crimes. Knowing him as I now do, to me he's not a monster, he's just "Danny" - a fascinating, talented and exciting man. I love him because of the way he is with me, and all I want is to be left alone with him, so we can continue what we set out to do: tame the beast within... "in a shocking and magical way."

I believe it is true, as Rilke suggested, that "all the dragons of our lives are really princes who are only waiting to see us be both beautiful and brave. Perhaps everything terrible is in its deepest being something helpless that only wants help from us."

Evil Mirrors

Danny Rolling recently sent me a poem he's written about seeing ourselves mirrored in the eyes of others. As I thought about Danny and the reflections he had seen, I was reminded of an old fable.

Hans Christian Andersen tells in **The Snow Queen** of an evil mirror created by the most evil troll of them all, the Devil. It has the power of reflecting anything good or beautiful, as loathsome and hideous. And if any good or kind thoughts pass through the mind of the person reflected in it, a horrible grin appears in the glass. The Devil delights in pointing his mirror at beautiful things, and watching the hateful images it reflects.

One day the little trolls at the school where the Devil was the Headmaster got hold of his mirror, and they flew all over the world with it, until there was no person who had not been distorted in it.

At last they flew up to Heaven to turn the mirror on God Almighty and all His Angels. Well, the closer the trolls brought it to Heaven, the harder the mirror grinned and laughed, until it laughed so violently the trolls couldn't hold it. When they dropped it, the mirror shattered into billions of splinters, some as tiny as a grain of sand. And those splinters are still flying around today, each one with the same evil powers as the whole mirror. If one gets into your eye, it will distort everything you see, and you will only be able to perceive the flaws, and not the virtues, of everything around you. And if one gets into your heart, it will make it turn to ice.

What was the message in the mirrors that Danny Rolling is said to have placed so purposefully next to the severed head of Christa Hoyt? What signal did he flash before our unwilling, still uncomprehending eyes? Was it only a mocking summons for us to dare pass through that silvered portal and enter a shrouded kingdom of horror beyond our worst nightmare, to confront evil incarnate?

Or was it a weeping child's only way to explain a broken toy, a broken life, a rage that may be at one and the same time unspeakably vile and totally innocent?

It is we who will decide the meaning of the evil mirror. Whose face did we see reflected there? His, hers... or our own?

There are many kinds of mirrors. When we look into each other's eyes, we are using the other person as a mirror, discovering who we are by virtue of what we see reflected there. This is the most elementary, prosaic level of mirroring. But by placing a mirror at an *angle*, we enter into a more sophisticated dimension, because we are sending the image of our mundane reality *out there* into the domain of the eternal. Capturing and projecting an image is like placing a mirror at an angle: once an act is written or recorded in any way, and that image is broadcast *out there*, this is the only worldly form of immortality we can know. Because it exists in this eternal dimension, the image takes on a life of its own that overwhelms the original by virtue of its greater power. That's what happens when your real life enters the Public Domain. Once you become a Public Figure, every act is immortalized as part of the whole drama.

The Gainesville Slasher went beyond snuffing out the lives of five Florida youngsters. He worked hard at the crime scenes to create an effect that would provoke a powerful reaction, even using evil mirrors to transform those hideous tableaux into a kind of *Street Theater of Horror*. And the dynamics of the theater have responded accordingly. The images projected in those evil mirrors have provoked the unwilling audience to a level of outrage that continues to mount, and has made the accused slayer into a "Special Case".

And since I announced that I am not only contracted to publish his true story, but engaged to marry him, I too have become a "Special Case". I am bemused to reveal that I have recently been immortalized in the annals of criminal justice by being enjoined with Danny Rolling as his co-defendant in an unprecedented move attempting to prevent us from publishing *The Rolling Papers*. (See Florida v. Rolling, London, et al., case no. 93-265-CA filed in April of 1993 in the Eight Judicial Circuit in and for Bradford County, Florida.) Stay tuned for breaking news from the Theater of the Real.

"Judge, there's just a whole lot of suffering and sorrow to go around in this world."

The above words were spoken by Danny Harold Rolling on the 21st of May, 1992, upon receiving five life sentences, plus 170 years, for armed robbery.

Yes there are a whole lot of sorrows in this ol' dark world. I know I've had my share. As a child, I lived a nightmarish existence. In our house, we didn't celebrate birthdays. I couldn't have friends over. Mom's family was not welcome, and our neighbors too were shunned.

It is difficult for me to speak about my father. One day I will open the floodgates of my mind and let all the strange fish tumble out. When I do, I know the dam is going to break.

For some reason, my Dad always seemed to cast a shadow over Christmas and New Years. Oh sure, we had the usual... the Christmas tree with different colored lights... there would be presents... there would be turkey and dressing... and there would be *DAD*. And we would all be walking on eggshells.

Dad just couldn't get it. It wasn't the presents or the brightly lit evergreen tree. It was about love. *LOVE*... a word my Dad did not know how to say or express. Poor Dad... he was always like an old grizzly bear with a quill in his paw... and we were the objects of his fury.

Dad was two people to me. There was the image of the policeman... the retired lieutenant... looked up to by everyone for 22 years... I can still see his shining badge. But when he came home and the uniform came off, Dad became someone else.

Dad drove Mom to the point where she had a complete nervous breakdown. I'll never forget it. I was about 9 or 10 years old the day they took my mother away.

A red and white ambulance screamed into our driveway. Two men dressed in white marched into the house. They put my Mom, sobbing and shaking, into a stretcher, and they took her away. We didn't see her for a while after that. But I shall never forget seeing her on the bathroom floor crying. I walked up to her to hug her neck and she started screaming! I told her, "It's OK, Mom, it's Danny." But she didn't hear me. I said, "I love you, Mom," as I looked into her confused, hurt-filled eyes, but she didn't see me. Dad had pushed her too far.

I wanted to shout at my Dad... to punch him... to hit him for how he bullied Mom. But I was just a little feller... and I was scared.

NO PLACE TO BE
by Danny Rolling

PRISON: Webster's Dictionary defines it as "an institution for confining people convicted of major crimes... penitentiary ... confinement or forcible restraint."

I've been asked, "What does it feel like to be in prison, and how does it sit with you that you have five life sentences and 170 years?" Webster's puts a pretty face on the beast by calling it a penitentiary. I define it simply as *HELL*.

Louisiana

If you want to know what prison is like, all I can say is lock yourself up in your bathroom for two months and don't come out. No TV, no radio, no nothing! That will give you an idea what it's like. Of course, there's much more to it than solitary. I've done time in five southern states: Louisiana, Georgia, Alabama, Mississippi, and now Florida. I've been on chain-gangs, road-gangs, solitary confinement... and each has its own distinct flavor.

Although anyone who has been in prison would just as soon forget his or her experiences in the joint, you never do. The culture shock of it changes you forever, branding you an outcast. My experience of incarceration began at age 16. As teenagers will experiment, I had my first taste of alcohol in the spring of 1971.

At 16 I had a high level of imagination. It was one way I vented my frustration and pain. One April afternoon, I was searching for adventure in the woods behind the old Sunset Drive-In.

With my bows and arrows in hand, I became an Indian Hunter in quest of the Great White Buffalo - although the prey were merely rabbits and snakes, and any other critter that had the misfortune of ending up at the other end of my arrow. This day, I had seen only a couple of rabbits... become bored ... and started to turn over things looking for snakes.

I came upon a piece of tin. "I'll betcha there's a big one under there!" I said in anticipation. I flipped it over and jumped back. A big black snake curled up ready to strike in defense. Immediately I pulled an arrow from its quiver, notched it, drew it back, aimed, and let if fly, pinning the venomous vermin to the bare earth.

As I watched in amazement, the snake writhing and biting the wooden thorn embedded through its scaly hide, I heard a boisterous laugh. I turned and saw a white-bearded old man sitting on the steps of his one-room rickety shack. All about his feet, ten mongrel dogs were barking and dancing about wildly.

The old man motioned for me to come over. I did so with caution... the dogs snarling and baring their yellow fangs. The old gentleman shouted, "Behave Now!" and the dogs cowered down.

He told me to step into his shack and take his .22 caliber pistol from his pillow and kill the snake.

As I stood over the snake, I took aim and blew its head off. I brought the smoking gun back to him and he chuckled, "Good shot, Boy."

We became good friends and on weekends and after school, I would clean out his old shack that would become full of empty beer cans and wine bottles. You see, he was a wino.

One day after cleaning out his place, he gave me half a gallon of Italian Swiss Colony Wine Muscatel... real rotgut stuff. I drank it all in about 30 minutes... and passed out in the weeds behind the Sunset Drive-In while the sun was shining high in the sky. When I awake, the stars were twinkling and the moon was grinning down at me from its heavenly perch.

"Oh, shit!" I said, struggling to my feet. "Dad's gonna kill me!" I staggered home only minutes before my dad came home from work. You see... my Dad was a policeman. Dad stormed in and we had an argument. I had never argued with him, because I was scared of him, but the alcohol gave me courage.

Dad threw me on the kitchen floor and handcuffed my hands behind my back, and called for a squad-car to take me to jail. I spent two weeks in Juve Jail. The food tasted plastic... the place smelled rank... I got into a fight... I was kept locked up... and I felt betrayed.

GEORGIA

Reidsville...Georgia State Penitentiary. My first taste of prison life, and it gave me one hell of a shock. The racial tension was so thick you could cut it with a knife. And sometimes you would have to.

While I was there, two riots broke out. A friend of mine got his kidneys punched out with a rat-tail file. Then three blacks caught this one guy on the third tier. Two of them held each arm, while the third butchered him. His only fault was being at the wrong place at the wrong time... and being white. He was in his twenties, and only had 90 days before his sentence was completed. Two months later, the brother of the slain man caught two of the blacks that killed his brother in the showers and stabbed them both to death.

One man working in the saw-mill was thrown into a woodchipper and left for dead... but somehow he managed to hold on with one hand. He lost both legs and one arm... but he survived.

There is no place safe in prison. Even the chow-hall can be your end. I once saw a man get his brains bashed out with an industrial can opener. Twice fights broke out in the mess-hall at Reidsville. At the time they still had guards armed with shotguns in the mess-hall towers, and whenever there was a fight they would pump buckshot into the room.

At Reidsville, there lived many wildcats that took up housekeeping under the buildings. There was this one black cat that I recall vividly. He would slink from under the building parallel to the mess-hall step up on a flat rock, and get himself a drink of cool water that dripped from a spigot there. How I grew to hate that cat! He became the symbol of everything I detested about Reidsville. While I was imprisoned there against my will, the cat chose to make it his home.

I wanted to kill it, remove it from my sight forever. But a nine-foot chainlink fence separated us. One day, I purposed to kill that black cat with the green eyes that taunted me. The day came. From his lair, the dark shadow crept into the light. Ignoring me, he stepped onto the flat slab and began to drink.

"Today is your day, bucko," I said and picked up a large round stone. All in one motion, I leaped on the fence, my left hand grabbed the fence and pulled me up, and with the right hand I threw the stone as hard as I could at the defiant drinking cat.

The noise startled the cat and he turned about quickly... just as the stone struck him dead center on his forehead and knocked him out cold. His feet just went out from under him. I looked on, fascinated. I could hardly believe it. See, it was an impossible shot, a one in a million chance I could hit that cat at that angle and that distance, while holding myself up on a nine-foot fence.

The cat did not move. I thought for sure it was dead, and went about my business. An hour later I passed back by the same spot on my way to chow. Lo and behold... the cat had crawled off. I thought, "Hmmm... maybe cats do have nine lives... but this one now has *EIGHT*."

Alabama

Staten Pen, in the lovely state of Alabama. I was transported to Staten at about 3.00 a.m. The lights of the prison could be seen miles away, surrounded by empty darkness, like a beacon warning careless sailors away.

Staten was not so bad as far as prisons go. Anyone who has done hard time would consider it a Boy Scout camp. Still ... it was a prison, and it held its own dangers and distress. You see... you can't paint a pretty picture of cold stone, barbed-wire fences and guard towers.

I was the baker while I was at Staten. Boy! Could I ever bake. Sometimes the only thing the fellows looked forward to was Cowboy Rolling's yeast rolls! Can you imagine? They hated to see me go.

They called me Cowboy in those days. When I first got to Staten, I was put on the road-gang, a squad of 39 hardened black convicts. I made the count 40... and I was the only white guy.

Early every morning, except Saturday and Sunday, we marched miles out into the fields. We dug ditches, planted crops, harvested, and when the sun hung low in the western sky, we marched back to the compound dirty and tired... under the constant eye of a lawman astride a magnificent horse with a shotgun in his saddle, and a .357 in his holster.

Dusty roads, from dawn till dusk, marching back... the cons would say, "Cowboy, sing that song." It never failed. I got so tired of singing it, but I'd sing it anyway:

"Oh, chaingang living...
Of your life you're given...
A-so many years...and a-so many tears...
Before you see your home again."

They loved it.

At Staten I had a good rep as a boxer. We didn't have a boxing ring. Instead, about 300 or so convicts would make a human circle and throw the two to fight in the midst. The only rule was you had to wear boxing gloves. I had several fights...the dust would fly... and I loved it! I never lost a match... at 38, I can still go.

I saw my first and only total eclipse of the sun at Staten. I shall never forget it. We were at the center of the path of the eclipse. A friend of mine purchased a piece of dark welder's shield that one of the fellows had broken into chips and sold for a dollar a chip.

We stood there on the sandy yard and gazed skyward. Just before the eclipse, time seemed to slow, as if the whole universe stood still. The birds began to act crazy, flying about singing weird songs... they were frightened. As soon as the moon passed in front of the sun, the birds fell on the ground, and there was a dead silence. The sky changed colors, from deep blue to a dark orange. Everything appeared like a double exposure. I grabbed the welder's piece of glass from my friend's hand and caught the eclipse at its peak. It was magnificent! As though God had stuck his mighty finger in the spokes of the universe, and everything went still.

Once the sun began to move from behind the moon, the birds began to fly again.. .the double exposure look came together crystal clear...the sky became blue again... and I felt small under the face of the Heavens. The experience left a longing in my already lonely heart.

Mississippi
Parchman Prison boasts of being the largest prison in the world, and it is easily that. It stretches out in all directions as far as the eye can see. Mississippi Delta farm land... its major crop: *KING COTTON.*

It was a blistering hot summer day when I arrived at its gates. They threw me into solitary confinement for a year and a half. My first cell was an oven... no air ventilated it. It was a closed cube built to simmer a man in his own juices. I spent three months in that cell in a dehydrated state before they moved me.

My next cell was miles away from the first one. I remember the lonely days with nothing to occupy my mind except watching the black birds that flocked outside my window. Ninety days passed, and I was moved again.

It had become fall, and my next residence was a place of torment. My first night there was cold and horrible. My cell was an ancient crumbling capsule. Someone down the long hall screamed all night long, and I slept fitfully.

The next dismal day, I awoke with my stuff... such as it was... floating in three inches of water. This phenomenon occurred every night. Finally one day the lieutenant came by my cell, and I pleaded with him to move me to a cell that didn't flood out. He did... but the sergeant of that cell block was a big mean black man who hated white folks, and I became the object of his scorn. He removed me from the nice clean cell the lieutenant had placed me in on the third tier... and threw me into the worst cell in Parchman Prison.

The hallway was at a grade, and my cell was the corner one at the bottom. It flooded out at least three times a week with raw grey-brown sewage. It seeped in through the floor and belched from the drain up the hall. The sludge would creep down the hall and bubble through the floor... and my cell would fill with filth. It's the most horrid smell I have ever known. It was winter, and between the creeping crud and the bitter cold... I went insane.

One day as the snow was falling from a grey sky and covering the hard brown ground, I watched from my cell window, as a lone sparrow flew down. It landed in the snow, and during the night, it froze to death. The thought of that little frozen sparrow left a cold spot in my heart.

Then there was the time I pulled the covers on my bunk back to go to bed... and a rat jumped out from underneath. He escaped under the narrow space between the cold steel door, and scampered gleefully away down the hall.

There were three spiders that had spun their sticky webs in the corners of the ceiling in my cell. I named them Ned, Ted and Fred, and when things became unbearable, I would speak to them as my friends. I fed them flies. I was quick enough to snatch a fly out of the air, then I would pull its wings off and throw it into the spider's web.

Ned and Ted were skimpy eaters. They began to ignore my offerings, so one day I became upset at their indifference and squashed them both with my shoe. Now Fred was different. He never turned up his nose at a fly or a moth. He would pounce on it with a vengeance, bite it, wrap it up in his silky bonds, and save it for a rainy day. I liked Fred. When I was moved a year later, Fred was well-fed and looking good.

When I was taken out of my solitary cell, I was put on the chain-gang. My first day out, I was loaded onto a modified trailer that had been cut in half length-wise. They herded 400 of us onto it like cattle. Front to back, crammed in like sardines. If someone farted, there was no place to go. You just held your breath. It was freezing cold, and I was not issued a jacket. In the early morning frost, the trailers drawn by old John Deere tractors rumbled off down dusty, bumpy roads, into the angry red eye of the rising sun.

When we got to our destination, we were unloaded and given wooden-handled hoes. I overheard some of the boys making bets as to whether or not I would last the day long. I pondered this, and decided I would endure, no matter what. And what a test it proved to be!

We were set to work against a square mile field of cane-grass. Our hoes cut the cane and beat the hard ground all day, except for 30 minutes to eat lunch and two 15-minute breaks. At the end of the day, I literally crawled back to the trailer. They had to send me to the hospital. When I finally got to see the doctor, he took one look at me and laughed, "There's nothing wrong with you! Get out of my sight!" Ha! That was Parchman. It's just the nature of the beast: kindness was preyed upon, the weak abused, and the ruthless respected.

I was forced to pick cotton and dig ditches until I was exhausted and sick. You had to get no less than sixty pounds of cotton a day or you were punished. Rows and rows of white cotton, gleaming in the noonday sun. Eighty pounds of cotton dragging in a sack behind me. Off in the distance dust devils whirling about like demoniac sentinels, keeping watch over the slaves. The guards on horseback would shout, "Awright girls! All I wanna see is assholes and elbows! Get that cotton!" And that's what we would do.

One day picking cotton, they brought the water tractor around as they did every day. We were filling our waterjugs. But I never used a jug, it just got in the way. Instead, I would kneel and drink from the spigot.

Someone threw water in my face. I stood up and looked about, but nobody said a word. So I knelt down again... I was thirsty... and again, someone threw water in my face. This time I jumped up and started punching the man nearest me.

Someone in the gang yelled, "It ain't him! He didn't do it!" I stopped fighting the man and asked him if he did it. "No," he said, so I left him alone. I turned toward the gang and demanded, "Whoever threw water in my face ought to be man enough to own up to it."

The biggest... meanest... ugliest... black man I ever saw in my life came forward and said, "I did it, Whitey. Whatcha gonna do about it?" I charged him, feet and fists flying! We ended up rolling in the dust like mad dogs. After that day... they no longer called me Cowboy. They called me *PSYCHO*.

Florida

And now... Florida State Prison in Starke, Florida ... gives new meaning to the words *HELL ON EARTH*. What more can I say? Prison is everything you don't want... and no place to be... period.

THE DEATH PENALTY
by Danny Rolling

The earliest form of execution I am aware of is described in the Old Testament in Genesis 40:9-22. This classic story is known to every Christian. Several thousand years before Christ, we see beheading as the common cause of execution, because Joseph said that Pharaoh would lift the baker's head from off him and hang his lifeless body on a tree for the birds to peck on. Quick, to say the least, but messy.

Later, in Numbers 15:32-36, we read of the Jews stoning their condemned. They found a man gathering sticks on the Sabbath, and the Lord said to Moses, the man shall surely be put to death. All the congregation stoned him, and he died.

The Romans were a bit more creative... they developed crucifixion, the same method that brought us salvation through the suffering of the Lord and Savior Jesus Christ, praise his holy name, and thank God above for his great love towards us sinners that he gave himself as ransom for us all (I Timothy 2:5-6).

As time ticked on, gunpowder was discovered, and so the firing squad soon followed: Kaa-*POW! OOOW!*

Hundreds of years later, Christopher Columbus sought out America, and it wasn't long before we were burning accused witches at the stake. If your neighbor got on your nerves, hey! All you had to do was point your finger and cry *WITCH!* That'd take care of 'em. Hmmmm. Maybe we could use that one today? Just kidding, folks.

During the French Revolution, the guillotine was constructed, a grisly sight to behold. Marie Antoinette said, "Let them eat cake," and they stretched her neck below the guillotine's heavy blade and relieved her of her head. Gasp!

How the West was really won? If you were apt to rustling cattle or stealing horses, well, you sure as shootin' better not get caught at it. Cause they would throw a scraggly old rope over a tree limb and put the noose around your neck... and you guessed it... hang 'em high! Whew-wee! What a way to go. Left for buzzard bait.

After the Civil War painted the American countryside red with the blood of our own, we Americans began to diversify and expand our means of execution. The gas chamber and the electric chair were added to our gallows.

I shall never forget the first time I saw the movie *Angels with Dirty Faces*, starring James Cagney. He played a real tough gangster type, but towards the end, you caught a glimpse of his humanity on his sorrowful face. When the guard said, "It's time," a chill ran up my spine. As I watched Cagney hang down his head and walk the last mile into the awaiting arms of the electric chair, it was so sad. There's no other way to describe it.

In my opinion, the death penalty has not accomplished anything other than sweeping our dirt under the rug, and the electric chair is inhumane. We don't even electrocute stray dogs. The Humane Society won't allow such cruelty to animals, yet we will fry our own.

I truly believe you can raise a child to become a decent law-abiding pillar of the community, or you can drive a child to become as uncontrollable as a whirlwind. Many of our criminals began this way, driven by cruel uncaring hands, destined to smash into the society that spawned them, like a tornado slams into a trailer park. "For they have sown the wind, and they shall reap the whirlwind." (Hosea 8:7)

The death penalty is not the answer. It is not even a viable deterrent. No, the answer lies deeper than that. It goes far back into the dawn of man himself. The day we chose to become wise, we became fools. Since the first man Adam and the first woman Eve, we have rejected the counsel of God and chosen rather to lean upon our own understanding, and there has been nothing but death and confusion ever since.

We rejected paradise for knowledge, and look where it has led us. Now we are all under the death penalty. Great and small, young and old must all return to the ground from whence we came: ashes to ashes, dust to dust. But there is hope for us all in our Lord Jesus Christ. Death for one who believes in Him is only a step into Glory.

We all must die, my friends, and as long as man refuses to seek the Lord God Almighty Jehovah for the answers to our violent world, greed will persist, hunger will remain, and the Death House will fill to the brim. Such is the wisdom of man, whose eyes have been opened to the knowledge he was not meant to retain.

God help us all...

5.8.93.

Dear Sondra

Time: 9.26 p.m. Saturday night. FSP Starke ... exactly 34 minutes from now ... Larry Joe Johnson (known by his fellow prisoners as "Time

Bomb") will be strapped in the *ELECTRIC CHAIR* and 300 amps 2,000 volts will race through his body burning his existence in this world away.

I have just prayed for Time Bomb, that if it must be so, God give him the strength to walk the last mile with courage to face the inevitable that reaches for all mankind.

The Grim Reaper hovers over Florida State Prison ... and it is a dark night indeed. The entire prison is lockdowned ... each prisoner confined to his cell ... the protesters have gathered outside the tall forbidding barbed wire fences of FSP ... lighting candles as they bid a fellow human being farewell.

At 9.40 p.m. the lights went out all over the whole prison, as the power and light company refuses to supply the prison with the electricity it seeks to *EXECUTE TIME BOMB...*

Five minutes to 10 ... my heart begins to squeeze within my chest as my pulse quickens ... I feel a sickness in the pit of my stomach. It is almost as though I am sitting in *THE CHAIR* myself ...

I can't move ... the leather straps hold me fast to the *WOODEN IRON MAIDEN OF DEATH...* the *METAL CAP* has been placed on my now shaved head ... an electrode is attached my leg ... the *BLACK HOOD* is placed over my head ... it is hard to breathe! ... I wait for the moment to come ...

Time 10.18 p.m. The lights just blacked out again as the prison generator that feeds the *ELECTRIC CHAIR* was switched off and the power company turned back on ...

LARRY JOE JOHNSON is dead. And the State *BLOODLUST* is satisfied for the time being ... and so the endless circle of an eye for an eye ... tooth for a tooth, continues ... and mankind has learnt nothing from its pilgrimage through the ages.

The Grim Reaper, drawn by Danny Rolling

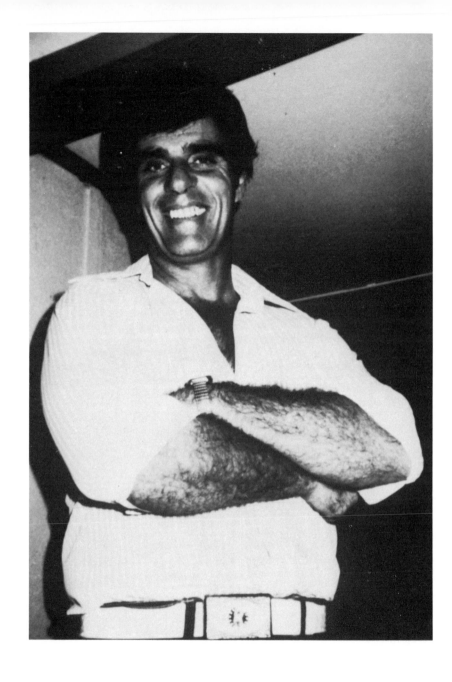

Joe O'Dell

Part Three

KNOCKIN' ON JOE

The Prison Letters & Diary of Joe O'Dell

JOSEPH O'DELL, III
by Sondra London

Blood Evidence

Joe O'Dell is on Death Row for a crime he did not commit. Helen Schartner was a middle-aged, middle-class secretary for the gas company, whose body was found in a muddy field one rainy winter's morning in 1985, battered, raped, sodomized, and strangled to death. She was last seen in the County Line Bar across the highway - the same country & western bar where Joe O'Dell was also seen drinking, chatting and dancing with several women - but not Helen.

Nor did they leave together, Joe left at least half an hour after Helen did. In fact, nothing connected him to the victim except that they were both in the same Virginia Beach bar. What did tie O'Dell to the crime was a tip from his estranged girlfriend Connie Craig, who told the cops O'Dell had stashed a bloody jacket and shirt in her garage that night.

After O'Dell was charged with the murder, rape and sodomy of Helen Schartner, the blood evidence on that jacket and shirt were tested by Jacqueline Emrich, who had just finished school. This was her first case. She concluded that the victim's blood was Type O, the "universal" blood type, and that enzymes and proteins in the bloodstains were of the same type. However, she failed to notate her procedures and her forensic conclusions have been seriously questioned. Because of this inadequate testing, the jurors were informed that the blood on Joe's clothing belonged to the victim - not accepting Joe's explanation that the blood came from a sailor whose nose he had bloodied in a fight that was broken up by the Shore Patrol.

He was defended by incompetent counsel, namely himself. The court had assigned him a military lawyer who had not even graduated from law school, and whose only legal experience was as an apprentice on domestic cases. This was his first murder case. He advised Joe to plead guilty to the murder. Joe refused, fired him and defended himself. For two years he prepared his defence, while his legal materials, books, pens, pencils, and paper were confiscated from him. He was limited to one law book, one pen and one legal pad at a time. He was only allowed to use the phone 15 minutes a day to call lawyers, investigators and witnesses. His mail was stolen. His witnesses were threatened and disappeared. One witness, Kathy Day, was raped at gunpoint and told that if she testified for Joe, she would be killed.

In addition, Mark David Pruett, a serial killer on Death Row for two other murders, confessed to killing Helen Schartner.

Nevertheless, Joe was convicted and sent to Death Row, but his story does not end there. He has become an adept jailhouse lawyer, and he continues to relentlessly purse his appeals both within the criminal justice system and in some rather creative extra-legal manoeuvres.

Let Freedom Ring

In 1988, he wrote to the philanthropist Percy Ross, whose column *Thanks a Million* appears in 200 papers, explaining his situation and pleading, "This is why I ask for $1,200. There is a new blood test used in forensic science called 'DNA Fingerprinting' - a positive identification of blood. These tests are run by a laboratory called 'Lifecodes' and would prove my innocence. If I were not innocent, I'd be insane to want these tests done. They would prove my guilt beyond a shadow of a doubt. Please take a chance on me by providing this blood testing. I can't begin to tell you how it feels to be awaiting my death when I'm innocent." Percy responded, "Based on the chance you may have fallen into a 'glitch' in our legal system, I'm willing to give you the chance to prove your innocence... I do, however, act with reservation, because if the testing proves guilt I'll feel as though I escorted you to the electric chair. Should it prove your innocence, we'll have righted a wrong and justice will have prevailed. I hope freedom rings."

Prosecutor Stephen Test responded to news reports of O'Dell's independent efforts to get his own DNA testing done by calling him "one of the most dangerous men alive... a psychopath... a real flimflam artist." He complained about the cost of convicting O'Dell. "He was afforded more resources, probably, than any criminal in the state's history. The costs were astronomical. O'Dell filed between 200 and 300 pages of motions weekly from his jail cell. He had 70 hearings on those motions. The total cost of the trial and hearings approached $250,000."

Meanwhile Percy Ross's readership responded with about 400 letters in support of giving O'Dell another chance to prove his innocence. One man even sent a $3,000 cheque to help in the case.

Freedom still hasn't rung quite yet, even though the Lifecodes DNA testing did show O'Dell had not committed the crime. He backed that up in 1992 by having the evidence examined by Dr. Alec Jeffreys of Leicester, England, who invented DNA fingerprinting, and who agreed that the blood was *NOT* that of Helen Schartner.

A Question of Innocence

O'Dell has been arguing in state appeals that the new blood evidence exonerates him, and that the trial court should not have allowed him to represent himself, due to his history of instability and his erratic behavior at trial. When those claims were rejected by the state courts, he persuaded a million-dollar Manhattan law firm to take his case and file an appeal with the Virginia Supreme Court. They filed the appeal, but put the wrong caption on it, calling it "Assignment of Error" instead of the required "Notice of Appeal". In April of 1991, the Virginia Supreme Court refused to hear his case, and so for that procedural error, Joe O'Dell is to die.

And so the appeal was taken to the United States Supreme Court. On December 2, 1991, the Court made an extremely rare :statement respecting the denial of the petition". Normally, no comment is offered when the Court turns down an appeal, but this time in a precedent-setting statement, the Court made an exception. "In short, there are serious questions as to whether O'Dell committed the crime or was capable of representing himself - questions rendered all the more serious by the fact that O'Dell's life depends upon their answers," the dissenting opinion, written by Justice Harry Blackmun, stated. "Because of the gross injustice that would result if an innocent man were sentenced to death, O'Dell's substantial federal claims can, and should, receive careful consideration from the federal court".

At the time of writing, the wheels of justice are still grinding - exceedingly slowly - towards the resolution of O'Dell's federal appeal and a reversal of his death sentence.

Life, Death & Frozen Sperm

Meanwhile, he has been in the headlines and on national TV on several occasions for some rather unusual petitions he has placed before the court.

In 1991, he and another Death Row inmate petitioned the State Court to allow them to have their sperm frozen before their executions, so their girlfriends could later inseminate themselves. "First of all, if you're thinking about being executed, you're looking at total extermination of your life. That's the end, that's finito. And I'm the only son in my family, and I got to thinking about my bloodline." His fiancee wanted to have his child to remember him by. "The right to procreate shouldn't be taken from a person just because the person is convicted of a crime," Joe explained to me. "Because I'm saying I'm innocent, and I've got evidence to prove I am innocent, but that remains to be seen right now. Say that they said OK, we're going to cut off Joe O'Dell's penis because he's guilty of this crime, and then they find out I'm innocent, they can't put it back on. I'm using that as an analogy to their taking my rights away from me because I'm convicted of a crime. Let's assume I'm telling the truth. And people tell me, you have no right to preserve your sperm, you have no right to have children. Well, I've got a fiancee that is 33 years old. Now, let's say the truth takes ten years to come to light. You see, by then she's too old to bear a child and we've been denied the right to have children, because society was so ignorant that they wouldn't allow me to have my rights when I was asserting I was innocent. It's just like if you kill the wrong person, you can't bring them back to life and say 'I'm sorry.' Well, if they take away my right to have children, then in ten years when I prove I'm innocent, there's no recourse. All I get is an 'I'm sorry', if I get that."

Naturally, there were mixed reactions to this controversial petition. Reporters came flocking, asking for his statements. And each time he gave them their sound-bites on the right to procreate, he explained that he was doing this so that he could tell people that he was *INNOCENT* and was going to be murdered. I'm not suggesting that O'Dell in insincere, because I happen to know that he really does want to preserve his lifeline by impregnating his fiancee. Still, that's not the point. If a convict has an original story that's interesting enough to break through the fog of media-hypnosis, it will get the attention of the public. Hopefully, somewhere in that process there will be some interest and sympathy generated for the convict's dead-serious concern about his dreadful situation. And that is the underlying dynamic behind this petition, and the next one he filed.

Kill Me on TV

On New Years Day, 1992, Joe O'Dell appeared on the Donahue show via satellite to comment on an even more sensational petition. The title of the show was *Kill Me on TV*, and that just about sums it up. O'Dell petitioned the State Court to allow him to have his execution televised. Once again, there was an important reason behind it. "Because I want society to see an innocent man executed." He explained, "People view capital punishment - and that includes the perpetrators of a capital crime before they are actually caught - they view execution in the abstract. In other words, you read about something happening, but you don't see it. But when you actually see something it becomes indelible in your mind. Even when a man is sentenced to the electric chair, it doesn't have an impact on him because he's seeing it in the abstract too."

One of the panelists quipped, "I've heard of people dying to get on TV, but this is too much." Lisa Sliwa, a street vigilante with the Guardian Angels, baited O'Dell mercilessly, dismissing his claims of innocence and repeatedly calling him a serial killer. But Phil Donahue was impressed with the seriousness of his gesture, and shocked the audience by stating that he would like the first televised execution to be broadcast on his show.

O'Dell continues to file various lawsuits and petitions at a prodigious rate, and his legal services are much in demand by his neighbors. It's hard for him to take time off from his legal research and writing in order to stretch his legs a little in the literary arena. But when he does, he manages to write some very compelling prose about life on Death Row, along with a series of poems about executions. He also has a half-dozen unfinished action-adventure novels in the works. He's so good at telling his own story that I hesitate to paraphrase what he has written. So I'll just get out of the way and let him describe our long-standing working relationship, which I hope will continue up to and beyond the day when those prison gates swing open and he comes walking out.

SONDRA LONDON
by Joe O'Dell

Sondra came into my life in a bizarre way. She was publishing the writings of a convicted killer in Florida, Gerard John Schaefer, who was doing some experiments with one of his fictional characters, Crystal Beavers. He wanted to know how realistic she was to his readers, so he decided to send some letters out to Death Row inmates he had read about. Some of these letters came to guys here on Virginia's Death Row, saying that she (Crystal... incognito Schaefer) was the president of an organization called Justice *NOW*, and that she believed all murderers and rapists should be executed, that justice delayed was justice denied, and that she wanted justice *NOW*. She also said she'd like to have a ticket to his execution. There was more, but you get the idea. Needless to say, the Death Row inmates went off about the letter. Frothing at the mouth and making death threats, they wrote not only to Crystal, but to lawyers, judges, and congressmen. I tried to calm them down, but to no avail. So I wrote a letter to Crystal myself, thinking it was a real woman I was writing to. Sondra, who was receiving the responses and then forwarding them on to Schaefer, read my letter, which was the only one that was sympathetic to Crystal, focusing on some of the poignant statements in the letter about being raped and abused. When Sondra read my letter, she responded, introducing herself and explaining the whole thing was a hoax. She also said she was sorry it had been taken the way it had, and hoped nobody was hurt over it.

One letter led to another. Sondra warned me at the beginning that she didn't have time for correspondence, but I was persistent, and soon we were writing to each other on a regular basis, and then I started writing stories. While they can't hold a light to some of Schaefer's stuff, still I keep on writing and with Sondra's help, I have begun to improve. The novel I am working on now is about a convicted serial killer in the guise of a woman who writes taunting letters to some Virginia Death Row inmates, who then escape from Death Row, go down to Florida, break the serial killer out of prison, and torture him.

With all the contacts that Sondra has with convicts, she has her hands full. She's a mama to some, an imaginary lover to others, and some even envision her as their rise to stardom in the literary field or the movies. She doesn't encourage any amorous relationships, and makes it clear to guys who come on to her that she's not interested, but some won't take no for an answer. Sondra has a lot of guys in prisons across America in love with her. She has received everything from death threats to marriage proposals, and schemes galore from imprisoned con men. She has interviewed, corresponded with, and talked on the phone to some of the most vicious murderers in the world. It would seem she would have a macabre personality dealing with all the lurid characters she writes about, but she doesn't in the least.

She recently visited me here on Virginia's Death Row, and we had a wonderful two-day visit talking over the phone through bullet-proof glass. She wore silver handcuff earrings, along with this sweater with 'CRIME DOES NOT PAY' and this stereotype criminal image on the front of it. I had to smile, thinking to myself, "Talk about balls! Here she is in the most dangerous prison in Virginia..." Can you image what all the hardened criminals were thinking? "Grr... snap... gnash.."

THE PRISON LETTERS AND DIARY
OF JOE O'DELL

November 19, 1990

Dear Sondra

I write this with a "red-face" after reading your letters, and after reading G.J.'s, I see that the analysis I made was in error concerning graphanalysis. (I have to admit, grudgingly of course, that the "Psycho Linguistical" analysis did not click when I did the analysis... guess I will have to turn in my "Dick Tracy" badge, huh?)

Yes, I know Eddie Odom (he and Bobby Lewis killed my best friend, Joe Richards... that's a long story, I'll tell you about it someday), Jimmy Carter (ugh! That guy is one persona non gratis... what a cesspool for a human-being). No, I do not know Henry Lucas, but I know of him. Each of the above-named individuals I have a plethora of true-life stories about.

I read the letter from Detective Kelly of the North Miami Police Department concerning a "confession" that Ottis Toole allegedly made concerning the murder of Adam Walsh. Sondra, Ottis Toole has made that confession to so many people, and believe me, I have personal knowledge that Ottis Toole was in prison when Adam Walsh was abducted from the Sears Department Store. I have been in touch with Leslie Groves (John Walsh's secretary) about this same thing, i.e. the "confession" of "sicko" Ottis Toole concerning the murder/abduction of that poor child! (I got a letter from John Walsh concerning the National Center for Missing and Exploited Children concerning my invention of implanting a micro tracking device in a child's tooth, that through a "transponder" off of a satellite, currently off of cellular telephone relay-stations, could pinpoint the whereabouts of any child within 10 feet anywhere on earth. There's so much to this, technology-wise, that would make it too complex for me to relay to you comprehensively. I was just looking for a copy of the letter I received concerning this... when I find it I will send you a copy.

Sondra, even though I know you don't have time for casual correspondence, I do know that you spent some time and energy on writing those two letters to me. I want to apologize to you for coming at you like I did... but in all honesty I have to admit, for the first time in my life I have came across someone who is a total enigma to me. (I do not mean that in a derogatory manner.) I just mean that you are not mediocre.

Yes, I knew Ted Bundy personally. What a waste! This guy could have been anything he wanted to be... and he was quite personable. I know that Bobby Lewis knew Ted quite well... they were really good friends. But I believe G.J.'s accounts of Bundy and himself are all a bunch of crap!

Please forgive me for jumping around on my subjects, but I am trying to write under some very extenuating circumstances right now (we are on lockdown, undergoing a major shakedown, and my deluxe suite (smile) is in shambles after the Gestapo went through it).

Sondra, relax! Nobody is going to come to Atlanta and hurt you or anyone else connected with you there. I can speak with certainty that nobody that is connected to Mecklenburg will be a part of anything like that. I have to get everyone together and explain the whole thing to them. Of course that is going to be a hard job, because a lot of these guys have limited intellect, and they do not approach situations rationally. I do believe though, that I can cool things on this end... so relax, I am in your corner, and I can take care of all the necessary things that need to be done that will quash any animosity that resulted from this whole misunderstood mess involving G.J. and "Crystal".

You were talking about all you were doing was "exploiting" G.J. to make a buck. Well now, that doesn't make you a bad girl! In fact I admire that in you... it's a hard world out there and you have to make a buck when you can, however you can when the opportunity comes around. You may laugh at this, but there was a certain amount of merit in what I said about the publicity aspect of all of this. If you would like I will help you set up some publicity on this thing so that you can sell your books on G.J. I know right now you are thinking, "Who in the hell does this joker think he is?" (Smile.) The only thing that has to be done is you have to keep everything within the confines of the law so that nothing backfires on you. Now I can write to *Geraldo* or *Sally Jessy Raphael* (I can't write Donahue, for I have him in court in New York right now for not paying me for my appearance on his show on April 26th with my friend, Dr. Jack Kevorkian, who as you may know is the inventor of the "Death Machine".) I can tell them about all of this nonsense about "Crystal", etc. and pretend to be terribly upset about the whole thing, etc. This would get you "National Television" coverage. You can tell about how you fell into this trap innocently and how you have been threatened, etc. This is an idea that you can kick around, but if you talk to me about it, be cryptic so that nobody can intercept what we are talking about.

I am sure that G.J. thinks that his macabre tales are a corner where he has the total market, but even though they are lurid and gross, you can bet I have heard stories from other serial killers, who prefer to remain anonymous, whose "Tales of Terror" would make "Popeye look like a punk!" (The only thing that really interests me, and is really phenomenal, is most of these tales came from Florida.) Garry Tillman, who is serving several life sentences at Avon Park Correctional in Florida, would kill his victims and cut out their private parts and put them in jars to view. Another man, whose name I will not reveal, would kill his female victims, cut off their breasts, cut out their vaginas, and he would take photos before and after he killed them, and would tag each photo, and personal items (just like in the article you sent to me), and he would take these body parts and have sex with them. He had a whole freezer full of these parts when he was arrested. He was arrested when he returned to a murder scene where the body of his victim was decomposed, and he took a hand of her decomposed flesh and masturbated with it around his penis. The police had the place staked out!

One time I wrote a hypothetical concerning Serial Killers. I hypothesized that when the news media sensationalized serial killings, and romanticized it and glamorized it, such as they did with Bundy, that potential serial killers who were in the latent or dormant state, were awakened, especially those that were *"NOTHING"* on the streets, and who had the lowest of self-esteem and wanted to be somebody. They would fantasize and then put their fantasies to work into becoming realities. In reality they wanted to get caught so they could enjoy the notoriety, make their niche in history, etc. (Do you think that there are female serial killers? Isn't it interesting that there are only male, and that for the most part that their victims are female? What do you think about this?)

Surely you jest when you say that "I have it all figured out!" On the contrary, I am really confused. Not about G.J. and his motives, etc., because that is patently clear to me, but about you! You have a lot of untapped potential, and I think right now you are struggling just to get by... you need a fresh start, and a new direction. (Life is stranger than fiction sometimes.)

I want to set something straight. I don't want to be your adversary in any sort of way. I know that this fiasco of G.J.'s caused quite a riff and got everyone agitated and off to a bad start, but I hope that we can put all of this behind us, and that we can maintain contact, professionally of course, and maybe come up with some ideas that will help the both of us in the future. To clarify another point, please don't get the idea that I am putting the hit on you amorously, for I definitely am not... I am engaged to a beautiful girl (Movie Star beautiful), and I love her very much. I'm telling you all of this because I know how guys in prison are... and I am sure that you received a lot of letters from guys in prison that preface things with business, and then later on try to make one thing lead to another. Just know that this is not my intention... besides, you don't like criminals! (Smile.)

G.J. is a brilliant guy in his own way and I have to say that I admire his penchant for getting things rolling. (Even the cops gave G.J. some credit for doing that ... Smile.) There is something sublime about all of this that is scary, and I am not sure whether it was intentional or unintentional, but I'll tell you, there is some sheer genius to all of this... only I don't know where to put the credit at!

My *LIFE STORY*! It would probably seem like *Leave It To Beaver* compared to G.J.'s! I don't get "off" on killing women and doing demented and aberrated things to them... necrophilia is just not my thing. I like *"LIVE"* women. My life involves a lot of women, but only because in my past I have been a philanderer. (Something I am not proud of... I've been married 3 times... once to a tiny little blonde named Judy (Jacksonville) who was an alcoholic; once to a little blonde doctor, Vicki (who was a psychiatrist and committed suicide), and my last marriage was to Kathy, a petite brunette, who I have an 8-year-old son by.) My life is full of "Hell-on-Earth", and is inundated crime and academics. (Weird combination, huh?) I've been dubbed by the prosecutors and the police as one of the most dangerous men on earth, but that was just to appeal to the readers of the newspapers and the viewers on television. The Police and the Prosecutors are afraid of my *MIND*, not of me per se! (I embezzled over a quarter of a million dollars from the State of Florida, and they have never figured out how I did it... my wife Vicki got all of the money, bought a new home, etc. just before she killed herself... I didn't get a cent of the money.) You can see why, as described in the brackets, why the police, etc. are afraid of my mind and not me per se. (There's a lot more they are afraid of that involves my mind, but that's another story.)

Sondra, G.J. seems to have a *"DEATH WISH"*. His fictional character, Crystal, who is on a crusade through the pseudo "JUSTICE NOW" organization, and who wants to see Death Row inmates "burn", etc. and his expose on the "Country Club" living that death row inmates allegedly enjoy, give me a little peek into this guy's mind. This guy has no allegiances... he is neither pro or con... he's playing both ends towards the middle, i.e. he is the "very" thing that he claims to abhor, yet he tries to depict through "Crystal" just the opposite. His dealings with the cop also show that he is trying to show that he hates child pornography, and wants to entrap pornographers that deal in children... an in-depth look at this man's warped mind will leave no doubt that he "gets-off" on child pornography! I don't say that arbitrarily, but through reading his letters and the response from the cop, and the totality of his psyche through the meager knowledge I have of him. His wanting to help the police solve the Adam Walsh murder by telling them about Ottis Toole's alleged confession to it. His hunger for attention is ravenous, as you already know.

His brief letter to you calling the guys on "Death Row" anal retentives (paraphrased), saying that they can't deal with controversy, and then his fit of infantile anger saying, "Burn Them," tells me this guy is not wrapped too tight! First of all, without being too analytic, how can he empathize with the men on Death Row and use the rationale that we are a bunch of assholes because we are in the dark about this so-called controversy he speaks of. While the idea of Crystal being gung ho for burning guys right away, then through some means she does a 180 degree flipside, and joins sides with those on Death Row that are not deservative of the death penalty, is a good idea, and would be good fodder for those in the know, it wasn't a good idea the way that it was carried out. (Like I said in one of my previous letters, G.J., like so many of his kind, has a high IQ, but there is a flaw in their rationale and their thinking things out, i.e. he can think from point A to point Z, but all of the other in-between that it takes to make a plan work, he just overlooks and lets twist-in-the-wind. No plan can work like that... if it does, it is just a matter of luck, and I don't like to use luck when I am planning something. G.J.'s flawed character is what got him where he is at, and it will keep him where he is at, and maybe more if he doesn't get a grip on himself... but I think it is too late for him to get help... this guy lives in a fantasy world and he is too far into it to come out.)

Go make your bucks little lady, and if I can, I will help you. Just keep yourself out of all this sort of mess that recently came up. I know you have better things to do with your time than waste money on long-distance telephone calls to lawyers and judges, and your friends in the FBI, not to mention people like Fisher, Joe Savino, and myself! You've got to understand Sondra, the people you are dealing with are not exactly the pillars of society... you are dealing with miscreants from all walks of life. Make your bucks and keep disengaged from any of the promotional schemes that G.J. and his flawed genius comes up with.

Before I conclude this lengthy letter, I think that G.J. should get his facts straight about the people he writes about. John Spinkelink was not a "homosexual". John killed the "homosexual" for making advances towards him in a motel room.... "forced advances". Another myth that G.J. talks about is the enema and diaper just before execution... that is mythical, and it does not happen! He is right about one thing though, the scams that are ran on women from Death Row prisoners through "Pen Pal" organizations. Most of the guys do it for commissary money and because they have nobody to love them... I'm not saying I sanction it or condone it, but I'm just saying the reasons why they do it. Does G.J. know the reasons? Sounds like he is talking from some more of his own true life experiences. (What do you think Sondra...?)

Take care "Mysterious Lady". Hope to hear from you, in synopsis of course, concerning this letter. Give "Ghastly Jerk" (isn't that what G.J. stands for?) all of our regards from Death Row... Smile Sondra... this is all a *TRIP*, huh?

Warm regards always,

Joe.

November 19, 1990

Dear Sondra

I know that you are probably getting tired of receiving letters from me, but this is just a short letter (Thank God, huh? Smile) to let you know that I did write to David A. Kelly of North Miami Beach. I wrote him a 3 page single-spaced letter, but I did not tell him the details about Schaefer and the "Crystal Beavers" scheme that caused all of the "flap"!

Sondra, why don't you get out of Atlanta and go to West Palm Beach and marry one of those rich old men there? (Smile.) You need to disassociate yourself from people like me, G.J., and the like. (Smile... I'm serious.) You'd have to watch out for guys like me and G.J. there though, i.e. guys that would be looking for a rich lady to take care of us! (Smile.) Wouldn't that be ironic...for you to go there looking for a rich old man, and some turkey would be there looking for a pretty rich girl, and you two hooked up! That would be the epitome of ironies, huh? (Smile.) (Okay, enough of that...)

I am not going to write to "Hazelwood" *(F.B.I. agent)*. I don't find it necessary. My primary reason for writing Kelly was to advise him about the Ottis Toole confession that G.J. is trying to negotiate for his own cynical purposes. (What an asshole... he has some nerve talking about us guys on the "Row"!) Sondra, Ottis Toole was incarcerated when the Walsh child was abducted and murdered. (I'm being redundant from my earlier letter of tonight... one of my biggest faults.)

G.J. is at Belle Glades (Glades Correctional) which is predominantly Cuban and Hispanic. He's playing an extremely dangerous game, and Sondra, he can thank you for no repercussions being forthcoming on him, i.e. friends of mine there. Just mention the name of Santas Trafficante to him, and tell him that I was his bodyguard in Tampa, and also saved his brother, Herman's, life. Also, that I was hired to fly the helicopter for Pedro Perez, out of Ebor City, Fla, during the revolution in Columbia, in which Pedro is (or was) a General. The bottom line to all of this being, G.J. stepped on the toes of people that could wipe him out like a fly! Don't worry Sondra, nobody will harm G.J.... but he'd better give his future "Play-Games" some second thoughts before putting them into action again.

Sondra, the thing that G.J. wrote about Jesse Tafero, *Jesse in Flames*. Could you send me a copy of it? The reason I am asking for this, is because Jesse was one of my closest friends... we shared things with each other every Christmas... cried together, and I am part of his family (not in the sanguine sense... but *FAMILY*). I used to fly from Miami to Starke with Carol, his lawyer, in her Lear Jet. We would have a party at the prison. (I also served time at that prison... then I went to work in Miami at Carol's law firm. At any rate, I want to see what that poem, or whatever it is, about Jesse, says. If it is at all derogatory, please don't have anything to do with it. When I say derogatory, I mean if G.J. is mocking Jesse's death in any way through his writings. Jesse's appeals were paid for the *FAMILY* if you get my drift! (G.J. is so full of crap...I keep thinking about when he was coming across as Crystal and the things that he said about Jesse, and how he knew the Trooper (Black) that Jesse allegedly killed, but in reality Walter Rhodes killed... I'll bet G.J. wished that he had never started any of this... little did he know that he would run into someone that would peek at his hole card.

Another thing that I didn't comment on in regards to G.J.'s comments about we "assholes" not being able to handle "controversy". What a *JERK*! What does he think we guys are under here... the "Fields of Ambrosia" or something? He's down because his latest appeal was just rejected. Well I am sorry to hear that, but I guess he never heard of "The Law of Reciprocity". It never fails... one begets what one puts out! He put out bad and he received bad in return. Men here have their appeals rejected every day... the difference being, these men die when their appeals are rejected... G.J. doesn't. Then he says that we don't know how to handle "controversy!" I know what you were saying is true about the people on the outside thinking that all men are guilty that are on Death Row, the crime colleges, etc. Still, one has to empathize with others before you can become judgmental and that applies to G.J. and his so-called research endeavor, which allowed him to bring into the lives of persons who are already in the pits of hell his unsolicited pseudo opinions under the guise of being "Crystal Beavers". Regardless of the well-intended reasons, and the rationale employed, it was terribly wrong. (I'm speaking from the perspectives of the others... for me, I could handle it, I just don't like the haughty attitude of Schaefer in calling us "F...ing assholes"!)

Anyway, I'm going to close this out for now. Take care of yourself and start making them bucks. (Money talks and bulllshit walks.) Be cool "Mystery Lady"!

Yours Joe.

1/2/91

You want to hear a good one? The guards had to come over here the other night and carry this guy out of here to the hospital. He had been giving himself head and his back went out of whack on him and he couldn't straighten back up! (Smile.) About a year ago they had to carry a guy out of here that had a homemade dildo stuck in his ass. (Smile.) There's some real sickos here believe me... two guys, Ricky and Timbo, (Ricky was executed in July) were caught sword fighting with their dicks and locked up! I never cease to be amazed at what goes on in these places... the perversion is rampant!

2/2/91

About B.L. (Bobby Lewis) and his outrageous lies concerning the women that visit him. No that isn't why women come to visit guys like B.L. Oh, it happens at times, but it isn't something that happens as a rule. I think that people like B.L. and G.J.S. equate their masculinity and desirability with convincing themselves and others how virile and sexually successful they are with the females... that is common amongst convicts. In actuality it is showing their low self-esteem and their insecurities with females. Braggadocio is common amongst men and their conquests all over the world... but in prison where the female is not so readily available, it becomes a real status symbol when a guy scores... it is like the *"FORBIDDEN FRUIT"* tasting so good. Even if it is a fantasy... the fantasy becomes a reality to the story-teller if he convinces his listener that he is a *REAL STUD*... you know JOHNNY WADD... JOHN HOLMES, etc.

Talking about the *PATHOLOGY* of *SCHAEFER* and *WOMEN*. I don't mean to get nasty talking, but *SCHAEFER* cannot see a woman as a human being per se, or an individual... he equates women as tits and pussy on legs and those parts are the only thing he sees and cares about. It is like Freud saying that everything that we do is connected with sex. With Schaefer, women are *NOTHING* but objects that were put on earth for the satisfaction of his lusts, regardless of how those lusts are satisfied. I mean he cannot get it in his mind that the females that he has killed had feelings, hopes, dreams, futures, families and someday wanted to be mothers and raise their babies. A synapse in his brain doesn't connect... It short circuits when this rationale comes into play. In his writings his *REAL* luridness doesn't fully emerge... he has esoteric things that he hasn't written about... that's why I asked you what he does about sex in the joint... it's like when the police interview a rape victim, they want to know what the rapist said to them during the rape... this gives the police a profile on the rapist and tells how his mind works. I'll give you an example. Remember me telling you about the guy that was giving himself head, and the guy that got the dildo stuck, etc. this tells me a lot about these people... and they are on Death Row for crimes against women. Self-sex practices reveal the real psychology of the person.

2/16/91

I know without a doubt that I am just a grain of sand in a vast desert, and there's nothing really significant about me. Mundanely I haven't made any worthwhile contributions to my fellow man... nor have I made my existence known other than as something that's distasteful and only worthy of being thrown in the garbage. Now some people would say that I have low self-esteem or low self-worth perception. No, I face the truth and that is the truth. All the bullshit about being gangsters, criminals, cops, DEA, FBI, CIA and all the other status quo monikers... that really doesn't mean jack shit! Those that are all of the status symbols aforementioned, *ARE*. Those that are not but want to be are *WANNABEES*. Everyone is seeking his or her own place on this planet... some make it and some do not. Some of us are cut out to be on Death Row... some are cut out to be guards... everyone has a place on this earth... but that place is ever-changing, and nothing ever remains the same. Those on Death Row either die by being executed, or they get life in prison and go on with life. Some eventually get out again... the guards retire, they go on with their lives... they die, and other guards take their places. Other Death Row inmates take the places of the ones that have departed. It is a cycle of life. All of us reach points in our lives where we have to make a *BIG* decision, i.e. *"WHERE DO I GO FROM HERE?"* Some think they have no choice and accept their fate, whatever that may be. Others fight and struggle, whether they are on Death Row, prison, on the outside, etc. The bottom line is, we all have some kind of choice no matter where we are, and no matter what our circumstances may be. *"EVEN THIS SHALL PASS AWAY"*. The main thing to keep in mind, is never to lose touch with the reality of who we are and what we are.

About my *TRUE CRIME STORY*... it's hard for me to write about my life... I just seem to get a mental block when it comes to writing about it. Just like when *UNSOLVED MYSTERIES* was doing a story on me... they had me on the phone every day, visited, got me to make audio tapes, etc. I just got to certain parts and things became so mentally painful that I couldn't get it out... I experienced some terrible mental confusion, which isn't the way I usually am... I'm usually articulate and come across pretty good. I'll tell you something that would make a good story, if I could only write down the incidents as they come to mind, and then compile them and put then in some type of order, is my life in prison and all of the things that have happened inside. There is a vast amount of humor, a lot of killing, drugs, sexual relationships with female employees, fraud, extortion, racketeering, and politics. I've had the whole population in my section of Death Row sit around me mesmerized for hours while I relate stories of the past in prison... even guards sometimes come around when I am telling the stories. The Warden and his staff have had me tell my stories to people that sat around with their mouths open in disbelief. All of these stories are true too.

Hell, my life has been one disaster after another. Runaway at age 9, meeting molesters on the highway that tried to engage me in homosexual affairs. A female schoolteacher that picked me up at age 10 in Baltimore, Maryland when I had run away from home and kept me in her home and slept with me and loved me... and at the time I didn't understand what was going on. Being placed in a mental institution and drugged and being sexually molested while

I was under the influence of drugs and passed out. The nurse named Janice Whiteley who had killed another patient at Southwestern State Hospital, Marion, Virginia, was the one who was sexually molesting me... squeezing the genitals until they had me in excruciating pain when I awoke... and I was handcuffed and chained the whole time. When I was hung up on a steel bar by handcuffs for 14 months and fed bread and water... when I was taken down I had to be hospitalized for malnutrition. Reform School at age 14, prison at age 16, prison at age 19, prison at age 33, and prison at age 44... Death Row. Stealing cars, armed robbery, kidnapping, murder in prison, assault in prison, and now murder, rape and sodomy. Now isn't this a hell of a story that is a tribute... a legacy to my loved ones? It's enough to gag a maggot! Yeah, I could write a story on my sordid past... but the truth is so hard to write about... it is *SO* painful. See I can make fiction anything I want it to be... I can be anything I want to be in fiction... but in my true life story I am only a sorry ass criminal that does stupid things and spends most of his life in prison. An anomaly to myself. A man with an IQ of 120 isn't supposed to do the things that I have done in my life... I have to be a few straws shy of being a bale... my elevator hasn't been reaching the top floor, or something.

Another thing... old G.J.S. pulled his "hole card" about his sexuality... him and *OTTIS* being *LOVERS*! God, give me a break G.J... cut me some slack man! Sondra, you'd better thank God or your *HIGHER POWER* that when you and G.J. were having your teenage sexual bouts, that you didn't get pregnant... your offspring would have had horns and a tail with a trident for a rattler! I'm not badmouthing G.J. for the sake of badmouthing him... these are true observations of the man... he's a sick guy, but I think I like him and even feel sorry for the poor sonofabitch! He must live in 24 hours a day torture... what a life to look forward to... FSP and memories of horror... childhood... then his teenage years... then adulthood. Damn I thought my life was screwed up! He wins the *OSCAR* on that count! Oh well, it's a rough life for all of us I guess.

3/4/91
You may not believe this, but when I was watching *TOOLE* on *A Current Affair*, I actually felt my stomach get queasy... the guy makes me sick. I looked at that smile on his ugly face and his flashing dentures, and thought about the perverted and sick mind that so shamelessly appears on National

Television and tells the world about his homosexual love for Henry Lucas, and how they killed close to 600 human beings. As I watched *TOOLE* I thought about the letter you had written me concerning your interview with him and the things that you said... and now I can see how you must have felt as you sat there listening to this sicko recite his life of murder. I felt one burst of compassion for him when he told about being raped, as a 6-year-old, and I thought to myself I shouldn't be so down on him, that society created him. Really it's a sad and shameful thing that created that man-monster that he became. There are many more like him out there being spat out of the so-called correctional systems everyday! There are many more being created like him through child abuse. The bottom line is, Ottis Toole is a sick puppy, but he wasn't born sick... he was created through abuse, and by being mentally retarded and nobody giving a damn about him. The same thing with Schaefer, and I know there is a correlation to all people that are like Schaefer and Toole. I deal with people like them each day, and I have to read their transcripts, pre-sentence reports, etc. and when I read their family history and background, I see the same thing over and over. You know, it is a funny thing about human nature... if a person has cancer of the liver, or heart trouble, or some other physical malady, that person receives sympathy. But just let that person be sick in their mind, and everyone hates them! I find myself falling into the same category as Jay North, that by reading about people like them, have not become like them.

3/9/91

Remember me telling you about my new typewriter coming in and it didn't work properly, and I sent it back? Well, I insured it for $450.00 when I shipped it. I waited and waited for the receipt to come back from the Post Office here, but it never came. I raised all kinds of hell, because I had the receipt from the accounting department where they had charged my account with the postage and the insurance charges. Come to find out that the girl that runs the post office hadn't even insured the typewriter, and the company never received it. The Warden had me in his office yesterday and he told Sgt. Lea that she would have to pay me out of her own pocket if the typewriter doesn't show up. He's suspicious, and so am I, that it was never mailed out, but was stolen. The Warden told her, "out of 350 inmates, why in the hell did you have to pick Joe O'Dell to fuck up with?" (Smile.) I'm giving them two more weeks and if the typewriter hasn't shown up by them, I'm coming for my money! Hell they stole my stamps on a regular basis, and that's why the Warden cut out the receiving of stamps coming in the mail. One time they stole $100.00 worth of stamps this lady sent me.

4/24/91
My lawyers just shelled out $4,000 to get some work done on my teeth. I made a joke about "No temporary fillings please" and they didn'tthink it was too funny. Smile.

5/5/91
Bobby Lewis's writing about the shanks, dope, zip guns, etc. on Death Row in Florida was no exaggeration. He told the truth there. I remember one time they had a shakedown, and Bobby Lewis was back there then too, this was in 1980, and they found machetes, knives, bullets for guns, and zip guns. Not to mention all the dope they found. Jesse Tafero and I talked about it in the Law Room. (That's how we made our contacts from P Wing to R Wing.)

This Death Row makes "Hooch" which is the name we give it here. (Alcoholic beverage from fermented fruit juice, etc.) There are no guns that I am aware of. Knives (shanks) are here I'm sure, but I don't own one. I have a one pound can of "Sea Mackerel" that I keep in my window that I can put in a pair of socks and knock heads if I need something to defend myself with. But usually there's not that sort of threat going on, and I usually handle anything that requires violence with my fists and feet, which I've had to do a time or two.

5/9/91
I don't know if I agree with the theory of Dr. [Joel] Norris about *SERIAL KILLERS*. I can't make a qualitative statement either way until I have more info on what his stance is, etc. I have my own theory about the phenomena of *SERIAL KILLERS* and what makes them tick, but it's just a theory. I have studied them in here and have gotten some real deep insight about their psyche. You cannot glean information from a *SERIAL KILLER* in a clinical setting, or in a professional interview. You have to get the information in a natural setting without the *SERIAL KILLER* realizing that he is being interviewed for research. I have gotten most of my information from the *SERIAL KILLERS* through subtle subterfuges. Most men on Death Row are poor, including myself, but compared to the rest I am doing pretty well, and

always have cigarettes, coffee, candy, and all sorts of munchies. These guys always come to me for the things they need, which gives me a chance to find out things in a way that they don't know I'm picking their brains. For example, when I was writing *EVIL PERSONIFIED*, I got in a rut about some things concerning murder, and I had to go to the experts, the *MURDERERS*, for the insight I needed for my book. I would stroke their forte, i.e. *KILLING*, by letting them read excerpts about killings, rapes, and all that sort of thing. I would watch them intensely as they would read my writings, and I could see the chemistry working in them. Their eyes would take on a gleam that I cannot explain or describe, and their breathing pattern would even change... the stimuli was there, and it's like a man in the throes of passion in a sexual act with a woman, he is at his weakest! The same way with a *SERIAL KILLER* when he reads about things that turn him on, i.e. killing.

Pruett, Spencer, and Poyner are the *KNOWN* Serial Killers on Virginia's Death Row, and I have interjected my probings about their crimes while playing cards, but not directly. The first thing a person has to do that wants to find out the *TRUTH* about what goes on in the mind of a *SERIAL KILLER* is to let him know that the subject turns you on immensely and that you don't have anything against a person that kills and rapes, or kills for other reasons. Once they see you approve of their actions, they will confide things that otherwise cannot be gleaned, certainly not in a clinical setting or on a professional interview. I've even had one of the *SERIAL KILLERS* take me on a mind trip into one of his rape/killings and ask me to create a scenario for him where he would take the victim and rape and kill them. (All of this neuron firing of the brain, etc. or the electrochemical discharges in the deepest lobes of the brain that are felt as uncontrollable impulses, may or may not have merit, I am not qualified to say. But I would go along with your theory more so than that theory on a neophyte stance. Don't get me wrong, Dr. Norris is more qualified in this subject in certain areas that I will ever be, but I just don't agree with the causal factors that he puts forth, and that would take me a book to explain, because I would have to give example after example, based on real-life experience with in-depth, uninhibited research with the perpetrators themselves, which is the best research that can be conducted.

I fully agree that the psychology of the *SERIAL KILLER* is almost impossible to understand. Another thing I agree with is that it doesn't stem from a hatred of the mother or father, or the hatred of one, and the love of another, nor that they were raped as a child. I don't go along with the pornography angle either, though in certain types of *SERIAL KILLERS*, pornography could play a role.

SERIAL KILLERS have to be sociopaths. But the strange thing about that is they can have emotions about their actions, and can express sorrow, etc. which is contrary to the way a sociopath is.

Freud said that everything is causal-connected to sex. I tend to agree with him, and it also plays a significant part in *ALL SERIAL KILLERS*.

Though I am sure that Dr. Norris has found this out, but for the sake of what I'm going to say, I'll go through it. You take your theory about the hormones, the testosterone, etc. and what it does to a *SERIAL KILLER*. You take your theory, combine it with Dr. Norris's, and I think that there might be a viable theory. (Dr. Norris's theory about the neurons, electrochemical discharge to the deepest lobes of the brains, kicking off the uncontrollable urges that drive the *SERIAL KILLER.)*

One of these nights (after I get my new *MEMORYWRITER* ... Smile) I will sit down and type you out a voluminous rundown on the things I have found out. I can take you on the actual trips of the *SERIAL KILLERS*, how they picked out their victims, what went through their minds, the physiological feelings, what turned them on, what turned them off, the elaborate schemes that they concocted to reach that *HIGH* that drives them. See Sondra, and I am sure you know this, where you and I have normal sexual feelings when the correct, and normal, stimuli are there, and where we reach the height of our sexual activity through an orgasm, the *SERIAL KILLER* has a mind orgasm FIRST, then a physical one.

Poyner loves to tell me how he raped and killed his victims. He brags to me how he would put his gun to their head and make them perform all sorts of sexual acts, then he would make them say, "Fuck me, fuck me... cum in my pussy... put that big cock in my little pussy... get me pregnant... give me a baby." He has told me this in about every episode that he relates to me, which is about 30 victims, but he is only sentenced to death on 5 of them, and some of the victims have never been found. He has taken me on the hunt with him, where he goes to the shopping malls and picks out a pretty female victim, and follows her all through the mall, looking at her ass, her legs, and all the while his mind is fucking her. By the time he finally follows her through the mall to her car and is ready to pull his gun and abduct her, he is out of his mind with lust for her. He has told me about how this one 17-year-old girl named Vicki, turned him on so much that when he abducted her at her car, that he couldn't wait to get her to the isolated place he had picked out beforehand, and he got behind the wheel of her car, grabbed her by the hair and put her head in his lap and made her suck him off while he drove to the spot where he raped her, robbed her, anally sodomized her, then without the least bit of concern, took his .38 and shot the kid in the temple. He told me that a lot of times he would sit in his car at the shopping centers and masturbate at the pretty girls that would walk by. He told me that he used to go into grocery stores with an overcoat on in the winter time, with a hole cut in the pocket, and would walk around and masturbate looking at the women shopping. On a couple of occasions he got a victim from that. Oh well, so much for that subject for tonight. It's a sick, sick, sick subject, and it is depressing.

May 27, 1991

Thursday morning, May 23rd, we woke up and found out that were on lockdown status, that afternoon the tactical team came in (about 20 of them) and handcuffed us and came in our cells and started tearing our cells apart searching. They spent the whole afternoon tearing up our cells... and then they left. It took me all night long to get my cell straightened back up and my papers in order. I figured that we might get out the next day, but the next morning we were still on lockdown status. That afternoon, much to my chagrin and surprise, here the tactical team came again. They handcuffed us and tore our cells apart for the second time. I was about to go crazy - I had just spent the whole night getting my papers and everything back in order... and here they come again: another shakedown.

For the two days that all of this was going on we were not allowed to make any phone calls whatsoever, not even to our lawyers. We weren't allowed to take showers or anything else. They took our televisions and radios, fans, etc. and took them apart looking inside of them. They didn't dare take this new typewriter apart... if they had of they would have voided the warranty and would have had to buy me a new one, and they didn't want to spend $300.00 for that.

My capital case comes up in June before the Virginia Supreme Court and at the same time we are filing into the Circuit Court of Virginia Beach on a Writ of Error Coram Nobis that is attacking my sentence and conviction solely on the innocence issue, i.e. DNA evidence and other corroborating evidence. The case is also going before the United States Supreme Court concerning the ignorant ruling the Virginia Supreme Court made about the caption of the appeal saying "assignments of error" instead of "petition for appeal" from a writ of habeas corpus. Without going into details about this, attorneys from all over America have stated that the ruling that the VSC made on my case is the most asinine and blatantly unconstitutional decision that has ever come out of a court! When those in authority in life/death cases care nothing about the innocence of the person whose life they have in their hands - those same people become murderers by proxy.

Death Row is designed to completely destroy a person. I have to fight it every day to keep my mind from going on me. Sometimes I catch myself drifting and falling into the trap that so many have fallen before. The prison administration has tried every trick in the book to get me to succumb, but so far I have not given up... and don't plan on giving up... though at times it is the most tempting thing I know. It would be so easy to just lay down and tell them to kill me and get it over with. Even though I did not kill the woman I am on Death Row for, that doesn't seem to bother me anymore. I don't look at it from the point that I am innocent... because innocence doesn't mean anything to my oppressors. They couldn't care less if a person is innocent or not. All they want is a body for a crime. And they don't care if that body is the guilty one or not. I know that I have to fight tooth and nail in order to win!

5/31/91

You know I think that there might be something really valuable to Dr. Norris's theory about the neuron transference and chemical imbalances, etc. which cause a freak synapse in the brain - that correlates to serial killers. The reason I say this is because I have had to totally re-evaluate my thinking on serial killers since the one that is still on the loose in Silver Springs, Maryland, has killed and raped 5 women in the past week. I just wonder what causes a person to all of a sudden become a rapist and killer! I mean wouldn't it be strange that a man 60 years old and a pillar of the community all of a sudden became a rapist and killer? What are the real causes? I think that Dr. Norris may just have something very valuable!

6/4/91

I wouldn't mind contributing my meager knowledge on the subject of *SERIAL KILLERS*. Most of my knowledge is derived from observations after conversing with one of them. Another aspect concerning *SERIAL KILLERS* is that each and every one of them has the trait of being very passive in a controlled environment. In a clinical setting, or when they are exposed to the media, they cannot portray their real selves, and their personalities take on a facade. I've observed the *SERIAL KILLERS* in here, and while they are telling their stories to me, they are looking around to make sure that nobody is eavesdropping, and they really get into the stories. It's like the camera in their mind is playing the reel and they are excited by the stimuli that the movie portrays in their minds. When they are around other people their personality clicks back to another setting, and they are *SUPER NICE GUYS* to the point of being sickening with their courteous ways. Maybe I should write a short book on my observations of *SERIAL KILLERS*, just for reference material, and then add to it as I learn more about them.

Sigmund Freud would not understand *SCHAEFER*! He is the epitome of anomalies! I really think that he enjoys the attention he gets from being abnormal. Like *MOOSE*, he couldn't get attention any other way than to be scarred and gross looking. Some people want attention so bad that they will do the most bizarre things to themselves to get it.

The thing about *SCHAEFER* and the *MADAM*, the *WHORES*, the *STRANGULATION* for kinky sex, sounds like another one of *SCHAEFER'S* far-out fantasies. Of course he is trying to impress you, but that's the most normal thing I have seen about him, for *ALL* men try to impress the important female figures in their lives - an inherent trait we men have!

SCHAEFER'S many-faceted personalities fascinate me too, but sometimes I wonder if he doesn't create these multi-faceted personalities because he knows that they turn people on. You know, I'm not convinced that

SCHAEFER isn't one of the smartest persons I have ever come across. His understanding of human nature is outstanding, but only when it comes to certain parts of the human psyche. He has a gap in his understanding, and it emerges and makes me look at him all over again. Maybe he has that synapse, i.e. a point at which a nerve charge in his brain passes from one basic reaction unit cell to another, but not in a moral way. You may want to pass this theory to Dr. Norris and find out what he thinks. The best way to describe what I just said, is the analogy of a wire with a short circuit, that sparks sometimes and makes contact, but at other times it doesn't.

6/15/91

Tell Dr. Norris that I'm glad he liked my poetry, and that he likes my research on *SERIAL KILLERS*. Did you catch your friend Roy Hazelwood on television with Faith Daniels when they were talking about Serial Killers in reference to that guy Dodd? That's one Serial Killer that makes me want to puke! The sick thing he did to those children was the most reprehensible act I have ever heard of! Like I told you one time... children, elderly people, and women are verboten for criminals in my eyes, and I could become a killer of those that commit acts against the aforementioned. I left out animals - I hate people that mistreat animals, especially dogs. Dogs are my passion.

6/27/91

As you know, almost every convict screams he is innocent when he gets busted. All my life I have been in one scrape after the other with the law, and consequently I ended up in jails, boys schools, prisons and now *DEATH ROW*. For the most part, everything I ever went to jail or prison for, I was guilty of. I have accumulated quite an unimpressive record during my lifetime, and believe me, it's something I am very ashamed of.

You have studied psychology and criminology, and you know that when a career criminal commits crimes, he has certain types of crimes he does, and there are certain crimes he will not do. Also criminals that commit sexual crimes do so at an early age, and it is an ongoing thing with them. What I am getting at, is a career criminal, such as myself, that has committed property crimes and armed robbery, without the slightest hint of any sexual hang-ups, i.e. never committed any crimes that were sexually related, does not in his middle forties all of a sudden become a rapist and killer. I'm sure that Dr. Norris will bear me out on this. Sexual crimes start at an early age, and I don't know of *ONE* case where a rapist started out in his middle forties. Though what I am saying is sound psychologically, it would not have any weight in a court of law. I'm telling you this to buttress some of the following things.

I have got to get my case *PUBLIC* any way possible. The *ONLY* way that will happen is through *BIZARRE* things happening that the public is interested in that I am involved in. I can't get too bizarre or I will take away from what I am trying to achieve, but bizarre enough to let the public know that I have been done *WRONG* and that if *AMERICA* stands for *EQUAL PROTECTION* and *JUSTICE AND FREEDOM FOR ALL*, that *SOMETHING* has to be done with this gross *MISCARRIAGE OF JUSTICE* that has been done to me.

The American Public has been inundated with the cries of criminals who claim they are innocent, only to find out after investigation, that they are in fact guilty. But the public has to know that there are cases of people that are innocent. You told me once that badmouthing the cops was not good due to the public having a need to know that their police were their heroes and protectors. Well I agree with that, but there are some bad apples in the police and court system too. I want to play on the fact that I'm not saying that *ALL* are bad, for I know that isn't true. But I have to show that I am suffering a miscarriage of justice that needs to be corrected. I mean, what does it take? I have disproved the *ONLY EVIDENCE* against me, and there is none that is even remotely inculpatory - it is all exculpatory now, and I think that it has to go before the *PUBLIC* - I have *NO CHOICE* in the matter other than laying down and just going through the motions of perfunctory appeals that one day will run out, and by that time it will be *TOO LATE* to do anything about it. One thing for sure, when a mistake is made, the government cannot go the graveyard, dig you up, and say, "Gee, we're sorry - we made a mistake!"

7/2/91

In the State of Virginia if a Death Row inmate, through his lawyer, etc. makes the slightest error in filing appeals, he is "*PROCEDURALLY BARRED*" from appealing any further. In other words if a person forgets to dot an "i" or cross a "t" the errant will be made to pay the penalty with his life. What makes it so ludicrous that this practice can go on, is the fact that the death-sentenced inmate depends on his lawyers to represent him and protect him through the appellate processes, and when the lawyer through omission, error, etc. makes the procedural error, the *VIRGINIA SUPREME COURT* will not relax their stringent rules, and the death-sentenced inmate is then condemned, without further appeals, to die in the electric chair. Oh, they can appeal further, but the appeals will be routinely rejected, citing the *"PROCEDURAL DEFAULT"* or *"PROCEDURAL BAR"*. It happened to *ROGER COLEMAN*. His lawyers filed his *NOTICE OF APPEAL* one day late. For that inadvertent error, *ROGER COLEMAN* will die in the electric chair. The same thing happened to me. I had a fear of having a *COLEMAN-THOMPSON "PROCEDURAL DEFAULT"* put on me, so over and over I cautioned my attorneys to be careful to not *"DEFAULT"* through any type of error. They assured me that they wouldn't and told me to relax and let them handle it. Well I trusted them, and it has cost me my life. They made the biggest error of *ANY* attorney in the *UNITED STATES*. When they filed my appeal, they put the title to the appeal as *"ASSIGNMENT OF ERRORS"*, instead of the required *"PETITION FOR APPEAL"*. The courts took that error and refused to even look at my appeal, and barred *ANY* of my issues from being reviewed by the *FEDERAL COURTS*. To make matters worse, my lawyers called me on the phone and told me that it was best that they withdrew from the case. They withdrew from the case and left me without any attorneys. I called, wrote, etc. to every attorney that I knew, asking for them to take my case. I got some inferential promises, but no commitments. Meanwhile the time limit for filing my *PETITION FOR WRIT OF CERTIORARI* was going on, and if that limit passed, then I would be getting an execution date at any time. So I ended up having to file it myself without any help.

I've been a fighter all my life, and I don't give up easily. But there's only so much fighting I can do under these circumstances. I see my friends getting execution dates: I see them going to the *DEATH HOUSE* and being executed. I don't see anyone giving them any help - all I see is someone holding their hands and selling them dreams and hope. I see them being stroked everyday with lies. The world is permeated with *EVIL* and this situation that I find myself in, and so many others are in, is the *EPITOME of EVIL*, with *EVIL* just dripping from those that we have to deal with on a daily basis. It's almost like the fight isn't worth the effort. Fight - for what? A life that isn't worth living? Still - I continue to fight for myself and for those that are not as strong as I am. I feel like God has made me a *SENTINEL* here, and that's the reason that I am here and haven't received *JUSTICE* yet. God wants me to fight this evil for myself and for the others that don't know how to fight for themselves.

To make our fight harder, the prison stopped furnishing us paper, envelopes, Xerox copying, and if we don't have the money to buy those things, then we are just up the creek without a paddle. There was a time when the courts would have *ORDERED* the prison to furnish us these materials, but the court system has broken down, and constitutional rights are out the door. Today it is my constitutional rights that are being violated, tomorrow it will be yours. Like Martin Luther King said *"INJUSTICE ANYWHERE, IS INJUSTICE EVERYWHERE!"* It's a known fact, that unless we have the materials to work with, then we cannot fight for our lives.

I am on *DEATH ROW* for a murder I did not commit, and I cannot describe to you the frustration, the heartache, the suffering, that all of this has caused me. A person that commits a crime can accept the punishment, even though he or she may not like it. But a person that is being punished, and is facing death, for something they did not do is a feeling I cannot describe in words.

2/20/92
Without all of the details, you know for the past few weeks we have been on lockdown/shakedown status, don't you? During that time I picked up a charge of *"POSSESSION OF DEADLY WEAPON"*. I was supposed to go to court today about it, but for some reason or another didn't. The charge is ludicrous... it was a two inch piece of metal that went on the tuning knob of the old television I used to have. At my preliminary hearing I told the judge that if I was going to be charged with that, then everyone in the prison, including the warden, should be charged for a deadly weapon for having a ballpoint pen. I illustrated that a ballpoint pen would penetrate easily six pieces of 20 lb.wt. copy paper, and that the so-called weapon wouldn't penetrate one. The judge had to laugh and agree with me that the ballpoint pen was the more dangerous weapon. I am demanding a jury trial, and I am representing myself if it goes to trial. I want to show the public that a bunch of idiots are running this institution. Anyway, that's the latest in the Joe O'Dell saga. Sub sole nolli novi. (Nothing new under the sun), and O tempore o more (Oh the times and the ways).

4/4/92
We are again on *LOCKDOWN*. Two guys overdosed and one died... the other is, or was in *INTENSIVE CARE*. So we are locked down tighter than Dick's Hat Band, with a *SUPER SEARCH/SHAKEDOWN* on the horizon. I get so sick of this. We stay locked down and searched more than any prison on earth. Every 30 days at least. We are always being told to pack up and move to another cell. I keep a spotless cell, and have no roaches or other pests, and they move me into a filthy cell with roaches crawling everywhere. Some of the men on Death Row are real filthy and don't even bathe. They smell like shit, and their cells are beyond belief... you wouldn't believe a human being could live like some of the men do. There are others like me that keep themselves impeccably clean, and it is us that are moved into these filthy cells. The psychology is, they know we will clean them. This is how the prison keeps the place clean. They tolerate the dirt balls, and make the rest of us clean up their shit!

I've got a big investigation going on here. One employee has already been fired and others are in line. There will be criminal charges forthcoming. I busted them for fraud, i.e. buying used products and selling them to us for *NEW*, and for top dollar. Overcharging, embezzlement, misappropriation of inmate funds, graft theft, etc. My lawyers have told me to be very careful. The ironic thing about it, is the warden is in there trying to bust them too, which surprised the hell out of me. He's not trying to cover anything up ... he honestly did not know this was going on. I've been knowing the warden for almost thirty years, and I didn't think he was stupid enough to be involved in anything like this, and it makes me feel good that he isn't.

4/21/92
I think I am *losing* it. One of my cats just had a litter of kittens and they are inside this drain pipe outside. It has been raining and I'm worried that the water will go into the drainpipe and wash the kittens away. The mama cat has been outside my window meowing for food. I have about went broke feeding her fish I buy out of the canteen. I can't wait to see the kittens... they were just born a few days ago. She came by to get fed in the morning all fat and belly dragging the ground, and that afternoon she came out of the pipe all slim and trim... so she dropped the little ones. (I told you I'm losing it. Tough cons are not supposed to be worried about little kitties... I'm supposed to say, "Fuck 'em... let the little bastards starve." Nope, I can't

do it, so I guess my reputation is shot, huh? Joe the "Wussy!")

5/3/92
I live around and with the most ignorant human beings on the face of this earth. There must be a correlation to *IGNORANCE* and *DEATH ROW*. No matter what is thrown at these guys they lay down and take it. We are being fed gruel that is not fit for human consumption and these guys are lapping it up like there's no tomorrow. I can't eat at all anymore. I guess it would do me some good, I will lose some weight, but it's no good for my health.

Roger Coleman was taken from Death Row Friday and moved to the *DEATH HOUSE* at Greenville. His execution date is the 20th of this month, and things are not looking too good for him. I hope and pray that he isn't executed, and I have a gut feeling he won't be, but who knows in this state?

My cat's had kittens and the kittens are only about 3 weeks old. (It doesn't seem but a little while ago that they were just kittens themselves), and they are outside my window right now playing and looking up at me. Most of them are Siamese, but three of them are totally white ... I believe they have Persian in them... they are beautiful. I feed them real good (Smitty and I feed them). This may sound crazy, but it's like those little creatures were put here just to see me through some tough times, because they sure make my life a lot better ... gives me something to love and care about. I worry about them all the time, especially when the lawn mowers are cutting the grass.

You would fall out if you were to see me right now. I had my head shaved and grew this monster-looking mustache. All the guys are saying I look *FIERCE* and *OMINOUS*, but we all know I'm just a *PUSSYCAT*, huh? Seriously, some of the people in here say the transformation is total, and that I resemble *MR. MOTO* the *JAPANESE WRESTLER*. Now that's taking it a bit far... I don't think I look like a *JAPANESE WRESTLER*... my eyes aren't even slanted!

5/9/92
You would not believe how sick I've been. I hate to ever complain about sickness, but there's an epidemic going on here. All of the guys have diarrhea, are vomiting and we are breaking out with boils and infections. It's our poor diet, and the filthy way our food is prepared. There is bacteria in

our food, and there is bacteria in our drinking water... even some of the guards are suffering from the same thing we are. We have sore joints, no energy, and we just cannot seem to be able to think clearly. Never, since I've been here, have I ever gone three days without writing letters or answering letters, but since this happened to me, I have been unable to do anything.

Roger Coleman is scheduled to die in eleven more days. He was taken to *GREENVILLE PRISON*, which is 54 miles from here, last week. That's where the electric chair is. One of my friends who was trying to locate me, called *GREENVILLE PRISON*, thinking that was where I was at, and the officer who took the call, who was the *PUBLIC RELATIONS OFFICER*, told my friend, "No, he is not here... we don't keep them here... we just *KILL THEM*." Now that's some good *PUBLIC RELATIONS* talk, huh? It gives you an idea of the mentality of the people who are in charge of the *MURDERS* of the people who are sentenced to death. I really feel for Roger Coleman, because these *LAST DAYS* have got to be the precursor to hell... he's actually living in hell now, and prayerfully, if he is murdered, he will not go to hell, but to heaven with our Lord. I firmly believe in Roger's innocence, and I have *STRONG* reasons for believing that. I haven't *ALWAYS* been convinced of his innocence, but now I have *NO DOUBTS* that *HE IS INNOCENT*.

If a person in Virginia commits a crime that reaps a *LIFE SENTENCE*, that person, with good behavior, will be paroled in less than 15 years. That's 15 years in a prison that has some normalcy to it, and where the prisoner can have contact visits with his loved ones, get out in the sunshine every day, have normal activities, etc. Men on *DEATH ROW* (some) serve up to, and beyond, 15 years, and then are *MURDERED*. Their 15 years was *PURE TORTURE*, with no contact visits, no sunshine, and no sense of normalcy. When they are murdered, they have already served a *LIFE SENTENCE* under the most heinous conditions.

Every single day on *DEATH ROW* I am handcuffed, while guards come into my cell with hammers beating on the walls, windows, the railings, the ventilators, etc. Not *ONE DAY* is missed. Can you imagine *EVERY DAY* listening to hammers banging for hours on 48 cells? It has about driven some of us crazy, and it has damaged my hearing, and the hearing of a lot of the other inmates. Each day, we are locked up for 19 hours out of 24. When we are not locked in our cells, we are out in a tiny area with four tables, and the acoustics are so bad that every word echoes, and it's hard to even hear the man next to you talking. Most of the inmates have gotten into the habit of screaming and yelling to be heard, and this creates a cacophonous madhouse... total audio chaos!

I hope this little poem will give you a lift in spirits: "If any little word of ours, can make one life the brighter; if any little song of ours, can make one heart the lighter; God help us speak that little word, and take our bit of singing, and drop it in some lonely vale to set the echoes ringing. If any little love of ours, can make one life the sweeter, If any little care of ours can make one step the fleeter, if any little help may ease the burden of another, God give us love and care and strength to help along each other." (I love this... it is called *A GOOD CREED.*)

5/15/92

When you think about all the *MIND CONTROL*, the *ASSASSINATIONS*, and all of the *EVIL* that is in this world with government officials, etc. do you ever ask yourself *WHY?* I mean, what is the real reason behind all of this? In the land of *EVIL DOERS*, those who practice evil have evil practised on them. Nobody can trust anybody, and it's just a matter of time before those who are ordering the deaths of people will have their own deaths ordered. It's like they know something *SUPER SECRET*, like the *SECRET TO ETERNAL LIFE*, and that they don't have to worry about *DEATH*... that *DEATH* is just a transition to their sought after life. It's crazy, but maybe not so crazy... it's crazy because I don't understand it all, and neither does anyone else who isn't a part of the elite evil doers.

I didn't explain what I really meant in the above paragraph. Hypothetically, or rather, in my own mind, I would rather be around people that I can trust, who are not liars, thieves, murderers, etc. I'd rather be around beautiful and clean things, rather than be around ugly and dirty things. I'd rather be able to relax and have peace and quiet, than be tensed up all the time with nothing but chaos around me. I like the finer things of life, but I'm not ready to sell my soul to have them, i.e. become a part of the *ORDER* that causes *DISORDER*, which is contrary to the *LAWS OF EXISTENCE*. Everything in this world has an opposite, and everything in this world has a *RIGHT* and a *WRONG* way of existing. The *PERFECT ORDER* of the universe, and all of the beautiful creations I've seen that are natural, tell me that there is *ONLY ONE RIGHT WAY*, and it certainly isn't with the filth and dung of the *EVIL DOERS*. All they represent is *DEATH*, and *EVERYTHING FILTHY AND NASTY*. They destroy, and their sole aim in their filthy existence is to ride roughshod over the weak... to become *GOD*. (I got off on a tangent here, but that's the way I think... I didn't always think like this, but I have gone through a metamorphosis, and a catharsis since being where I am, and the things I said in the foregoing two paragraphs, are just a modicum of what I see and believe in.)

Schaefer's release *(WISHFUL THINKING/ DREAMING/ NIGHTMARE/ ETC)* is all bullshit and you know it. He's full of plans and schemes, and it is like his whole world revolves around you. He thinks he can get mad at you, play on your fears to control you, and then do whatever he feels like. It's typical of his dealings with females. He sees a female as a *THING* and not a living, breathing, feeling human being, and therefore your feelings do not count... just his.

Reading Schaefer's letters and how he switches up in his them, tells me the guy has a real weird mind. (I already knew this.) Why would he think you'd like to have the address of the lawyer who wants to hear from guys who have been mistreated, etc., by FSP officials? Can you see the psyche behind that? It is to show you that something is going on, and he's in the *KNOW* of it. He has this image of himself as being *VERY IMPORTANT*, and you are the nucleus of his reason for wanting to be important, and everything in his twisted life hangs on you, but he doesn't want to expose his vulnerability, his image that he thinks you have of him. (Does he really know what you think of him? I think not.)

5/20/92
It's 3.25 a.m. now, and I'm wide awake. I can't seem to get myself on a regular sleeping schedule. I sleep a few hours, stay up a few hours, and this goes on all the time. The result of this piecemeal sleeping arrangement is that I never feel rested, never have any energy, and walk around like a *ZOMBIE* all the time. I'm burned out, Sondra. I'm totally burned out from all this shit. Same shit every day... same ugly mugs to look at every day... it gets to me. (The State of Virginia has created a *MONSTER*. There's no way anything with a badge will ever be able to arrest me again... I would die

right then and there!)

My lawyers are still dragging their asses. The Attorney General wrote them a letter and said if they didn't file my appeal within a couple of weeks, that they were going to seek an *EXECUTION DATE* for me. I got all over my lawyers about that.

I've been studying the *"TRILATERAL COMMISSION"* (the article you sent me and some other stuff) and what it is all about. Our whole country is under a dictatorship by some rich and powerful people who dictate to the government what they should and should not do. The *NEWS MEDIA* is owned and controlled by them, and they cover up anything that doesn't suit them. The American people are the most gullible people in the world. They believe everything that the news media feeds them, and are like a bunch of *ROBOTS* walking around. I call American society *"THE JOHNNY AND JENNY SOCIETY."* What that means is, "Give me my little Honda car, my VCR, my TV dinner, my credit card, and fuck everything else." That's what America is comprised of. Meanwhile, the government and the chosen elite, get fat off of the *"JOHNNY AND JENNYs"* and live a good life. Man, it is so fucking sad. Take a hundred people like me, give us AK 47's, some C-4, and some other goodies, and we could put a stop to all this shit.

Roger Coleman is scheduled to die tonight. That's a sad story. Our watermelon eating governor, "Uncle Remus", decided there wasn't enough evidence to convince him that Coleman is innocent. At the least the governor should have granted a stay of execution to give Coleman's lawyers a chance to develop the evidence that is pouring in. I have a feeling if they execute Coleman, that the State of Virginia is going to be sorry. One thing the Coleman case has taught me, and I hope it has taught others as well, and that is *"YOU DO NOT WAIT, UNTIL THE LAST MINUTE TO DO INVESTIGATION."* See, that's where my lawyers are fucking up... and no matter what I do, what I say, etc., they do what they want to do. Experience is the best teacher, and I know, because I live with these people, and I've watched 10 of them walk that last walk, and I've studied each and every one of their cases... the ones whose cases were properly investigated, i.e. Giarratano and Bassette, got commutations... the others got the *GRIM REAPER.*

You were talking about living in peace and quiet, having some leisure time, being able to take hot baths, etc., and you were saying that you couldn't take the banging, etc., that I go through here everyday. You asked me if I didn't have some fear about repercussions due to all the lawsuits I file against these people. The answer is *YES*. In some ways I have *FEAR*, but mostly I proceed with caution. Vulnerable is a misnomer here, it is more like *HELPLESS* and at their *TOTAL MERCY*, which of course they have *NONE*! I try not to be paranoid, and work hard at it, but I really think that I am being slowly killed by bad food, contaminated water, etc. It was like the time that they served us ice cream, and we were all on the lockdown. Everyone got strawberry ice cream but me... I received chocolate and almost died. I was sick for four days and almost didn't survive. All the guys swear they tried to poison me... tried hell, they did poison me, and it was only pure *WILLPOWER* that I survived. It would be so easy for them to poison me through my commissary orders. When I order from the commissary, they fill the order by placing my items in bags, and they deliver the bags to my cell. I know that sounds paranoid, but I am observant and cautious... that wouldn't do any good if they were really after me, but I'm not going to just be careless either.

5/27/92

I thought one of my newborn kittens (a month old) had become lost. I looked and looked for him (he is snow white and his name is Gabriel), and he was nowhere to be seen. Then all of a sudden, like a white flag being waved in surrender, this tiny white tail shot up in the air out of the grass, and here comes little Gabriel trotting across the grass. He had been hidden in the grass. He looked up at me with his tiny white face and started meowing real loud. There was a slice of bread on the ground and he ran over to it and picked it up in his tiny mouth... the bread was too heavy for him, so he started dragging it. Then he got mad at it and jumped back, leaving the bread in front of him, then he charged full steam ahead and attacked the bread. Breadcrumbs were flying everywhere as little Gabriel tore into that bread. Then here his mama came, Mrs. "Bootie Boots", and she ran over to see what her youngster was doing. Then Gabriel ran over to her and they started playing all over the yard... Gabriel would chase Mom, and then she would turn around and chase him... then they fell on the ground and rolled all over. Bootie Boots is black with a spot of white on her face and white boots on her paws. Gabriel is totally white... his daddy, "Snowball" is totally white just like him... Gabriel is a carbon copy of his daddy. (All of Gabriel's brothers and sisters were killed when a lawnmower ran over them.)

Olly the Possum came in and was eating some of the food that was thrown out for the cats. He ate a veal patty, and started weaving back and forth... unsteady on his feet, went out to the road and keeled over dead. He laid in the road for four days. Watching that poor animal die from some food we had given him made us all sad. It also scared us, because we know the food here is so rotten that it is unfit for human consumption. We have been told by employees that I cannot name, that the good food is being stolen by the prison officials, and we are getting fed all the bad food... spoiled food, and food that they have bought that has been discarded by the vendors. Not only that, but they have stolen all the new towels, sheets, blankets, etc., and we haven't had clean towels, sheets, etc. for two weeks. I had to wash my own in my sink and hang them to dry on the bars outside my cell. (I live on peanut butter and jelly and Cheerios... things that are bought from the commissary... without that food I would probably die... I also eat these little bags of instant soup... they only cost 23c a bag, and taste pretty good. I can buy stale bread for 58c a loaf... it isn't so stale that it tastes bad, so I don' complain too much. I just try to survive... that's the name of the game.)

5/31/92

I've really got some great lawyers now. There was a four page article on my main lawyer, Patricia Shwarzschild, in the paper the other day. (My name was mentioned in the article due to her taking my case.) I have the best legal representation of any inmate on Death Row., I have the largest law firm in New York on my case, which is PAUL, WEISS, RIFKIND, WHARTON & GARRISON, which has 300 partners and over a 1,000 Associate Lawyers, and I have Hunton & Williams of Richmond, the most prestigious law firm in Virginia. I am the only criminal case that they are handling. I have 56 lawyers assigned to my case, and I don't know how many investigators. Since Coleman was executed, things have picked up in my case. My case is much stronger than Coleman's, and everyone is concerned that Virginia is going to execute another innocent man. I know that a lot of people had ambivalent feelings about Coleman's case, but believe me, that man was innocent. There was a lot of lies told in his case, and there was a lot of cover-up. It makes one wonder what the purpose is in executing an innocent person, especially when those who are doing the executing know that the man is innocent. The only reason, and I mean the only reason, that I am still on Death Row, and not free, is because of Rules instead of Justice. When I get into Federal Court with my case, it will be a different ballgame. Virginia is coming to the point where Death Row cases are concerned, where there is going to be nationwide attention focused. We have a black man here named Earl Washington, who has DNA evidence that proves he was not the rapist, and that he could not have killed the woman he is accused of. The evidence had been hidden for 10 years. We have another who shot a cop in the arm, the cop's arm flew backwards from the bullet hitting him in the arm, and his gun went off and he shot himself in the head, which killed him. The prosecution claimed that the other man's bullet did it. Only one shot was fired... that shot hit the cop in the arm... the cop couldn't have shot himself in the arm. Another man had a dream that he killed someone, (Terry Williams) and he told the police about it. They took his dream and made it into a confession. They went to the cemetery and dug up a man's body who had been dead for 7 months, and who died from drinking too much, which was termed alcohol poisoning, and they charged Terry with murder, even though there was nothing showing he had been murdered. There are about 9 cases here like that, and people from all over America are focusing in on Virginia and how they are killing innocent people with their stupid laws instead of the truth and justice. Just like my case... the cops, the prosecutors, the attorney general, etc., they know I am innocent. They are pacifying their consciences and justifying executing me, by my past record and nothing else. They figure I should die for my past crimes, and being innocent of this one is inconsequential!

I spent about an hour yesterday working with Mr. Montgomery, the institutional attorney, in figuring out where each man's case on Death Row was. I was amazed to learn that there are so many whose cases are without any appeals left. Either there is going to be a giant blood bath in Virginia, or something is going to have to happen with the death penalty soon. We have about 10 who are at the end of their appeals, and with blood-thirsty Virginia, there will be executions one behind the other. Texas does it without causing any public outcry, so I have no doubt that when it starts in Virginia, the same apathetic response will be heard from Virginia, i.e. "Ho, hum, so what!"

6/14/92

I wish I could send you copies of everything I have for you to read so you could see the monster I'm up against. The sad thing about it, is I'm not the only one up against the *MONSTER*... even you are up against the monster, but in a different way. The *MONSTER* is the corrupt people we have running our government and our government-run facilities. Everyone is out to make a buck, and they will do what they have to do to make that buck, and in here they are stealing us blind. To give you an example of what I'm talking about: these people have deals with vendors to sell to us inmates all of the rotten and putrefied food products that the vendors have to dispose of. We are charged *TOP PRICE* for these products, plus a 15% markup. When I filed a lawsuit against the people who were doing this, and forced them to show what they did with their stale products, and produce records of the destruction of the products, here is the verbatim response I got from Mr. Charles E Rawlings, General Manager of MCLEAN TOMS INC., PRINCE GEORGE, VIRGINIA, who furnishes all of the potato chips, nachos, corn chips, cookies, candies, etc. etc. Here's his response to my *SUBPOENA DUCES TECUM*: "We keep no records of the disposal of our products. We give them to a local farmer who feeds them to his pigs." Then the attorney general told the judge here in Mecklenburg that he, the judge, should not even consider the case. He said, "Who is interested in a bag of potato chips, your Honor?" I told the judge we weren't talking about a bag of potato chips, that we were talking about hundreds of thousands of dollars worth of products that had *EXPIRED* and were supposed to be disposed of. That the local farmer Mr. Rawlings was talking about *MECKLENBURG CORRECTION CENTER*, and the *PIGS* the products were being fed to were the *INMATES* at Mecklenburg Correctional Center. It is hard to believe that the Attorney General's Office, who is supposed to protect the people from criminals is fighting to cover up criminal activities. It's all a big cover-up, and I wish I had someone like Ross Perot that I could drop this on to investigate. The prisons would be bursting at the seams with guards and prison personnel. I'm not going to give up, I'm going to continue writing letters, filing lawsuits, until *SOMEONE* will look into this. I've tried *60 Minutes, 20/20*, and all of the shows that expose things like this, but none of them seem to be interested.

The warden and his *MOTLEY CREW* had me in an interview trying to get me to stop filing all of the lawsuits. I refused, so as the meeting concluded, this one big fat sweat hog goes and calls my female lawyer in New York and said that I had received a package from one of my legal staff (female) that contained *PUBIC HAIRS*. My lawyer, Susan, called me and asked me about it. I blew my stack and raised hell. It was a bald-faced lie. Then when the sweat hog who had made the call was confronted with it, she denied doing it. We have proof that she did, and there is going to be some repercussions behind it. This will show you the extent these people will go to cause problems. My lawyers have told me not to file any lawsuits on it yet, but I'm going to eventually... that cannot happen without some heads rolling... no way.

6/22/92

We have one to be executed soon. Edward Fitzgerald. His execution date is for July 23rd. Damn, July is a bad month for the guys on *THE ROW*. Ricky went on July 10th, and Richard Whitley went on July 6th ... now Fitz is scheduled to go on the 23rd of July. He seems to be handling things pretty well. Of course Fitz isn't one to go around crying the blues. He is the same old Fitz, laughing and playing and not letting this horror get to him. I'll tell you, this place is one big *ENIGMATIC NIGHTMARE* to me ... I don't understand the psychology of it all. I mean I think I do, but when I get down into the heavy thinking concerning it, my mind goes blank. I know one thing, I know who the enemy is, and I know who the *EVIL ONES* are. The *EVIL ONES* don't think that they are *EVIL*, but believe me, when someone kills other human beings with premeditation and enjoyment, then they are *EVIL*. I don't know of *ONE* person on *DEATH ROW* who can say he enjoyed killing his victim. Most of the killings that people are here for happened due to circumstances, and not premeditatively planning them. Of course prosecutors will argue that for a split second the person had the rationale to form malice and premeditation. Technically that might be true, but not *ONE* sat around for years planning the murders of their victims. Not *ONE* tortured their victims for years before killing them. Not *ONE* told his victim what day, what time, etc., that he was going to kill them, and offered them a *LAST MEAL* before they killed them. Victim's families I have compassion for, but not one victim's family member has ever gone through what the family members of a condemned man's family goes through. Years and years of anguish, heartache, pain of knowing that their loved one is going to be murdered ... even getting the very day, the hour, the minute, and having it broadcast on television, radio and the newspapers ... then instead of sympathy for their loss after their loved one is murdered, they are looked at with disdain and scorn, like they did something atrocious. It makes absolutely *NO SENSE* ... it boils down to *EVIL!*

6/28/92

Never in my life have I been around such ignorance like I'm around here on Death Row. These guys worry about all this petty crap, but don't give a hoot about their circumstances. I have these guys coming up to me asking me to file complaints on petty crap that I wouldn't waste my time on. Check this out. I had one wanting me to waste my time complaining to the warden about the guards turning the television around so they can watch it when we are locked up. So what? We have our own televisions in our cells, and who cares if the guard is watching the television in the outside area? In fact I'm glad they are watching television, that way they won't be bothering me. Another complaint. The guards are talking on the telephone. So what? While they are talking on the telephone they aren't bothering me. Another complaint. Ronnie has ice in his cell, and it isn't right. Hell, so what? We all have ice in our cells... I have an ice cooler, so why should I care about what Ronnie or anyone else has in his cell. These are the type of complaints these guys write the warden about. Like, so and so is taking a shower when he is supposed to be locked in his cell. Can you believe the pettiness of these people who have death sentences? I tell them I can't waste my time on that kind of crap, and then look at them like they are crazy, because whether they know it or not, they are snitching! I spend my time attacking the administration... the establishment on issues that mean something. Like they don't give a damn - the sycophant-types- that they are being stolen blind by the prison commissary, their food is being stolen and they are being fed gruel. That their visits are being curtailed. Their prison pay cut from $38.00 a month to $13.80 a month. That they have to pay for their paper, envelopes, toothpaste, razor blades, deodorant, etc., which they did not use to have to do. That we do not get the benefit of the 15% markup on every dollar we spend. That the library gives us the dregs of the books. Our personal property is being stolen. Money orders and mail being stolen. It goes on and on, but the bottom line to it all, is they don't even care about their cases, and will not lift a finger to help their attorneys. I'm not talking about uneducated people either, not for the most part. We have computer experts, writers, lieutenant commanders in the Navy, business men, etc., but they are the main ones who don't give a damn. I just don't understand this kind of thing...

it is beyond my comprehension. What do you think it is? Is it that they are afraid to face reality due to the gravity of their situation?

7/3/92

Booty Boots had a green snake playing with it last night. Snowball and BB Head Boots just sat there and watched her play with the snake. Every time Booty Boots would claw the snake, she would sling it three or four feet... then Snowball and BB Head would go sniff where the snake had been before. Little Gabriel got *"CATNAPPED"* by the female guard who patrols the perimeter fence. He has a good home now, so I'm not upset, though I miss the little rascal. I looked out the window last night and thought I had a new kitten, because this was a tiny little mis-colored creature. I seen the cats about ten feet away just looking... it was dark, so I couldn't see too well... I threw meatloaf down to the creature... it was a baby Skunk. A beautiful baby Skunk. Booty Boots got jealous because I was feeding the baby Skunk, so she ran at it... the baby Skunk hunched down, fluffy tail in the air... they stood there looking at each other for a few seconds, then Booty Boots went at the Baby Skunk, then jumped back... the Baby Skunk turned his tail to Booty Boots and let her have a whiff of that Estee Lauder... Booty Boots yelped, jumped in the air and all the other cats took off meowing and Snowball rolled over in the grass and snatched a patch of his white fur out, then ran into the drainpipe. I heard laughter from all the windows. All the other guys were watching the show. The baby Skunk went back to eating... then we all had to close our windows... that little fella sure put out a *STINKER*!

The thing about the *ELECTRIC CHAIR*. That would probably be a blessing to him. The guy has *NOTHING* to live for but countless years of hell in prison. I'd rather be dead than live in that rathole for life. That is *HELL* in itself! The guy has already exhibited his desire to *END IT ALL*, so if he gets the chair, what is the difference in how he goes... he still has that option of taking himself out. I know that sounds cold on my part, but actually, I feel like Carl Panzram, people like that are being done a favor when they end this life of hell-on-earth. Some people are *"PAST REDEMPTION"* with their lives. (I started to write a book about some guys here on the *ROW*, and that was going to be the title of the book, *PAST REDEMPTION*.) I think he is PAST REDEMPTION, and his life on earth has NO meaning in the realm of what life is all about. Prison isn't *ANY* life at all. I mean if a guy goes out and screws up like robbing a store, breaking and entering, and something along that order, gets five or ten years, his life still has some redemptive value, and he can straighten himself out and go on and make a *NEW LIFE* for himself. What has he got to look forward to? The *"LAW OF SELF-PRESERVATION"* would have to be very strong for me to want to continue life under the circumstances that guy's life is under. I know I am on *DEATH ROW*, and I *KNOW* that in his shoes, I would opt for death! No question about it!

7/12/92

I know exactly what you mean about dreams, delusions, etc., some guys who are in prison, Death Row, etc., say over and over that they have this going or that going, concerning their release. I hear it all the time in here from men who have *NO CHANCE* of *EVER* seeing freedom again, and I look at them when they say something about what they are going to do when they get out. I know they are living in an *"ALICE IN WONDERLAND"* world. Reality hurts too bad for them to face the fact that it is *ALL OVER WITH* insofar as having a *FREE LIFE* again. (God what a horrible thought! No more pussy, no more good times, just being around a bunch of crying-ass, hairy-ass men, and all the decadent bullshit that goes on. What a world to look forward to spending the rest of one's life in! Not me... I'd rather be dead than be up against a fate like that!)

7/27/92

I know you must be getting tired of all these *DOWN* letters, but if I write you a cheery letter, I would be phony, and I know you don't want to hear a bunch of fantasy. I'm not the only one that is down here. We are *ALL DOWN*! All executions are atrocious.... I don't call them executions... I call them murders. That is one of the definitions in my *FRANKLIN ELECTRONIC DICTIONARY*, and it goes along with the way I feel, so I call it *PREMEDITATED MURDER* that is worse than *ANY* other type of premeditated murder.

When Eddie Fitzgerald was murdered Thursday night it just took a lot from me and the other guys. Shaking us down, tearing our cells apart, then after we straighten our cells back up, here they come two days later and make us pack up all of our belongings, and move us into roach infested, filthy cells. The highlight for the hell they put us through and to cap it all off, they murder

Eddie! We have to go through this again the 15th of August and also on the 15th of September with Davis and Jones, then there will be Timmy Bunch and a couple more following. It has gotten to be too much for some of the guys, and they are giving up their appeals so that the horror and torture will end for them. I try to talk them out of it, but it hasn't worked yet. I can guarantee everybody *ONE THING*, I will *FIGHT* them all the way... I *WILL NOT* give up... to give up is to let them win, and I don't want them winning.

8/4/92

Think about this for a minute. Just hypothesize about this being a *CRIME FREE SOCIETY*. Just think that tomorrow all crime ceased, and all persons convicted of crimes were given a second chance and released, and that there would *NEVER* be any more crime ever. What do you think would happen to the economy? Prisons are an *INDUSTRY*... a *VERY PROFITABLE* industry at that. All the guards would be out of work. All the released convicts would be looking for work. There aren't enough jobs now, so where would the jobs come from? They can take that bullshit about "Let us make tougher laws to prevent crime," and shove it up their asses, because they don't want to stop crime.

8/13/92

Glad you like the *KITTY CAT STORIES*. I love my little kitties, and they love me too. I'll tell you, I am thinking seriously about writing a book concerning the things that they do. I'd write the book just for the joy of reading it myself. I know my family would get a kick out of reading it. Animals are a lot of fun... especially cats and kittens. They love to play like children and they are such a joy for me to feed and love. I get tired of hearing who got executed in this state and that state, who is going to be executed next here, and all the *DEATH, DEATH, DEATH*! Damn, I like to hear things about *LIFE*... things that make me happy.,.. not things that make me glum.

I hadn't heard about the serial killer that killed 25 women. Send me some material on it when you get a chance. I know you have your hands full with D.H.R. [Rolling] right now, and I think you are right not spreading yourself too thin. I also think you will be the top authority on *SERIAL KILLERS* when the dust goes down. G.J.S. can't stand it because he's in some tough competition. He's like a Beauty Queen who has lost all of her beauty and the young beauties come in and take away all of his/her glory. The new killers coming into the limelight now have him all worked up, because he is no longer an interesting celebrity... he has become mediocre and "Ho Hum... Schaefer who?"

8/17/92

I know you most likely understand this better than I do, but every convict has these fantasies about some movie star falling in love with them, some famous writer, singer, reporter, lawyer, etc. I see this every day on the *ROW*, and there are guys in here who will do *ANYTHING* to get a female lawyer. (I got my female lawyers by accident... it was just a coincidence that they are both very pretty and sexy... it has nothing to do with my dreams and fantasies. Smile... I'm a dirty old man, huh?) Anyway, what I am saying here, is these convicts sit around in their cells daydreaming and sex is on their minds all the time. They envision themselves as some hero figure, that women just swoon over, and they fancy themselves as *MEN OF THE WORLD*, handsome, debonair. Blacks have a penchant for playing these roles, thinking all white women want some black dick. I hear them signifying all the time. When a female contacts a convict in a professional capacity, the convict automatically goes into *FANTASY MODE* and starts entertaining ideas how he might persuade her to be his woman. Some play real coy, they all tell lies to make themselves what they are not, trying to impress the female, without the slightest idea whether she is married, has a boyfriend, etc. I've tried to tell these guys in here. "What woman wants a man who is in prison, isn't going to get out, etc." A woman would have to be nuts or desperate to want a man who she will never be able to have a life with. But that's the way it is, and there are women like that... pretty women too. So the guys still do their fantasizing, hoping someday that their dream girl will appear on the horizon, provide them with all their needs, in return for a bunch of lies written on paper, and lies spoken through Plexiglas and over a telephone.

Convicts sit around watching television, and some of the programs take on a *REAL LIFE DRAMA* for them, and they get into them and they see their lives being like the lives of the characters on the screen. When female guards or female food workers, or nurses come around, there are certain guys who cannot help themselves, they've got to make up an excuse just to talk to her. The Mail Lady is stopped every morning by the same sex fiends, who lust on her under the pretext of something being wrong with their mail. The nurse, the same guys are always sick or have a headache or something. The Grievance Lady, the same guys file frivolous grievances just so they can lust on her. It goes on and on. The bottom line to all of this is, convicts are a bunch of "Alice in Wonderland" characters, who live in a fantasy world. They are liars, and will tell a woman anything to get what they want. I know this, because I've been down that road myself. I guess with age, wisdom... I no longer do any of that crap.

You are up against a monster with your type of work, and I mean that literally. You deal with irrational people all the time. I mean, here's a guy who can be so sweet and gentle, then something sets him off and he suddenly becomes a crazed killer. There's no trusting, no relaxing, etc. around people like that. I like my people predictable, and I am sure you do too! One thing about being married to a man in prison, or on Death Row... it's a very safe relationship.

Did you read some time back about this guy in prison whose wife filed for divorce on him, saying she had met another guy and wanted to marry the guy? The guy in prison begged her to come see him one last time. She agreed and visited him. When she was leaving after the visit, the convict asked her to give him a last kiss. She agreed and was kissing him... he took his teeth and bit her top lip clean off and swallowed it, and yelled all sorts of obscenities at her as she was screaming and bleeding profusely. In a moment this guy ruined this woman's face, her life, etc. So you see, you have to be careful around unpredictable people, especially convicts.

8/26/92

Would you believe I've got seven more kittens? God Almighty, I've got so many kitties now I can hardly feed them. I don't know where they are all coming from. They are beautiful kittens. These have Persian in them and are little fluff balls. The mama cat is Persian, the daddy cat is just a big white tom cat. He's the same tom that impregnates all the females... he's the biggest tom cat I've ever seen. His name is Frostie, and he's a mean SOB too! You aren't going to believe this, but it is the truth... Frostie is so big and mean that he was chasing one of the German Shepherds the other day. I've never seen a cat chase a dog before.

Pepe La Pew, the tiny baby Skunk, came in last night and all the kittens, cats, including Frostie, broke camp and got out of Dodge. Pepe is one mischievous little guy. He sprays everywhere and we have to close the windows. For a little guy he sure puts out a *BIG STINK*! He interrupted the kittens while they were eating, and when the kittens took off, he feasted off of their food. He got confused and couldn't figure how to get out of the fenced in section he was in, so he curled up next to the fence and went to sleep. He was still there this morning. I looked out the window just in time to see a guard open the fence gate, and Pepe (brave little guy) jumped up and ran right for the gate... the guard saw him and took off running... Pepe ran one way, the guard ran the other. (Smile) That was just what I needed to wake up... I laughed until tears came down my face. Benny Hill couldn't touch these animals and their comical antics.

Talking about ignorance... This one guy in here is bugging me to file a *DISSOLUTION OF MARRIAGE*. I asked him why was it so important for him to divorce his wife when he will not lift a hand to do anything about his death sentence. He said his wife was a whore and had a baby by another man. I asked him what did he expect her to do while he is on Death Row and knowing he would *NEVER* get out again? He said she disrespected him. He has been on Death Row 8 years and I guess she was supposed to sew that thing up for him and cross her legs forever. The beat goes on...

8/31/92
Hell, you are getting fucked without getting kissed! I told you once, you don't let convicts call shots... they will try to control you the first time you get weak on them. I know convicts better than anyone, and I know that they are very attuned to fine details, and the first thing they look for when they come to prison is a way to break out, and the next thing they do is look for a weak spot in another human being. There's *NO HONOR* amongst most convicts, and they will definitely take advantage of a woman if given half a chance.

I kept thinking it was thundering outside, so I cut my fan off and my television down, and listened... it was those assholes in Building #2 beating on their lockers. A real nuthouse. They put their radios in the windows and they all have "*GHETTO BLASTERS*" and play *RAP* music all night long. *Brenda Got a Big Old Butt*, and all that bullshit! They keep Death Row awake day and night. They are in solitary confinement and have nothing better to do than irritate us!

9/8/92
Your friend has 10% of your heart. I think maybe that 10% he has may be tainting the other 90%. I'm not badmouthing him, but if he was a part of this, if it took on being a three-way conversation, he would be the first one to admit that he is a *CON MAN*, and that he has very little loyalty. Respect in his circles comes from being able to *BEAT* people. It's a sign of strength. Whenever someone gets over on another, the one who got over is considered the strongest and is given the respect that goes along with it. It is the law of the criminal jungle! Different cultures have different values, as you well know, and the criminal culture has its own set of rules, as you also know, and those rules do not comport to the rules of society... they are totally different. What is commendable in society is condemned in the criminal society. He is a *STAND UP CITIZEN* in the criminal society, but his violation of one rule of the criminal society, is at odds with another rule, which is *THE LAW OF SELF PRESERVATION*, which is what he is doing... he is trying to survive. With all of that being said and done, I want to give you a little bone to gnaw on. If a person will do those things, then what do you think he will do to you if the opportunity that he will benefit comes to pass? It doesn't take a genius to figure that one out! Again, I am not badmouthing him, but I have a loyalty to you that I will not betray, and I don't have any commitments to him, other than I like him, and wouldn't do anything to hurt him... yet, I owe it to you to point out how I see things. The bottom line, "Don't let your right hand know what your left is doing!"

Guys like your other friend, who have killed women, men, and have done weird things in their crimes, are not an enigma to me. I may not understand them totally, and do not claim to... but I do understand the machinations that drive them to do the things that they do. It is a complex maze of things that criminologists, psychologists, etc., have correctly perceived, but not totally. Like a cake that requires so many ingredients, the makeup of a killer like him is a combination of ingredients that make him come out to what he is when the process is complete. To go into all the *CAUSES* of what started the cake to baking would take a book. But there are the usual things, frustration, rebellion, anxiety, abuse, anger, sexual frustration, fantasies, hatred, feelings of omnipotence, infallibility, challenges, game-playing, hero emulating, delusions of grandeur, aberrated logic, jealousy, celebrity syndrome, feelings of not belonging, feelings of total alienation, feelings of being something special, feelings of being nothing, feelings that the world is against them, supreme being syndrome, necrophilia syndrome, predator syndrome, histrionic syndrome, general-delusion/confusion, fetishes, voyeurism, pornographic stimuli, anatomical preoccupation, i.e. body parts, sexual dysfunction, sexual toys, lack of conscience, sees his acts in a movie reel inside his head, and like a director or producer, enhances those acts in a mental script, then as he commits them, he has become director and producer of the movie he has created, schizophrenic, paranoid, appears normal, usually very intelligent, enjoys games like Chess, usually a loner, temperament fluctuates, moody, intellectual vanity, clever at figuring out *"BRAIN TEASERS"*, usually poor at mathematics (this is a key to the puzzle), concentration poor, meanders in conversations and writing, perceives himself above reproach, usually closer to the mother than the father, the Oedipus Complex/Syndrome, etc. The foregoing just touches the basic ingredients for the serial killers, who have many faces, personalities, etc. All, or some, are in *EVERY* serial killer.

You wanted me to give you some insight concerning psyche. You are as well qualified to psychoanalyze him as I am. Of course I have the prison experience, being around people like him, etc, but I probably can't tell you much that you don't already know. The one thing I want you to understand; guys like him are lonely, seeking the answer to all of their problems, and *ANYONE* who approach them, they feel that "This could be it!" Also, you are a female and you know that guys like Danny have a propensity for falling in love with the first female that pays them the least attention. They fantasize about any female that comes into their lives. The scenario in their minds takes them from prison and their circumstances, and they put their *ALL* into the belief that the female is their female goddess who will deliver them from their hell-on-earth. There is *NO* loyalty involved, just demented delusions created by aberrated fantasies, and the first time their bubble is burst, and the fantasy isn't according to Hoyle, then they "go off!" The "celebrity syndrome" is prevalent in this instance, and people like him feel that they are movie stars and that everyone is vying for their attention, etc. and that they can call the shots! They live for attention, and when they don't get it, they will do something, anything, regardless of the consequences (The anomaly of the disregard for consequences has always intrigued me. In these people, there seems to be a *TOTAL LACK* of regard of the consequences of their acts.) to get this attention, and when they don't, they will regress to an infantile posture, and go into temper tantrums, pout and rant and rave unintelligibly!

Another thing worth noting. Every serial killer I have ever known, read about, etc. is creative! Look at Ottis, even though he is illiterate, has a dysfunctional mind, he is still creative. Of course his creations are that of someone from *ROMPER ROOM*, but still, in his own way, creative. Schaefer, he is creative, and like a Chameleon, can change up on his creativity. He takes fact and turns it into fiction, instead of fiction into fact. He plays out in fictional roles the reality of his life. Schaefer is one of the most diabolical human beings I have ever known, and his penchant for creating evil schemes is beyond the scope of any adjective I know that would describe them. Danny is creative, as you well know, and he has many faces he can put on. Many personalities. He can be Jesse James in his mind. Cole Younger, John Dillinger, or anyone else he wanted to be. He can be a Rock Star, a Poet, a charming mesmerizer. He can captivate the gullible and naive. That is how Bundy would trap his victims... through his hypnotic charm, like a Cobra coming out of a basket to the tune of the snake charmer. There are so many things that these type of people's psyche entails, that a book would have to be written to cover it all.

There are things that haven't been written about, or at least I have never read anything about it, that involve serial killers. Like Phallus Worshippers, there are Vagina Worshippers, Breast Worshippers, Anal Worshippers, and to put it in perspective, there are "Anatomical Worshippers", but some have special body parts that they are especially attracted to. Mystery, intrigue, the unknown, play a significant part in all of this. The voyeur, the stalker, they all have a sexual thing that gets put in gear whenever they can observe someone without that person knowing it. It's like the *MALL STALKERS* who go to the Shopping Malls to observe women. They walk around observing a variety of women, and to them they are shopping like everyone else, but they are shopping for victims. They see a woman that appeals to their sexual fantasy and they mark her for a victim, and then they act on it. (Another Bundy speciality.)

Remember I told you one time that the way to really peek at Schaefer was to observe him unobserved? The reason I said that is because some of the serial killers here on Death Row have been caught during shakedowns with all sorts of weird objects that were constructed and concocted from their aberrated imaginations. Though they appeared normal under known observation, the implements found in their possession during the shakedowns told another story. In one guy's cell they found pictures cut out of magazines (pornographic) where this guy took the vaginas and penises and placed them in a pictorial outlay that satisfied his own fantasy. He had a homemade pussy constructed out of rubber gloves, inside a toilet paper roll, and even had a reservoir built in for lubrication. (Hmmmm, now that's not such a bad idea. Smile.)

Well, I just got interrupted, this guy named Mueller, who raped and killed a 9-year-old little girl and bit her little non-developed breasts off, just set himself afire. The smoke is about to run me out of here... they just brought in the exhaust fans... carried him out after dousing the flames. Guess the thoughts of what he did to that poor little girl got to be too much for him. He is the most hated man on Death Row. For some reason I cannot get a modicum of sympathy for the guy in my heart... guess I am cold-hearted, but not so much, because I sure have sympathy for the little girl he so brutally murdered and cannibalized!

9/14/92

I just read this big article about Virginia's Death Row in the Washington Post. Of course my name was listed, but nothing specific said... I was just a statistic. The information given about the crime was erroneous, and my age was wrong. The article depicted the horror of *CAPITAL PUNISHMENT*. After reading the article I became nauseated... the article came during lunch... great timing, huh?

While reading the article in the Washington Post, I realized something. I was reading about the crimes the men are on Death Row for. Reading about people I know, and how I know them, and then reading about the crimes they are charged with, freaks me out. I don't know the person that is being described as a killer who stuck a knife in a body 180 times, or shot an infant in the head, or took a hammer and beat the brains out of someone. The people the papers are talking about are aliens to me. The people I know, who have the same names listed in the paper, are seemingly normal human beings. They are not the people depicted in the newspaper. People reading the paper about the Death Row Inmates can only see what the paper describes, which is the *MONSTER* portrayal. Another thing I realized after reading the article. I was looking out of the window and I saw some of my buddies from prison and reform school. One of my old chums, Shorty Breeden, who was in reform school with me, is serving five life sentences for robbing a Roy Rogers restaurant and shooting, execution-style, four of the restaurant workers to death. Shorty was walking around the prison yard. He had no *DEATH SENTENCE*. He had a long criminal record when he committed the murders... yet he did not get the death penalty. Not that I would want Shorty to receive the death penalty, but in comparison to the men on Death Row, where is the *JUSTICE*? It is all arbitrary and capricious, with a wide range of disparity!

I'll tell you how economical I've become. The other guys spend 39c apiece for air fresheners, and they have to use at least three a week. I buy Irish Spring Soap to bathe with, and I take the bars when they get small and cut them into small pieces and put the pieces in an Irish Spring Soap box with holes punched into it. I take a piece of dental floss and tie the box to the front of my fan and turn it on. My cell smells fresh and clean with the Irish Spring scene. The air fresheners the other guys use have a sweet and sickening smell to them. Some smell like KOOL AID, and that is really nauseous smelling. Even if I could afford the air fresheners, I would still make my own. I wash my cell down with laundry detergent that I buy out of the commissary, which has a clean smell to it. (I splurge on this.) The mop water that the state furnishes has this disinfectant smell that I cannot stand! I have smelled this so much in my life that the smell alone puts me into a state of depression. I know enough about psychology to know that smell plays a big role in the psyche of a person. Color is another thing. I keep my walls decorated with bright and cheery cards (mostly Garfield). I have Garfield balloons all over the place. I made my own carpet out of a blue blanket. I try to keep my cell (my home for now) as cozy and comfortable as possible. My television combo/cassette recorder/radio/monitor and all of my other electronic equipment is situated like an entertainment center. I have everything positioned where I can sit in my chair and reach it. I wish they would allow me to take a photo of my cell so you could see what it looks like. I'm sure you would be surprised. It is anything but a dark, dank stereotyped prison cell, although it could look like that. I have curtains on my window.

9/20/92

People like Danny and Schaefer have been in my life for many years. I have observed them closely (not them per se, but people like them), and I see the lack of self-esteem that they have. They feel that they have to do something unique to be somebody, and even those who do it for other reasons have the same delusions of self-importance. It is like I told my whole cell block the other day, "Who in the hell is a *BIG WHEEL*" on Death Row? Big Wheel over what?" I asked them did they realize just how silly all of their prison politics, snitching to the man, and all the silly games that they were playing, really was?" All I got was some blank stares. Then I asked them "Do you have a world outside of this stupid place? Is your sole existence in this hellhole?" Again the blank looks.

A lot of people cannot exist in a free environment and function perfectly in a controlled one. In fact that has been said about me, but seriously, the evaluation on me was wrong, because I love being free and functioning in a free society. The mistakes I made in my life cost me *BIG TIME* and then this miscarriage of justice put the finishing touches on everything. Anyway, before I digressed, some of the men in here want to be somebody, so to put their mark on the world and to get some recognition, they revert to all sorts of bullshit. One guy is the *KING* booze maker. Another is the *DOPE MAN*. Another is the Queen Bee (faggot). Then there is the SNITCH who gets all sorts of favors from the guards for his information. The *GREAT MERCHANT/DELICATESSEN MAN*. The *BEST POKER PLAYER*. The *BEST GREETING CARD MAKER*. The *STRONGEST*. The *BEST BASKETBALL PLAYER*. The *BEST JAILHOUSE LAWYER* (Smile) The *FATTEST*. The *SKINNIEST*. The *UGLIEST*. The *BEST LOOKING*. The *BIGGEST STUD*. Whose *COCK IS THE BIGGEST*. Who *HAS THE MOST WOMEN*. Who has *THE BEST PORNOGRAPHIC COLLECTION*. It goes on and on... who can eat the most. Who can fart the loudest. You would not believe the lengths prisoners will go to in order to get attention and recognition. These observations are worthy of a criminologist's investigation. I guest it is inherent in everyone to want to be something unique. Nobody wants to be a *NOBODY*.

I study people all the time. Strange creatures roam the space in prisons... on the outside too. Human nature and human psyche is something I wish I had taken seriously when I was going to college. I learned just enough to be ignorant. There are things, however, that I have learned that have not been discovered and put in the textbooks yet. I have learned the psychology that criminologists and psychologists have never learned. I am still learning and will never know it all. There is so much to learn about criminals. I think the word criminal should be changed and each type of offense a person commits have a special classification as to what his *RAP SHEET* will depict. Society just dumps everyone into a criminal category. Robber, rapist, murderer, burglar, forger, counterfeiter, etc. The point I am trying to make, and not doing it very well, is that everyone is a potential criminal in most of the categories. The thing that differentiates the criminal from the non-criminal is not the person per se, but the act of crossing the line while the other person did not cross the line.

Everyone is a potential murderer... that has been proven over and over. Every man can commit rape if the passion and circumstances are there. It goes on and on. Most people, not all, have committed what is termed a criminal offense. Another example is those that were caught and those that were not. So if that is the case, it boils down to what is known. A person could wear the cloak of respectability and society would look kind on him, but that same person could be a murderer, rapist, etc. who has gone undetected. So, society respects what they know about a person, not what the person actually is. It is like the woman whose virtue was impeccable and was loved by all. Then one day someone who knew her in the past put the story out that she was a trollop in another place and time. Instantly she is scum and looked upon as trash. So it isn't the person that is really being looked at, but what is known or not known about that person.

You were talking about me being able to see your friend for what he really is. He isn't unique in the sense I evaluated him. He is a typical convict who has been around rogues all his life. He has been *USED, ABUSED* and *FUCKED OVER* all his life. His traits were developed by *SURVIVAL* and his will to *GET BACK*. His conscience was *DESTROYED* and he feels no remorse for conning someone. In his mind and in his world/society, his tricks of the trade are *RESPECTABILITY* and *RECOGNITION*. He isn't a big man and he has to have something going for him that will make up for his lack of stature. Inherently he isn't a bad person, but he was made to be what he is, and I can readily identify with it, because I was once just like him. My conscience was *DEAD*, but it came alive much to my surprise. My emotions were *DEAD*, but they too were resurrected. The *MORALS* of my prison society are known by me thoroughly, but they are not the *MORALS* I live by anymore. I am climbing out of my *SNAKE PIT* and *SLIME BALL* society insofar as *JOE* goes. I have the knowledge of this society, and that is to my advantage, but it does not appeal to me to take advantage of people, hurt people, etc. I feel better about myself since I got some self-respect, and my thinking was changed by education. I am still lacking in the education I want and need, but I am far from the ignorant person I was once, and my whole concept of life has changed through education...

CONTRIBUTORS

THE FOLLOWING INMATES OF
FLORIDA STATE PRISON
P.O. BOX747
STARKE
FLORIDA 32091
USA:

ROBERT FIELDMORE LEWIS
032695

MARK DEFRIEST
073061

GERARD JOHN SCHAEFER
039506

OTTIS ELLWOOD TOOLE
090812

DANNY HAROLD ROLLING
521178

WAYNE HENDERSON
P.O. BOX 290
36152 REPRESA
CALIFORNIA 95671
USA.

JOSEPH O'DELL, III
P.O. BOX 500
BOYDTON
VIRGINIA 23917- 0500
USA

TO EXPRESS SUPPORT FOR O'DELL,
ALSO CONTACT:
CLIVE STAFFORD-SMITH
SOUTHERN CENTER FOR
HUMAN RIGHTS,
83 POPLAR STREET NORTHWEST
ATLANTA
GEORGIA 3030
USA. Tel. 404 - 688 1202

**COMING SOON / AVAILABLE NOW FROM
NEMESIS LOGO TRUE CRIME**

"Monsters of Weimar"

(ISBN 1 8987743 10 6 - £7.50 / $11.00),

the long-awaited book that tells the tales of how Germany was terrorised by *true-life human vampires* between the wars. For the first time in the English language, True Crime fans will be able to read the classic *"Haarmann - the Story of a Werewolf"*. Nothing, not even the stories of Dennis Nilsen and Jeffrey Dahmer, exceeds the horror of how this maniac capturedyoung men to feed his bloodlust, and to stock his butcher store with the flesh of their young bodies... No less infamous was *"Peter Kürten -the Vampire of Düsseldorf"*, a monster so disturbed even the thought of his execution filled him with pleasure... "Monsters of Weimar" also includes an introduction on "lust murder" by COLIN WILSON, and an essay on the classic films inspired by these cases.

THE FAMILY
by Ed Sanders

(ISBN 1 8987743 15 7 - £9.99)

THE FAMILY has been updated to the present day, with five new chapters. Published in a 500-page edition by NEMESIS, this classic case history tells the only complete story of the *"Manson family"*, This new edition contains rare, exclusive stills, many from the shocking new movie, *CHARLIE'S FAMILY* - plus an introduction by the film's director, Jim Van Bebber, who tells why *THE FAMILY* is the only truly essential volume for readers fascinated by the madness of Manson and his followers.

"Ed Sanders has done nothing less than risk his own life...It is only fitting that such a risk should produce such a terrifying book!" -
THE NEW YORK TIMES